Pre-Algebra
Student Guide

Illustrations Credits
All illustrations © K12 unless otherwise noted

About K12 Inc.
K12 Inc., a technology-based education company, is the nation's leading provider of proprietary curriculum and online education programs to students in grades K–12. K¹² provides its curriculum and academic services to online schools, traditional classrooms, blended school programs, and directly to families. K12 Inc. also operates the K¹² International Academy, an accredited, diploma-granting online private school serving students worldwide. K¹²'s mission is to provide any child the curriculum and tools to maximize success in life, regardless of geographic, financial, or demographic circumstances. K12 Inc. is accredited by CITA. More information can be found at www. K12.com.

Printed by RR Donnelley, Willard, Ohio, USA, May 2012, Lot 052012

Table of Contents

Unit 11: Perimeter and Area

Unit 12: Square Roots and Right Triangles

Unit 13: Solid Figures

Unit 14: Counting and Probability

Unit 15: Statistics

Unit 16: Semester Review and Test

Student Guide

Order of Operations

Suppose you are following instructions to replace the batteries in your portable radio. The directions tell you that you must first use a screwdriver to remove the screw from the battery compartment cover. Next, you must remove the cover and take out the old batteries. Then, you insert the new batteries and replace the cover. Though these steps may seem obvious to you, the order in which they occur is very important.

In this lesson you will learn about the order of operations. The order of operations refers to the order in which to perform operations in mathematics, no matter what problem is being solved

Goals for the Lesson
- Use the order of operations to simplify a numerical expression.

Graded Activities in This Lesson
Lesson Quiz (computer graded)

Materials
"Order of Operations" in Pre-Algebra: A Reference Guide and Problem Sets, pages 5–9

Optional
Order of Operations Solutions

Keywords and Pronunciation
grouping symbols: symbols—such as parentheses ( ) and braces { }—used to enclose an expression

Learn: Order of Operations [online]

Note: As you read through the lesson online, use the spaces below to take notes on each screen.

Notes:
What is the order of operations?

Worked Examples: Order of Operations [online]
Notes

Mathcasts: Simplify an Expression [online]

View the video to see how to solve a typical problem.

Summary: Order of Operations [online]

- Use the order of operations to simplify or evaluate expressions.

- First, perform operations within grouping symbols. Examples of grouping symbols are parentheses or a fraction bar.

- Second, perform all multiplication and division in order from left to right.

- Third, perform all addition and subtraction in order from left to right.

Offline Learning: Order of Operations [offline]

Skills Update

Print and complete the Skills Update.

In the Book

Review pages 5–9 in the Reference Guide.

Do the Math

Simplify this expression:

$4 \cdot 8 - 6 \div 2 + 1$

If you didn't know about the order of operations, you might be tempted to perform the operations from left to right. You would get a different answer than you would get if you were to use the order of operations. Let's compare the two ways.

If you worked in order from left to right, you'd get	If you followed the rules for order of operations, you'd get
$4 \cdot 8 - 6 \div 2 + 1$ $32 - 6 \div 2 + 1$ $26 \div 2 + 1$ $13 + 1 = 14$	$4 \cdot 8 - 6 \div 2 + 1$ $32 - 3 + 1$ $29 + 1 = 30$
The correct simplified expression is 30. The answer 14 is not correct.	

Try adding parenthesis to the same expression as shown below. Do you get the same answer? Why or why not?

$4 \cdot (8 - 6) \div 2 + 1$

What is the value of this new expression?

Simplify. $4 \cdot (8 - 6) \div 2 + 1$

$4 \times \underbrace{(8 - 6)} \div 2 + 1$ Perform the operation within parentheses.

$\underbrace{4 \cdot 2} \div 2 + 1$ Perform multiplication…

$\underbrace{8 \div 2} + 1$ …and division in order from left to right.

$\underbrace{4 + 1}$ Perform addition.

5 Simplified value.

The simplified value is 5.

Compare this solution to the expression without any grouping symbols, which had a value of 30.

Sometimes you will see grouping symbols added when they aren't absolutely necessary. Consider the original expression:

$4 \cdot 8 - 6 \div 2 + 1$

You could write this expression as follows:

$(4 \cdot 8) - (6 \div 2) + 1$

The parentheses aren't really necessary because they don't change the order of operations. They do, however, make the order a little easier to see.

Problem Sets
Complete Problems 1–19 odd on page 8 of *Pre-Algebra: A Reference Guide and Problem Sets*.

Lesson Assessment: Order of Operations Quiz [online]
Now go back online to complete the lesson quiz.

Answers

Skills Update

1. $m = 321$

2. $(30 \div 5) \div 2 = 3$

3. $5\frac{5}{7} + 2\frac{1}{3} = 8\frac{1}{21}$

4. 26 inches

5. about 129 inches (answers may vary)

Skills Update

1. Use the commutative property to solve for *m*.

    $548 + m = 321 + 548$

2. Complete the number sentence to make it true.

    $(30 \underline{\quad} 5) \div 2 = 3$

3. Compare. Write ≠ or =.

    $5\frac{5}{7} + 2\frac{1}{3} \underline{\quad} 8\frac{1}{21}$

Refer to the graph below for Problems 4 and 5.

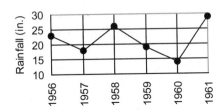

Yearly Rainfall

4. What was the approximate rainfall in 1958?

5. Find the approximate total rainfall from 1956 to 1961.

Student Guide

Variable Expressions

You've probably heard of facial, verbal, and artistic expressions. But are you familiar with mathematical expressions? Some mathematical expressions are "numerical expressions" —which is just a way to represent a number. For example, 2 + 3 is a numerical expression that represents the number 5. Other mathematical expressions are "variable expressions" —expressions that contain a variable. For example, $n - 4$ is a variable expression.

Goals for the Lesson
- Evaluate a variable expression.

- Simplify a numerical expression.

Graded Activities in This Lesson
Lesson Quiz (computer-scored)

Materials
Skills Update

Pre-Algebra: A Reference Guide and Problem Sets, pages 10–13

Optional

Variable Expressons Solutions

Keywords and Pronunciation
coefficient: a number that is multiplied by a variable in a variable expression; in an expression such as $3x$, the numerical coefficient of x is 3

numerical expression: an expression that represents a certain number (for example, 4 + 6 represents 10)

variable: a symbol used to represent one or more numbers

variable expression: an expression that involves a variable

Groundwork: Preparing for the Lesson [online]

Notes: (As you read through the lesson online, use the space below to take notes on each screen.)

Learn: Mathematical Expressions [online]

This activity will introduce you to variable expressions. Use the space below to follow along with the example provided online.

Notes

Learn: Variable Expressions [online]

In this activity, you will get a more in-depth understanding of variable expressions. Answer the questions below to follow along with the online instruction.

Notes

When a variable are immediately next to each other with no symbol between them, what operation is implied?

What is a term?

What is a numerical coefficient?

If a variable stands by itself, what is its coefficient?

Learn: Evaluating Variable Expressions [online]

In this activity, you will learn to use the order of operations to evaluate variable expressions. Use the space below to follow along with the online instruction.

Notes

What should you do first when you evaluate a variable expression?

Worked Examples: Variable Expressions [online]

Notes

MathCast: Evaluation Expressions [online]

View the video to see how to solve a typical problem.

Summary: Variable Expressions [online]

- A *variable* is a letter that represents a number, and a *variable expression* is an expression that contains a variable.

- A *term* is a number, a variable, or the product of a number and a variable.

- The coefficient of a term is the number that is multiplied by the variable.

- When no coefficient appears in front of a variable, then the coefficient is 1.

- To evaluate a variable expression, replace the variable with a given value, then follow the order of operations to simplify.

Offline Learning: Variable Expressions [offline]

Skills Update

Print and complete the Skills Update.

In the Book

Review pages 10–12 in the reference guide.

Complete Problems 1–29 odd on pages 12–13.

Complete the Extension in the Student Guide for additional practice.

Do the Math

Try applying what you've learned to your road trip.

You are going to the beach, and you plan to spend one day driving on a road that has a speed limit of 55 miles per hour. If you drive at the speed limit, how far will you travel in 1 hour? 2 hours? 3 hours?

To solve this problem, you can write numerical expressions that describe the number of miles traveled in 1 hour, 2 hours, and 3 hours.

Number of Hours	Miles Traveled (numerical expression)	Miles Traveled (simplified)
1	55 • 1	55
2	55 • 2	110
3	55 • 3	165

Do you see a pattern in the table? To find the miles traveled, you multiply the number of hours by 55 miles per hour.

You can write a variable expression that describes how far you will travel in any number of hours. If you travel for h hours, you will travel:

$55 • h$, or $55h$ miles

This variable expression could be very useful to you. Suppose you needed to know how far you will travel in 8 hours. Just substitute the number of hours for the variable h. If you travel for 8 hours, you will travel:

$55 • 8 = 440$ miles

How about 3.25 hours? If you travel for 3.25 hours, you will travel:

$55 • 3.25 = 178.75$ miles

Think: Can a variable have more than one value?

Yes, a variable can have more than one value. Variables are symbols that represent one or more numbers.

Problem Sets

Complete Problems 1–29 odd on page 12 of *Pre-Algebra: A Reference Guide and Problem Sets*.

Extension [optional]

Complete the sentences below.

1) If the value of $100 - x$ is 64, then $x =$? .

2) If the value of $4 \cdot c \cdot c$ is 196, then $c =$? .

3) If the value of $8 \cdot a \cdot b$ is 160, and $b = 5$, then $a =$? .

4) If the value of $51 \div a \cdot b$ is 17, and $a = 3$, then $b =$? .

Lesson Assessment: Variable Expressions Quiz [online]

Now go back online to complete the lesson quiz.

Answers

Skills Update

1. Turkey

2. 10

3. 3

Extension

1. 36

2. 7

3. 4

4. 1

Skills Update

Soccer Team's
Favorite Sandwiches

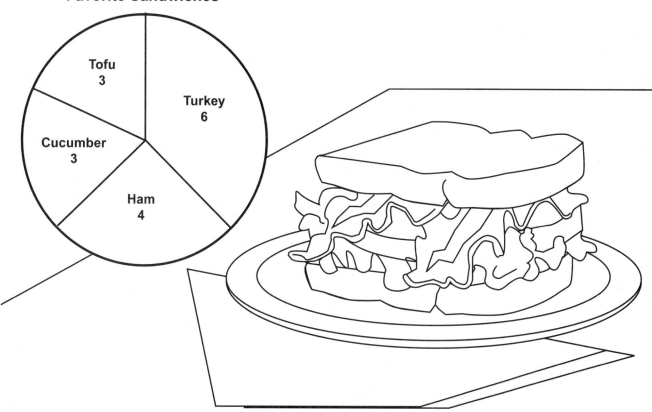

A soccer team is planning a party. The coach takes an inventory of the players' favorite sandwiches.

Here are the results.

1. Which is the most popular sandwich?

2. How many people favor sandwiches with meat?

3. How many more people prefer turkey to tofu?

Student Guide

Writing Expressions for Word Phrases

The ability to translate words into mathematical expressions is a powerful skill used in mathematical problem solving. In this lesson, you will learn strategies to help you master this skill.

Goal for the Lesson
- Write a variable expression for a word phrase.
- Write a word phrase for a variable expression.

Graded Activities in This Lesson
Lesson Quiz (computer graded)

Materials
Pre-Algebra: A Reference Guide and Problem Sets, pages 14–17

Optional
Writing Expressions for Word Phrases Solutions

Keywords and Pronunciation
none

Groundwork: Preparing for the Lesson [online]
Review previously learned material about variables and mathematical expressions.

Note: As you read through the lesson online, use the spaces below to take notes on each screen.

Learn: Variables [online]
In this activity, you will learn to translate between word phrases and variable expressions. Use the space provided here to follow along with the online instruction.
Notes
What is a variable?

What are some words or phrases that indicate the operation of addition?

What are some words and phrases that indicate the operation of subtraction?

What are some words and phrases that indicate the operation of multiplication?

What are some words and phrases that indicate the operation of division?

Worked Examples: Writing Expressions for Word Phrases [online]
Notes

Mathcasts: Translate [online]

View the video to see how to solve a typical problem.

Summary: Writing Expressions for Word Phrases [online]

- To translate a word phrase, determine whether the word phrase describes addition, subtraction, multiplication, or division.

- Use parentheses to indicate the order in which operations should be performed.

Skills Update: Practice Your Math Skills [online]
Complete the Skills Update online.

Offline Learning: Writing Expressions for Word Phrases [offline]

In the Book
Review pages 14–16 in the Reference Guide.

Problem Sets
Complete Problems 1–31 odd on *pages 16 - 17.*

Extra Practice
Very different situations can be described by the same variable expression. Write a variable expression for each word phrase.

1. Mary's age, if she is 25 years older than Harry, who is *x* years old

2. The amount of money in a piggy bank that holds *q* quarters

3. The length of a board that was originally *x* cm long and 20 cm were cut from it

4. The distance you traveled if you were going *x* miles per hour for 4 hours

5. Gary's weight, if he weighed *x* pounds last year and has since gained 15 pounds

Lesson Assessment: Writing Expressions for Word Phrases Quiz

[online]
Now go back online to complete the lesson quiz.

Answers

Extra Practice

1. $x + 25$
2. $0.25q$
3. $x - 20$
4. $4x$
5. $x + 15$

Student Guide

Comparing Expressions

When you simplify different numerical expressions, you are likely to get two entirely different answers. However, sometimes you can simplify two different expressions and get the same answer. In either case, you can use mathematical symbols to compare the values of each expression.

Either or both of the expressions you are trying to compare may contain a variable. Whether one of these expressions is greater than, less than, or equal to the other expression depends on the value of the variable. In this lesson, you will learn to compare numerical expressions and to determine if a given value is a solution to a mathematical sentence that involves an unknown quantity.

Goals for the Lesson
- Use a less than, greater than or equality symbol to compare two numerical expressions.
- Determine whether or not a value is a solution of an open sentence.

Graded Activities in This Lesson
Lesson Quiz (computer graded)

Materials
Pre-Algebra: A Reference Guide and Problem Sets, pages 18–21

Optional
Comparing Expressions Solutions

Keywords and Pronunciation
equation: the number sentence that indicates that two expressions are equal

inequality: a mathematical sentence formed by placing an inequality sign between two expressions

open sentence: an equation or inequality that contains one or more variables

solution: a value that makes an open sentence true

Groundwork: Preparing for the Lesson [online]

As you read through the lesson online, use the spaces below to take notes on each screen.

Notes

Learn: Inequalities [online]

In this activity, you will learn to use inequality signs when comparing two quantities.

Notes

Explain the meaning of each inequality sign below.

$<$

$>$

k

|

Learn: Open Sentences [online]

In this activity, you will learn about open sentences and how to determine whether or not a value is a solution to an open sentence.

Notes

What is an open sentence?

What is a solution to an open sentence?

How do you determine whether a given value is a solution to an open sentence?

Worked Examples: Comparing Expressions [online]
Notes

Summary: Comparing Expressions [online]

Inequalities allow you to compare two quantities or expressions using one of four inequality symbols.

< less than

≤ less than or equal to

> greater than

≥ greater than or equal to

You can determine if a value is a solution to an open sentence by substituting the value for the variable and seeing if the statement is true or false.

Equations usually have one solution. For example, the equation $x + 7 = 9$ is true only if the value of x is 2.

Inequalities usually have more than one solution. For example, the inequality $x < 3$ is true for any number less than 3, such as 2.999, 1.05, or 0.

To determine whether a given value is a solution to an open sentence, substitute the value for the variable and simplify each side. If the resulting sentence is true, then the value is a solution. If the resulting sentence is false, the value is not a solution.

Skills Update: Practice Your Math Skills [online]
Complete the Skills Update online.

Offline Learning: Comparing Expressions [offline]

In the Book
Review pages 18–21 in the Reference Guide.

Complete Problems 1–27 odd and 31–33 on pages 20–21 of the Reference Guide.

Do the Math
Chances are, you make comparisons on a daily basis. Sometimes these comparisons involve the use of formulas.

For instance, suppose you needed a box for storing books, and you narrowed your choices down to two boxes that appear to be the largest ones you could find. You want to choose the box that has the greater volume so that you can pack as many books as possible in to it. The first box is 2 feet wide, 3 feet long, and 2 feet tall. The second 1 foot wide, 2 feet long, and 4 feet tall. Which box should you choose?

Substitute the values for the length, width, and height into the formula for the volume of a rectangular box with length l, width w, and height h, $V = lwh$.

First Box

$V = lwh$

$\quad = 3 \cdot 2 \cdot 2$

$\quad = 12$

Second Box

$V = lwh$

$\quad = 2 \cdot 1 \cdot 4$

$\quad = 8$

The volume of first box is greater. You should choose the first box.

Problem Sets
Complete Problems 1–27 odd and 31–33 on pages 20–21 of the reference guide.

Lesson Assessment: Comparing Expressions Quiz [online]
Now go back online to complete the lesson quiz.

Student Guide

Replacement Sets

Have you ever taken a test **that** required you to choose the correct word to complete a sentence? If you chose correctly, the completed sentence was true. If you chose incorrectly, the completed sentence was false.

Like word sentences, open sentences are either true or false, depending on the value that replaces the variable. In this lesson, you will learn how to find which value or values in a set of numbers, if any, make an open sentence true.

Goals for the Lesson
- Find the solutions to an equation with a given replacement set.

- Find the solutions to an inequality with a given replacement set.

Graded Activities in This Lesson
Lesson Quiz (computer graded)

Materials
Pre-Algebra: A Reference Guide and Problem Sets, pages 22–24

Optional
Replacement Sets Solutions

Keywords and Pronunciation
replacement set: a given set of numbers that a variable may represent

solution set: a set of values that are solutions of an open sentence with a given replacement set

Groundwork: Preparing for the Lesson [online]
Notes

Learn: Equations, Inequalities, and Solutions [online]

This activity explores the replacement set method of solving equations and inequalities.

Note: As you read through the lesson online, use the spaces below to take notes on each screen.

Notes

What is a replacement set?

What is a solution set?

Mathcast: Solve an Inequality [online]

View the video to see how to solve a typical problem.

Summary: Replacement Sets [online]

A replacement set is a given set of numbers that a variable may represent.

A solution set is the number or set of numbers taken from the replacement set that make the equation or inequality true.

Notes

Offline Learning: Replacement Sets [offline]

In the Book
Review pages 22–24 in the Reference Guide.

Complete Problems 1–19 odd on page 24.

Do the Math (optional)
For each of the following equations and inequalities use the replacement set {2, 4, 6}:

$$3x - 4 = 14 \qquad \frac{x}{4} + 2 = 9 \qquad 4x > 7 - x$$

Because the replacement set is small, the easiest way to solve the equations is to substitute each value from the replacement set for the variable and then determine which values make the equations true.

$$3x - 4 = 14$$

$3(2) - 4 \overset{?}{=} 14$ Replace x with 2.

$\qquad 2 \neq 14$ Simplify to determine if the equation is true.

$3(4) - 4 \overset{?}{=} 14$ Replace x with 4.

$\qquad 8 \overset{?}{=} 14$ Simplify to determine if the equation is true.

$3(6) - 4 \overset{?}{=} 14$ Replace x with 6.

$\qquad 14 = 14$ Simplify to determine if the equation is true.

The only value in the replacement set that results in a true statement is 6. The solution set to $3x - 4 = 14$ in the given replacement set is {6}.

$$\frac{x}{4} + 2 = 9$$

$\frac{(2)}{4} + 2 \overset{?}{=} 9$ Replace x with 2.

$\qquad 2\frac{1}{2} \neq 9$ Simplify to determine if the equation is true.

$\frac{(4)}{4} + 2 \overset{?}{=} 9$ Replace x with 4.

$\qquad 3 \neq 9$ Simplify to determine if the equation is true.

$$\frac{6}{4} + 2 \overset{?}{=} 9 \qquad \text{Replace } x \text{ with 6.}$$

$$3\frac{1}{2} \neq 9 \qquad \text{Simplify to determine if the equation is true.}$$

None of the values results in a true statement. There is no solution to $\frac{x}{4} + 2 = 9$ in the given replacement set, so the solution set is empty, $\{\varnothing\}$.

$$4x > 7 - x$$

$$4(2) \overset{?}{>} 7 - 2 \qquad \text{Replace } x \text{ with 2.}$$

$$8 > 5 \qquad \text{Simplify to determine if the equation is true.}$$

$$4(4) \overset{?}{>} 7 - 4 \qquad \text{Replace } x \text{ with 4.}$$

$$16 > 3 \qquad \text{Simplify to determine if the equation is true.}$$

$$4(6) \overset{?}{>} 7 - 6 \qquad \text{Replace } x \text{ with 6.}$$

$$24 > 1 \qquad \text{Simplify to determine if the equation is true.}$$

All the values result in a true statement. So, the solution set to $4x > 7 - x$ using the given replacement set is $\{2, 4, 6\}$.

Problem Sets

Complete Problems 1–19 odd on page 24 of the reference guide.

Mid-Unit Assessment: The Basics Test [online]

Now go back online to complete the Mid-Unit Assessment.

Student Guide

Related Equations

If you earn $20 and then spend the $20 at the movies, how much will you have left? Nothing, of course! Adding $20 to your pocket and then subtracting $20 leaves you zero dollars and an empty pocket. In this case, the operation of subtraction "undoes" the operation of addition. This is an example of an inverse operation.

Goals for the Lesson
- Use inverse operations to write a related equation.

Graded Activities in This Lesson
Lesson Quiz (computer graded)

Materials
Pre-Algebra: A Reference Guide and Problem Sets, pages 28–29

Optional
Related Equations Solutions

Keywords and Pronunciation
inverse operations: mathematical operations that undo each other, such as addition and subtraction or multiplication and division

related equations: a set of equations that all communicate the same relationship between three values, but in different ways

---

Groundwork: Preparing for the Lesson [online]
Complete this activity to get ready for this lesson.

Note: As you read through the lesson online, use the spaces below to take notes on each screen.

Learn: Introduction to Inverse Operations [online]
Notes
What are inverses?

What are inverse operations?

What are related equations?

Write two related equations for $x + 5 = 12$.

Write two related equations for $4y = 28$.

How can you use related equations to solve an equation?

Worked Examples: Related Equations [online]
Notes

MathCast: Using Related Equations [online]

View the video to see how to solve a typical problem.

Summary: Related Equations [online]

- Inverse operations can be used to solve an equation.

- Addition and subtraction are inverse operations.

- Multiplication and division are inverse operations.

- Related equations are equations that all communicate the same relationship among three values, but in different ways.

Offline Learning: Related Equations [offline]

Skills Update

Print and complete the Skills Update.

In the Book

Review pages 26–28 in the reference guide.

Problem Sets

Complete Problems 1–9 odd and 23–26 all on pages 28 and 29 of the reference guide.

Lesson Assessment: Related Equations Quiz [online]

Now go back online to complete the lesson quiz.

Answers

Skills Update

1.

n	n • 1.5
2	3
2.5	3.75
3	4.5
3.5	5.25

2. $.\overline{33}$

Skills Update

1. Complete the table.

n	$n \cdot 1.5$
2	
2.5	
3	
3.5	

2. Change the fraction to a decimal.

$$\frac{7}{21}$$

Student Guide

Problem Solving

Each day, we face and solve many real-world problems that involve math. Having an approach to solve these problems can help make them easier to solve. One way to approach problem solving in math uses the five-step plan.

Goals for the Lesson

- Write an equation for a word sentence.

- Write an equation for a word problem.

- Solve a word problem using related equations.

Graded Activities in This Lesson

Lesson Quiz (computer graded)

Materials

Pre-Algebra: A Reference Guide and Problem Sets, pages 30–35

Optional

Problem Solving Solutions

Keywords and Pronunciation

Groundwork: Preparing for the Lesson [online]

Notes

Learn: Five-Step Plan [online]

Note: As you read through the lesson online, use the spaces below to take notes on each screen.

Notes
What are the five steps of the five-step plan?

Mathcast: Coin Problem [online]

View the video to see how to solve a typical problem.

Summary: Solving Problems [online]
You can use the five-step plan to solve just about any word problem.

Offline Learning: Solving Problems [offline]

Skills Update

1. Express $\frac{41}{40}$ as a percent.

2. Solve for n. $\frac{2}{5} = \frac{n}{65}$

3. What are the prime factors of 126?

For Questions 4–6 state whether an angle with the given measure is acute, right, or obtuse.

4. 90°

5. 45°

6. 99°

In the Book
Review pages 30–31 and pages 33–34 in the Reference Guide.

Problem Sets
Complete Problems 1–15 odd on page 32, and 1–17 odd on page 35 of the Reference Guide.

Extension (optional)
Write a word problem that can be described by each equation below.

Equation 1: $6 + c = 54$

Equation 2: $100 + 6x = 250$

Lesson Assessment: Solving Problems Quiz [online]
Now go back online to complete the lesson quiz.

Answers

Skills Update

1. 102.5%

2. 26

3. 2, 3, and 7

4. Right

5. Acute

6. Obtuse

Extension

Answers will vary.

Student Guide

The Basics Review

You have finished studying some of the pre-algebra basics, which include the order of operations, evaluating expressions, comparing expressions, solving equations, and solving word problems. Now it's time to pull together what you have learned. Throughout the review, see how the skills you have learned relate to the Pre-Algebra big ideas.

Goals for the Lesson
- Review the concepts and skills learned in the unit.

Materials

"Pre-Algebra Basics" in *Pre-Algebra: A Reference Guide and Problem Sets*
Preparing for the Unit Test

The Basics Practice Problems

Unit Review: The Basics [online]

This is your chance to review the big ideas of Pre-Algebra you have learned in this unit. Under Review These Activities, you will find activities from previous lessons that will review each big idea. Choose the topics you feel you need to review. Under Try These, you will find interactive problems that will test your understanding of each big idea. As you work through this lesson, take notes in the spaces provided.

Big Idea

A number is any entity that obeys the laws of arithmetic; all numbers obey the laws of arithmetic. The laws of arithmetic can be used to simplify algebraic expressions.

Big Idea

Expressions, equations, and inequalities express relationships between different entities.

Big Idea

The laws of arithmetic can be used to simplify algebraic expressions and equations. Solving an equation means finding values for the variable or variables that make the equation a true statement.

Big Idea

If you can create a mathematical model for a situation, you can use the model to solve other problems that you might not be able to solve otherwise. Algebraic equations can capture key relationships among quantities in the world.

Summary: The Basics Review [online]

In this unit you covered the following topics:

- Using order of operations

- Evaluating expressions involving addition, subtraction, multiplication, and division of whole numbers

- Using a replacement set to solve equations

- Solving word problems

- Translating a word phrase into an algebraic expression

- Translating word problems into equations

- Describing strategies for solving word problems

Offline Learning: **The Basics Review** [offline]

How well have you mastered the goals of this unit? Complete the The Basics Practice Problems. These problems are similar to the problems you will have on the Unit Test.

You can also

- Review the The Basics unit in *Pre-Algebra: A Reference Guide and Problem Sets*

- Review the notes in your Student Guide

- Read and follow the instructions in Preparing for the Unit Test

Tucker

Practice Problems

The Basics

For questions 1–3, simplify the expression.

1. $5 \cdot 4 - (8 + 2)$

   $5 \times 4 = 20 - 10 = 10$

2. $(14 - 3) \cdot (7 + 2)$

   $14 - 3 = 11 \cdot 9 = 99$

3. $\dfrac{4 \cdot 9 - 6}{1 + 2 \cdot 2}$

   $\dfrac{4 \cdot 9 - 6}{1 + 2 \cdot 2} = \dfrac{30}{6}$

For questions 4–6, evaluate the expression if $a = 3$, $b = 1$, and $c = 5$.

4. $2a + 3b - c$

   $2 \times 3 + 3 \times 1 - 5 = 4$

5. $\dfrac{5c - b}{4a}$

   $5 \times 5 = 25 - 1 = \dfrac{24}{12}$
   4×3

6. $6a - (b + c)$

For questions 7–9, write a variable expression for each word phrase.

7. The product of five and a number decreased by three

8. The sum of 2 and number decreased by 4

9. Eight increased by the difference of a number and seven

For questions 10–12, write an equation for each word sentence.

10. A number minus five is fourteen.

11. The product of two and a number increased by four is twelve.

12. Nine less than the product of a number and six is fifteen.

For questions 13–14, find the solution set for each inequality if the replacement set for x is {4, 5, 6, 7, 8}.

13. $4x + 6 \le 5x$

14. $2x - 1 \ge x + 4$

For questions 15–19, write a related equation that you could use to solve each equation.
15. $x - 4 = 12$

16. $y + 4 = 20$

17. $3m = 18$

18. $\dfrac{y}{2} = 14$

19. $\dfrac{8}{n} = 4$

For questions 20–21, solve the following open sentences.

20. $2x - 5 = 9$

21. $\dfrac{c}{3} - 4 = 10$

For question 22, write an equation for the given word problem.

22. Helen withdraws \$450 from her bank account. The balance in her account is \$840 after the withdrawal. Write an equation that can be used to find the amount, m, in her account before the withdrawal.

Answers

1. 10

2. 99

3. 6

4. 4

5. 2

6. 12

7. $5n - 3$

8. $(2 + n) - 4$ or $(n + 2) - 4$

9. $8 + (n - 7)$

10. $n - 5 = 14$

11. $2n + 4 = 12$

12. $6n - 9 = 15$

13. $\{6, 7, 8\}$

14. $\{5, 6, 7, 8\}$

15. $x = 12 + 4$

16. $y = 20 - 4$

17. $m = \dfrac{18}{3}$

18. $y = 14 \cdot 2$

19. $n = \dfrac{8}{4}$

20. $x = 7$

21. $c = 42$

22. $m - 450 = 840$

Name _____   Date _____

Preparing for the Unit Test

Review the Concepts and Skills Learned in the Unit

To prepare for the test, you should review the skills, concepts, and keywords learned in the unit. As you review, ask yourself the following:

What were the key concepts in the unit? Why are they important?

Key concepts are the main points of the unit. Look through the reference guide pages and Student Guides for this unit. In the space below, create your own list of key concepts. Then, compare your list to the list provided in the Student Guide for the unit review.

As you create your list, think about why the concept is important. How does each concept relate to other mathematical concepts you've learned? What kinds of problems can you solve using the concept?

What types of problems will I need to be able to solve?

Look through the Reference Guide and select a few typical problems from the chapter. Make sure you still remember how to solve the problems. Rework some of the problems if you feel you need extra practice.

Were there any concepts that I found difficult to understand or master?

Review the examples and problems for any concepts or skills you found difficult.

Choose a few problems that were difficult for you. In the space below, rework the problems until you're comfortable with your mastery of the concept or skill.

What were the keywords in the unit, and do I understand the meaning of each keyword?

You can find unit keywords online or in the unit review. Don't forget: The Reference Guide glossary can also be a useful way to review keywords.

Jot down any keywords and definitions that you feel are important.

What properties, formulas, and rules will I need to know for the test?

Properties, formulas, and rules are located in the blue-bordered boxes in the Reference Guide.

Record any properties, formulas, or rules from the unit in the space provided. Then, you'll have them all in one place for easy reference and quick memorization.

Unit Assessment

The Basics Unit Test, Offline

Answer each question in the space provided.

(8 points)

1. Compare the expressions below using <, >, or =. Show all of your work.

   $(14 - 6) \div (6 - 2)$ _____ $4 \cdot (10 - 8) - 2 \cdot 2$

Score

   Answer:

Score	___ of 8

Student Guide

Integers on a Number Line, Part 1

Positive and negative integers can be used to measure temperatures, elevations, and much more. In this lesson you will learn to identify and graph positive and negative integers on a number line. You will also learn to compare integers.

Goals for the Lesson
- Graph positive and negative integers on a number line.
- Determine the integer coordinate of a point on a number line.
- Compare positive and negative integers.

Graded Activities in This Lesson
Lesson Quiz (computer-scored)

Materials
Pre-Algebra: A Reference Guide and Problem Sets, pages 39–44

Optional
Integers on a Number Line Solutions

Keywords and Pronunciation
coordinate: the number associated with a point on a number line

integers: all positive and negative whole numbers including zero {… –2, –1, 0, 1, 2, …}

number line: a line on which each point represents a number

origin: the point on a number line whose coordinate is zero

opposites: two nonzero numbers that are the same distance from zero on the number line

Groundwork: Preparing for the Lesson [online]

Take a look at some different situations which can be represented by positive and negative integers. Can you think of any other situations where positive and negative integers are used?

Notes

Learn: Integers on a Number Line [online]

As you work through the activities record any notes and answer the questions below.

Notes

What is the difference between a point and the coordinate of a point?

Explain how to find the opposite of an integer.

Learn: Comparing Integers [online]

Notes

How can you use a number line to compare integers?

Write an inequality that is equivalent to −1 < 15.

Worked Examples: Integers on a Number Line, Part 1 [online]

Notes

Summary: Integers on a Number Line, Part 1 [online]

- The set of integers is the set of all positive and negative whole numbers including zero: {... –3, –2, –1, 0, 1, 2, 3 ...}.

- On a number line, zero is the origin. Positive numbers are to the right of the origin and negative numbers are to the left of the origin.

- Opposites are two numbers that are the same distance from zero a number line. Zero is neither positive nor negative, so it does not have an opposite.

- On a number line, numbers increase in value as you move from left to right and decrease in value as you move from right to left.

Offline Learning: Integers on a Number Line, Part 1 [offline]

Do the Math
Review pages 39–41 in the Reference Guide.

Problem Sets
Complete Problems 11–27 odd and 30–32 on pages 43–44 of the Reference Guide.

Lesson Assessment: Integers on a Number Line, Part 1 Quiz [online]
Now go back online to complete the lesson quiz.

Student Guide

Integers on a Number Line, Part 2

You can use a number line as a way to find the opposite and the absolute value of an integer. In this lesson, you will learn how you can use the number line to find the absolute value of a number, solve an absolute value equation, and solve an absolute value inequality.

Goals for the Lesson

- Solve a simple equation involving absolute value.

- Solve an inequality involving absolute value.

- Find the absolute value of an integer.

Graded Activities in This Lesson
Lesson Quiz (computer-scored)

Materials
Pre-Algebra: A Reference Guide and Problem Sets, pages 41–44

Optional
Integers on a Number Line Solutions

Keywords and Pronunciation
integers: the whole numbers and their opposites (for example, ... −2, −1, 0, 1, 2, ...)

number line: the positive number of any pair of opposite nonzero real numbers; the absolute value of 0 is 0; the absolute value of a number *a* is written as |*a*|

opposites: a pair of numbers that sum to zero, such as −4 and +4

origin: the graph of zero on a number line or in a rectangular coordinate grid

---

Groundwork: Preparing for the Lesson [online]
What real-world situations can you think of where positive and negative integers are used?

Notes

Learn: Exploring Absolute Value [online]

As you work through the activities record any notes and answer the questions below.

Notes

How do you find the absolute value of a number?

Learn: Solving Absolute Value Equations and Inequalities [online]

Notes

How can you use a number line to solve an absolute value equation?

How can you use a number line to solve an absolute value inequality?

Worked Examples: Integers on a Number Line, Part 2 [online]

Notes

Mathcasts: Absolute Value [online]

View the video to see how to solve a typical problem.

Summary: Integers on a Number Line, Part 2 [online]

The absolute value of a number is its distance from zero on a number line. Since absolute value represents a distance, its value is always positive. Even if the number inside the absolute value symbol is negative, its absolute value is positive.

The solution to an absolute value equation or inequality is the set of all numbers for which the equation or inequality is true.

Offline Learning: Integers on a Number Line, Part 2 [offline]

Do the Math
Review pages 41–42 in the Reference Guide.

Problem Sets
Complete Problems 13–27 odd on page 43 in the Reference Guide.

Extra Practice (optional)
Complete Problems 14–28 even, and 32 on pages 43-44 in the Reference Guide.

Lesson Assessment: Integers on a Number Line, Part 2 Quiz [online]
Now go back online to complete the lesson quiz.

Student Guide

Adding Integers

Think about the person who delivers mail in a tall office building. All day long she goes up and down on an elevator. Suppose she begins at the mail center on floor 5 of the building and goes up 7 floors and then down 10 floors. Where is she now in relation to floor 5? If you think of the elevator as a number line, you can find the answer. In this lesson you will learn to add integers.

Goals for the Lesson
- Add positive and negative integers.
- Evaluate simple expressions for integer values of the variables.
- Compare expressions involving addition of integers.
- Use addition properties to find solutions to equations involving addition.
- Evaluate absolute value expressions with sums of integers.

Graded Activities in This Lesson
Lesson Quiz (computer-scored)

Materials
"Addition and Subtraction" in *Pre-Algebra: A Reference Guide and Problem Sets*

Optional
Adding Integers Solutions

Keywords and Pronunciation
absolute value: the distance from 0 to the graph of a number on a number line; the absolute value of a number a is denoted by |a|

Groundwork: Preparing for the Lesson [online]
Work through the activity to review absolute value and answer the question below.

Notes

In your own words, define absolute value.

Learn: Using Number Lines to Add Integers [online]

As you work through this activity, record any notes that may help you remember the information and answer the questions below.

Notes

Explain why you move to the right on a number line when you add a positive number.

Learn: Using Rules to Add Integers [online]

As you work through this activity, record any notes that may help you remember the information and answer the questions below.

Notes

In your own words, write the rules for adding integers.

Learn: Evaluating Expressions [online]

As you work through this activity, record any notes that may help you remember the information.

Notes

Addition Properties [offline]

Two useful properties of addition are the identity property for addition and the property of inverses for addition. The properties are summarized here.

Identity Property of Addition

There is a unique real number 0 such that for every real number a, the sum of any number and zero is equal to the number. Zero is called the additive identity.

Examples:

$4 + 0 = 4$

$0 + (-12) = -12$

Property of Inverses for Addition

The sum of any number and its opposite is equal to zero. Opposites are also called *additive inverses*.

Examples:

$-3 + 3 = 0$

$25 + (-25) = 0$

Worked Examples: Adding Integers [online]
Notes

Summary: Adding Integers [online]

A number line is one method for adding integers.

You don't always need the help of a number line to add positive and negative integers. In fact, there are certain rules you can use that make adding positive and negative easier.

- If the signs of the addends are the same, add their absolute values. The sum has the same sign as the addends.
- If the signs of the addends are different, find the difference of their absolute values. The sum has the same sign as the addends with the greater absolute value.

When comparing two expressions that involve addition of positive and negative integers, start by evaluating the expression on each side using the rules of addition. Once each expression is simplified, use the appropriate symbol to make a true statement.

Notes:

Offline Learning: Adding Integers [offline]

In the Book
Review pages 45–48 in the Reference Guide, through the Application: Banking example.

Problem Sets
Complete Problems 1–11 odd and 19–29 odd on pages 48-49 of the Reference Guide.

Extra Practice (optional)
Complete Problems 29–30 on page 49 of the Reference Guide.

Lesson Assessment: Adding Integers Quiz [online]
Now go back online to complete the lesson quiz.

Student Guide

Subtracting Integers

The opposite of up is down and the opposite of cold is hot. Similarly, the opposite of a positive number is a negative number and the opposite of addition is subtraction. In this lesson, you will use this concept of opposites to subtract integers.

Goals for the Lesson
- Subtract integers.
- Evaluate expressions involving a difference of integers.

Graded Activities in This Lesson
Lesson Quiz (computer-scored)

Materials
Pre-Algebra: A Reference Guide and Problem Sets, pages 50–52

Optional
Subtracting Integers Solutions

Keywords and Pronunciation
difference: the solution to a subtraction problem

opposites: a pair of numbers that sum to zero, such as −4 and +4

Groundwork: Preparing for the Lesson [online]
Work through the activity to review absolute value and answer the question below.

Notes

Explain how to add integers.

Learn: Subtracting Integers [online]

As you work through this activity record any notes that may help you remember the information and answer the question below.

Notes

How can you rewrite the expression –2 – 12 using addition?

Learn: Evaluating Expressions [online]

As you work through this activity record any notes that may help you remember the information.

Notes

Worked Examples: Subtracting Integers [online]

Notes

Mathcasts: Value of the Expression [online]

View the video to see how to solve a typical problem.

Summary: Subtracting Integers [online]

In this lesson, you have learned how to simplify expressions involving the subtraction of integers by rewriting the expression using addition.

You have also learned how to evaluate and simplify variable expressions involving a difference of integers.

Offline Learning: Subtracting Integers [offline]

In the Book

Review pages 50–51 in the Reference Guide.

Problem Sets

Complete Problems 1–29 on page 52 of the Reference Guide.

Extra Practice

For additional practice, see Problems 15 and 25 on page 53 of the Reference Guide.

Lesson Assessment: Subtracting Integers Quiz [online]

Now go back online to complete the lesson quiz.

Student Guide

Decimals on a Number Line

Like integers, decimals have opposites, absolute values, and they can be plotted on a number line. Using a number line is also a good way to represent, order, and compare decimal values. In this lesson you will build on your knowledge of positive and negative integers and learn more about decimals.

Goals for the Lesson

- Graph positive and negative decimals on a number line.
- Determine the decimal coordinate of a point on a number line.
- Compare positive and negative decimals.
- Put a set of decimals in order.

Graded Activities in This Lesson
Lesson Quiz (computer-scored)

Materials
Pre-Algebra: A Reference Guise and Problem Sets, pages 53–57.

Optional
Decimals on a Number Line Solutions

Groundwork: Preparing for the Lesson [online]
The Groundwork reviews what was learned in the previous lesson. As you work through this activity record any notes and answer the question below.

Notes
Write another inequality that is equivalent to –3 < 2.

Learn: Graphing and Identifying Decimals [online]
As you work through this activity record any notes and answer the questions below.

Notes

Explain how to choose a scale when you are graphing decimals on a number line.

Find two decimals between 3.6 and 3.7. Explain how you found your answer.

Learn: Comparing Decimals [online]
As you work through this activity record any notes and answer the question below.
Notes

Explain how you can use a number line to order decimals.

Learn: Ordering Decimals [online]
As you work through this activity record any notes and answer the question below.
Notes

How does graphing decimals on a number line help you order them? Explain.

Worked Examples: Decimals on a Number Line [online]
Notes

MathCast: Ordering Decimals [online]
View the video to see how to solve a typical problem.

Summary: Decimals on a Number Line [online]

- Positive and negative decimals can be graphed on a number line just like positive and negative integers.

- To set up a number line, chose an appropriate scale.

- Positive decimals lie to the right of the origin. Negative decimals lie to the left of the origin.

- You compare decimals by using the inequality symbols >, <, and =.

- When ordering decimals it may be useful to graph the decimals on a number line. The decimals will appear in order from least to greatest as you look from left to right.

Offline Learning: Decimals on a Number Line [offline]

In the Book

Review pages 53–56 in the Reference Guide.

Problem Sets

Complete Problems 1–29 odd on pages 56–57 in the Reference Guide.

Extra Practice (optional)

Complete Problems 2–28 even on pages 56–57 of the Reference Guide for extra practice. (optional)

Lesson Assesment: Decimals on a Number Line Quiz [online]

Now go back online to complete the lesson quiz.

Student Guide

Adding Decimals, Part 1

You have already learned how to add together two integers. In this lesson, you will learn how to add together two signed numbers that have a decimal component. First you will use a number line to think through the addition process. You'll then figure out a shortcut for adding two signed decimals.

Goals for the Lesson
- Simplify an expression involving addition of positive and negative numbers.
- Evaluate an expression involving addition of positive and negative decimals.

Graded Activities in This Lesson
Lesson Quiz (computer-scored)

Materials
Pre-Algebra: A Reference Guide and Problem Sets, pages 58–60

Optional
Adding Decimals Solutions

Keywords and Pronunciation
absolute value: the positive number of any pair of opposite nonzero real numbers; the absolute value of a number is the distance of its graph from the origin; the absolute value of 0 is 0; the absolute value of a number a is denoted by |a|

sum: the result of an addition; the numbers added are *addends*

Groundwork: Preparing for the Lesson [online]

In this Groundwork, you'll be reviewing the skill of adding two integers.

Notes

Learn: Adding Decimals on a Number Line [online]

Below are a few blank number lines for you to use while working through this activity.

Tips:

- Always start the arrow representing the first addend at zero on the number line.

- Always start the arrow representing the second addend where the first arrow ended.

- Make sure you've chosen an appropriate scale on the number line for the problem you're doing.

- Make sure that you draw the lengths of the arrows as precisely as possible. Double check that your lengths are correct!

- The sum of the addition problem is where the number where the last arrow drawn is pointing.

Notes

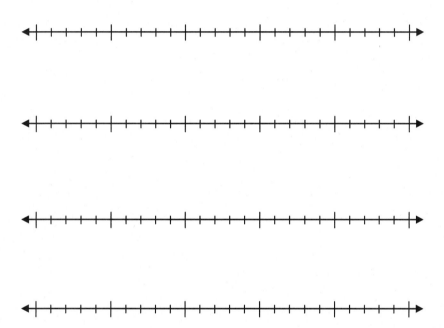

Learn: Rules for Adding Decimals [online]

This activity combines two skills you already know—adding decimals, and adding signed numbers. Even when it's not convenient to draw a number line, it can be helpful to think about one.

- Where would the first arrow point?

- Is the second arrow going to make the sum closer to zero, or further away?

- Will the second arrow go through zero and change the sign of the sum?

Notes

Worked Examples: Adding Decimals, Part 1 [online]

Notes

Summary: Adding Decimals, Part 1 [online]

The number line is a good way to visualize adding positive and negative decimals.

Instead of using a number line, however, you can use rules to add positive and negative decimals. These rules are the same as the rules that you used for adding positive and negative integers earlier in this unit.

Offline Learning: Adding Decimals, Part 1 [offline]

Skills Update

1. Write a variable expression for the word phrase: the product of 3 and a number n increased by 8.

2. Simplify the expression: $2[(4 - 1)^2 - 2 \cdot 3]$.

3. Which members of the replacement set $\{-3, -1, 4, 15\}$ make the inequality $x \geq -1$ true?

4. Write an equation for the word phrase: a number r divided by 4 is 6.

5. Ten people pay a total of $62 for tickets to a show. If 3 adults attend and the price of a child's ticket is $5, what is the price of a single adult ticket?

In the Book
Review pages 58–60 in the Reference Guide.

Problem Sets
Complete Problems 1–8, 21–25 odd on page 61 in the Reference Guide.

Lesson Assessment Adding Decimals, Part 1 Quiz [online]
Now go back online to complete the lesson quiz.

Student Guide

Adding Decimals, Part 2

Knowing how to add positive and negative decimals allows you to solve many different types of problems. In this lesson, you will learn about several different applications of decimal addition. You will also learn problem-solving strategies.

Goals for the Lesson

- Compare two expressions involving addition of positive and negative decimals.

- Use related equations to solve an equation.

- Solve a word problem involving addition of decimals.

Graded Activities in This Lesson

Mid-Unit Test (computer-scored)

Materials

"Adding Decimals" in *Pre-Algebra: A Reference Guide and Problem Sets*, pages 58–61

Optional
Adding Decimals Solutions

Keywords and Pronunciation

absolute value: the positive number of any pair of opposite nonzero real numbers; the absolute value of a number is the distance of its graph from the origin; the absolute value of 0 is 0; the absolute value of a number *a* is denoted by $|a|$

equation: a number sentence indicating that two expressions have the same value; an equation compares expressions using the = symbol.

expression: a group of mathematical symbols that represents a numerical value; most expressions contain numerals as well as operation signs or grouping symbols or a combination of these elements; an expression containing one or more variables is called a *variable expression* or *algebraic expression*

inequality: a mathematical sentence that compares numbers or expressions using one of the symbols $<, >, \leq,$ or $\geq$

inverse operations: operations that undo one another; for example, subtraction is the inverse operation of addition

sum: the result of an addition; the numbers added are *addends*

Groundwork: Preparing for the Lesson [online]

In this Groundwork, you'll be determining the sign of a sum of signed numbers.

Notes

Learn: Comparing Expressions with Signed Decimals [online]

When comparing two expressions, simplify both expressions then compare their values.

You can also look for shortcuts. For example, if you know that one expression has a positive value and the other expression has a negative value, then you can compare them without having to simplify.

Notes

Learn: Solving Subtraction Equations [online]

You can solve subtraction equations using the inverse operation: Addition. For example, the equation

$x - 7 = -5$ is correctly undone using the addition sentence $x = -5 + 7 = +2$

Notes

Learn: Solving Word Problems [online]

You don't have to use the five-step problem solving plan if you can see how to solve a word problem right away. The problem-solving plan is most helpful when you don't know how to get started on a problem. However, you should *always* make sure that you read word problems carefully. Make sure you know what question is really being asked before you start making calculations!

Notes

Mathcasts: Related Equations [online]

View the video to see how to solve a typical problem.

Summary: Adding Decimals, Part 2 [online]

You can apply your understanding of additing positive and negative decimals toward solving problems. These problems include

- comparing two expressions
- solving equations
- solving word problems

Offline Learning: Adding Decimals, Part 2 [offline]

Skills Update [offline]

1. Simplify the expression: $(38 - 20) \cdot (2 + 3) \div 9$.

2. Find the solution set to the equation $7r + 12 = 26$ with the replacement set $\{0, 1, 2, 3\}$.

3. Simplify the expression: $|-8| + |8|$.

4. Evaluate the expression $2a + 5b - 2c$ when $a = 3$, $b = -1$ and $c = 7$.

5. Rewrite the numbers in order from least to greatest: 0, 8.6, −10.2, 6.3, −1.7.

In the Book
Review pages 58–60 in the Reference Guide.

Problem Sets
Complete Problems 27–33 on page 61 of the Reference Guide.

Mid-Unit Assessment: Addition and Subtraction Test [online]
Now go back online to complete the Mid-Unit Assessment.

Answers

Skills Update

1. 10

2. {2}

3. 16

4. – 13

5. –10.2, –1.7, 0, 6.3,. 8.6

Student Guide

Subtracting Decimals, Part 1

You learned that the concept of opposites can be used to subtract integers. You learned that you can turn any subtraction problem to an addition problem by just adding the opposite. This can be applied not just to the subtraction of integers, but also to the subtraction of all numbers.

Goals for the Lesson

- Simplify an expression involving subtraction of positive and negative numbers.

- Evaluate an expression involving subtraction of positive and negative numbers.

Graded Activities in This Lesson

Lesson Quiz (computer-scored)

Materials

Pre-Algebra: A Reference Guide and Problem Sets, pages 62–64

Optional
Subtracting Decimals Solutions

Keywords and Pronunciation

difference: the result of a subtraction

opposites: two numbers that are the same distance from zero on a number line but on opposite sides of zero; opposites are also called additive inverses because their sum is 0 (the additive identity)

absolute value: the positive number of any pair of opposite nonzero real numbers; the absolute value of a number is the distance of its graph from the origin; the absolute value of 0 is 0; the absolute value of a number a is denoted by $|a|$

Groundwork: Preparing for the Lesson [online]

In this Groundwork, you will review what you know about adding and subtracting signed numbers.

Notes

Worked Examples: Subtracting Decimals, Part 1 [online]

In these problems, you will combine what you know about adding signed decimals with what you have learned about subtracting integers. Even though we aren't using number lines to find the answers to these problems, using a number line can be a good way to visualize the numbers you are subtracting. Remember that when you are subtracting a number, the arrow points in the *opposite direction* than it would if you were adding that number.

Notes

Summary: Subtracting Decimals, Part 1 [online]

When subtracting positive and negative numbers, add the opposite of the number.

When a minus sign immediately precedes a variable, think of it as "the opposite of" the variable.

When subtracting a series of numbers, begin by rewriting each number being subtracted as the addition of its opposite.

Offline Learning: Subtracting Decimals, Part 1 [offline]

Skills Update [offline]

1. Write <, =, or > to make the statement true.
   -4.5 ___ -5

2. Evaluate $3y - z + 4$ when $y = 4$ and $z = 5$.

3. Write an equation for the word sentence: four times a number equals 56.

4. Add: $-7 + (-3)$.

In the Book
Review pages 62–64 in the Reference Guide.

Problem Sets
Complete Problems 1–8 and 21–25 odd on page 65 of the Reference Guide.

Lesson Assessment: Subtracting Decimals, Part 1 Quiz [online]
Now go back online to complete the lesson quiz.

Answers

Skills Update

1. >

2. 11

3. $4x = 56$

4. −10

Student Guide

Subtracting Decimals, Part 2

Many real-world problems involve subtracting decimals. Getting your change back at the store, changes in temperature—these are just a couple of examples. In this lesson, you will learn how to apply the subtraction of decimals to solve problems.

Goals for the Lesson
- Solve an equation involving subtraction of positive and negative decimals.
- Solve a word problem involving a difference of decimals.

Graded Activities in This Lesson
Lesson Quiz (computer-scored)

Materials
Pre-Algebra: A Reference Guide and Problem Sets, pages 62–65

Optional
Subtracting Decimals Solutions

Keywords and Pronunciation
equation: the number sentence that indicates that two expressions are equal

Groundwork: Preparing for the Lesson [online]
In this groundwork, you'll be practicing your skills in solving equations. In other words, you'll be finding the value of the variable that makes the equation true. Later in this lesson, you'll learn to solve the same type of problem, only the problems will include signed decimals.

Notes

Learn: Solving Equations with Subtraction [online]

Writing related equations are a good way to review how to solve equations.

For example, look at this equation:

3 + 1 = 4

The related subtraction problems are:

4 − 1 = 3 and 4 − 3 = 1

When solving an equation, you can just write all of the related equations, then choose the one that has the variable by itself on one side of the equal sign.

Notes

Learn: Solving Word Problems [online]

Use the five-step problem-solving plan when you are solving word problems. Each step in the plan is designed to help you think through the problem, document all of your work, and arrive at a sound answer.

Notes

Mathcasts: Transformation - Subtraction [online]

View the video to see how to solve a typical problem.

Summary: Subtracting Decimals, Part 2 [online]

In this lesson, you have applied your understanding of how signed decimals subtract to several different types of problems.

- You have learned how to solve equations with addition by writing a related subtraction sentence.

- You have solved a word problem using the addition of signed numbers.

Offline Learning: Subtracting Decimals, Part 2 [offline]

Skills Update [offline]

1. Simplify $-3.82 + (-4.69)$.

2. Find a solution to the equation $3x - 7 = -10$ from the replacement set $\{-2, -1, 0, 1\}$.

3. Evaluate $4a - 3b$ when $a = 3$ and $b = -2$.

4. Simplify $-4.5 + (-3.7) + 4.5$.

5. Write $<$, $=$, or $>$ to make the statement true: $(3.4 + -2.7)$ __ $(-5.8 + 4.9)$.

In the Book
Review pages 62–64 in the Reference Guide.

Problem Sets
Complete Problems 27–33 on page 65 of the Reference Guide.

Lesson Assessment: Subtracting Decimals, Part 2 Quiz [online]
Now go back online to complete the lesson quiz.

Answers

Skills Update

1. -8.51

2. $\{-1\}$

3. 18

4. -3.7

5. $>$

Student Guide
Addition and Subtraction Properties

Occasionally you might decide to rearrange the furniture in your bedroom. You have the same things in your room, but your room looks different. Or, you might decide that you can't make your room the way you want it with the things you have, so you might get rid of some of your stuff, or you might bring in new things.

In math, it's important to be able to tell the difference between rearranging an expression and changing it. In this lesson you will learn some ways you can rearrange an addition or subtraction expression without ever changing its value.

Goals for the Lesson
- Identify the commutative, associative, and opposite of a sum properties.
- Use an addition property to evaluate an expression.
- Use a property of equality to solve an equation

Graded Activities in This Lesson
Lesson Quiz (computer-scored)

Materials
Pre-Algebra: A Reference Guide and Problem Sets, pages 66–70

Optional
Addition and Subtraction Properties Solutions

Keywords and Pronunciation
none

Groundwork: Preparing for the Lesson [online]
In this groundwork, you'll be testing out a few of the properties that you will be learning about later in this lesson.

Notes

Learn: The Addition Properties [online]

Here are a few hints to help remember the names of these properties.

COMMUTATIVE is a word that is similar to commute, commuter, or commuting. When you commute to work or school, you follow the same route in each direction — you just change the **order** that you see things along your way! The commutative property is about the order in which you see the addends in an expression.

ASSOCIATIVE is a word that is similar to associate. When you associate with people, you spend time with them in a group. The associative property has to do with grouping symbols, and how addends are grouped together in an expression.

OPPOSITE OF A SUM is a property that is about exactly what its name suggests. There is a sum in an expression, and the opposite is taken of the entire sum.

Notes

Worked Examples: Addition and Subtraction Properties [online]

At first, the helpfulness of the addition properties may not be obvious to you. After all, it probably *is* obvious to you that 8 + 7 and 7 + 8 are equivalent expressions. With expressions more complicated than that, you might still not see that the addition properties matter. But, rest assured, learning about these properties and how to use them to simplify expressions can help you become a better prolem solver.

Notes

Summary: Addition and Subtraction Properties [online]

Now you know about three properties of addition and their applications.

Knowing how to use these properties of addition is important for you to be able to simplify expressions and solve equations efficiently.

Offline Learning: Addition and Subtraction Properties [offline]

In the Book
Review pages 66–69 in the Reference Guide.

Problem Sets
Complete Problems 1–27 odd on pages 69–70 of the Reference Guide.

Lesson Assessment: Addition and Subtraction Properties Quiz

[online]
Now go back online to complete the lesson quiz.

Student Guide

Equations Involving Addition and Subtraction

Suppose you have two sets of coins with equal values: One set includes a quarter, a dime, and a nickel; the other set consists of two dimes and four nickels. If you add a quarter to each set, are their values still equal? What if you instead remove a dime from each set? Would they still have equal values?

Goals for the Lesson

- Use transformation by addition to find an equivalent equation.

- Use transformation by subtraction to find an equivalent equation.

Graded Activities in This Lesson
Lesson Quiz (computer-scored)

Materials
Pre-Algebra: A Reference Guide and Problem Sets, pages 71–74

Optional
Equations Involving Add / Sub Solutions
Calculator

Keywords and Pronunciation
none

Groundwork: Preparing for the Lesson [online]
This groundwork uses what you know about inverse operations to simplify expressions. Make sure you look for ways you can simplify the problem before you make any calculations!

Notes

Learn: Properties of Equality [online]

In the previous lesson, you learned about how you can rearrange expressions so the value of that expression stays the same. In this lesson, you are learning about how you can change two equivalent expressions so that they stay equivalent. Together, these two concepts will allow you to successfully solve equations using algebra.

Notes

Learn: Transformations [online]

You can think of an equation as a balance. Whatever operation you apply to one side of the balance, you must also apply to the other side to maintain equality.

Remember to check your answer. You are still new at solving equations, and this step allows you to be sure that you solve the equation correctly. If your check *doesn't* work — in other words, you don't get a true statement when you plug your solution back into the original equation — look carefully at how you solved the equation and see if you can find your mistake.

Notes

Mathcasts: Transformation - Addition [online]

View the video to see how to solve a typical problem.

Summary: Equations Involving Addition and Subtraction [online]

Applying transformations to an equation results in a sequence of equations that are equivalent to the first equation; the transformed equations all have the same solution.

When you transform an equation, the goal is to arrive at a *simpler* equation.

To solve a subtraction equation, use the inverse operation of addition to transform the equation.

When you have solved an equation, check your solution to be sure you have not made any errors in transforming the equation. To check, simply substitute your answer for the variable in the original equation.

Offline Learning: Equations Involving Addition and Subtraction

[offline]

In the Book
Review pages 71–74 in the Reference Guide.

Problem Sets
Complete Problems 1–21 odd on page 74 of the Reference Guide.

Lesson Assessment: Equations Involving Addition and Subtraction Quiz [online]

Now go back online to complete the lesson quiz.

Student Guide

Addition and Subtraction Applications

In this lesson, you will apply what you know about adding and subtracting numbers and writing and solving equations. Use the five-step problem solving plan when solving all word problems.

Goals for the Lesson
- Solve a word problem involving addition of positive and negative numbers.
- Write an equation that can be used to solve a word problem involving subtraction of positive and negative numbers.

Graded Activities in This Lesson
Lesson Quiz (computer-scored)

Materials
Pre-Algebra: A Reference Guide and Problem Sets, pages 76–80

Optional
Addition and Subtraction Applications Solutions
Calculator

Keywords and Pronunciation
none

Groundwork: Preparing for the Lesson [online]
To find the solution to a word problem, you often have to solve an equation for a variable. Practice this skill in this groundwork.

Notes

Worked Examples: Addition and Subtraction Applications [online]
Always use the five-step problem-solving plan when solving word problems.

Notes

Summary: Addition and Subtraction Applications [online]

When solving word problems involving subtraction of positive and negative numbers, use the following suggestions.

- Use the five-step plan when solving these and all word problems.
- Apply the rules that you learned for adding and subtracting positive and negative numbers.
- Use the appropriate property of equality to solve equations.

Offline Learning: Addition and Subtraction Applications [offline]

Skills Update [offline]

1. Simplify: $12 + 4 \cdot 4 \div 2 - 3 \cdot 2$.

2. Write an inequality for the word phrase: 3 times a number n increased by 2 is less than 7.

3. Evaluate the expression $|x + y|$ when $x = -3.4$ and $y = -2.7$.

4. Solve the equation $-n - 8 = -3$.

5. Order the numbers from least to greatest: $-2.4, -5.1, 3.6, -0.2, 1.5$.

In the Book

Review pages 76–79 in the Reference Guide.

Problem Sets

Complete Problems 1–21 on pages 79–80 of the Reference Guide.

Lesson Assessment: Addition and Subtraction Applications Quiz

[online]

Now go back online to complete the lesson quiz.

Answers

Skills Update

1. 14

2. $3n + 2 < 7$

3. 6.1

4. $n = -5$

5. $-5.1, -2.4, -0.2, 1.5, 3.6$

Student Guide

Addition and Subtraction Review

You have finished studying the addition and subtraction unit, which includes graphing integers on a number line, adding and subtracting integers, graphing decimals on a number line, adding and subtracting decimals, addition and subtraction properties, equations involving addition and subtraction, and applications of addition and subtraction. Now it's time to pull together what you have learned. Throughout the review, see how the skills you have learned relate to the pre-algebra big ideas.

Goals for the Lesson
*   Review the concepts and skills learned in the unit.

Materials
"Addition and Subtraction" in *Pre-Algebra: A Reference Guide and Problem Sets*
Preparing for the Unit Test

Unit Review: Addition and Subtraction [online]

This is your chance to review the big ideas of pre-algebra you have learned in this unit of this course. Under Review These Activities, you will find activities from previous lessons that will review each big idea. Choose the topics you feel you need to review. Under Try These, you will find interactive problems that will test your understanding of each big idea. As you work through this lesson, take notes in the spaces provided.

Big Idea

A number is any entity that obeys the laws of arithmetic; all numbers obey the laws of arithmetic. The laws of arithmetic can be used to simplify algebraic expressions.

Big Idea
Expressions, equations and inequalities express relationships between different entities.

Big Idea
The laws of arithmetic can be used to simplify algebraic expressions and equations. Solving an equation means finding values for the variable or variables that make the equation a true statement.

Big Idea

If you can create a mathematical model for a situation, you can use the model to solve other problems that you might not be able to solve otherwise. Algebraic equations can capture key relationships among quantities in the world.

Summary: Addition and Subtraction Review [online]

In this unit you covered the following topics:

- Graphing integers on a number line

- Adding integers

- Subtracting integers

- Graphing decimals on a number line

- Adding decimals

- Subtracting decimals

- Addition and subtraction properties

- Equations involving addition and subtraction

- Addition and subtraction applications

Offline Learning: Addition and Subtraction Review [offline]

How well have you mastered the goals of this unit? Complete the Addition and Subtraction Practice Problems. These problems are similar to the problems you will have on the Unit Test.

You can also

- Review the Addition and Subtraction unit in *Pre-Algebra: A Reference Guide and Problem Sets*

- Review the notes in your Student Guide.

- Read and follow the instructions in Preparing for the Unit Test

Practice Problems

Addition and Subtraction

For questions 1–2, write the opposite of the given integer.

1. −4

2. 19

For questions 3–5, state the property illustrated.

3. $-12 + (3 + 14) = (-12 + 3) + 14$

4. $-(15 + 9) = -15 + (-9)$

5. $-18 + 9 = 9 + (-18)$

For questions 6–8, simplify the expression.

6. $-14 + 9 - 3$

7. $-5 - 13 - 4$

8. $8 - 12 + 20$

9. Solve $|x| = 14$.

For questions 10–13, use the number line to graph the given numbers.

10. –4

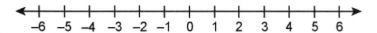

11. 2

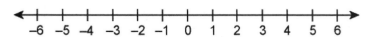

12. –0.4

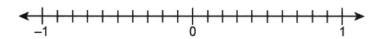

13. 0.3

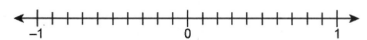

For questions 14–16, evaluate the expression if $a = 4$, $b = -8$, and $c = -5$.

14. $|a - b| - |c|$

15. $|a| - |b - c|$

16. $|a + c| - |b|$

For questions 17–22, solve the equation.

17. $x - 7 = -12$

18. $y + 16 = 14$

19. $m + 3 = -10$

20. $n - 12 = -10$

21. $4.2 + p = -5.6$

22. $-7.8 + r = 3.9$

For questions 23–25, evaluate the expressions if $x = 2.4$ and $y = -3.5$.

23. $x + y$

24. $x - y$

25. $-y - x$

For questions 26–29, use < or > to compare the values.

26. −6.2 _____ −6.5

27. 2.24 _____ 2.18

28. −9.4 _____ 8.5

29. −0.24 _____ −0.25

Answers

1. 4

2. −19

3. Associative Property of Addition

4. Opposite of a Sum Property

5. Commutative Property of Addition

6. −8

7. −22

8. 16

9. −14 or 14

10.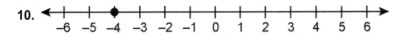

11.

12.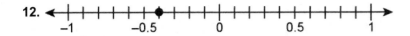

13.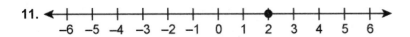

14. 7

15. 1

16. −7

17. $x = -5$

18. $y = -2$

19. $m = -13$

20. $n = 2$

21. $p = -9.8$

22. $r = 11.7$

23. −1.1

24. 5.9

25. 1.1

26. >

27. >

28. <

29. >

Unit Assessment

Addition and Subtraction Unit Test, Offline

Answer each question in the space provided.

(6 points)

1. At the mall, Leona bought a T-shirt and a book for a total of $22.95. The book cost $12.25. How much did the T-shirt cost?

   A) Write an addition equation that models the problem.

   B) Solve the equation

   C) Answer the question.

Score

(14 points)

2. Today Carly's bank account contains $82. Yesterday she made a withdrawal of $25. What was the bank account balance before Carly made the withdrawal?

   A) Write an equation that models the problem.

   B) Solve the equation.

   C) Answer the question.

Score

Score	___ of 20

Student Guide

Multiplying Integers and Decimals, Part 1

Now that you know how to add and subtract positive and negative numbers, you can learn how to multiply positive and negative numbers. This lesson will focus on the rules for multiplying two or more signed numbers.

Goals for the Lesson

- Multiply positive and negative numbers.

- Determine the sign of a product with three or more factors.

Graded Activities in This Lesson
Lesson Quiz (computer-scored)

Materials
Pre-Algebra: A Reference Guide and Problem Sets, pages 85–88

Optional
Multiplying Integers and Decimals Solutions

Calculator

Keywords and Pronunciation
factor: any of two or more numbers multiplied to form a product

integers: all positive and negative whole numbers including zero {… –2, –1, 0, 1, 2, …}

Groundwork: Preparing for the Lesson [online]
In this groundwork, you will practice multiplying positive numbers. You will find that this is excellent practice for multiplying integers!

Notes

Learn: Multiplication on a Number Line [online]

This problem walks you through a problem that should be easy for you to think about and solve. The point of this activity is to explore rules for multiplying positive and negative numbers.

Remember that multiplication is just repeated addition. For example,

$5 \cdot 7 = 7 + 7 + 7 + 7 + 7$ (five sevens added)

$5 \cdot 7 = 5 + 5 + 5 + 5 + 5 + 5 + 5$ (seven fives added)

Since you already know how to *multipy* integers, we will use this definition of multiplication to figure out the rules for multiplying decimals.

Notes

Learn: Determining the Sign of A Product [online]

Be careful when reading problems that involve multiplying three or more factors. Sometimes, you will be asked to find the product. When that's the case, use one of the strategies you learned in this section. Sometimes you will only be asked to find the sign of the product. For that type of problem, you don't have to spend time actually calculating the product!

Notes

Summary: Multiplying Integers and Decimals, Part 1 [online]

When multiplying two signed numbers with decimals, we use the following plan to figure out the answer.

1. Ignore the signs of the numbers and multiply as usual.

2. Determine the sign of the answer.

Offline Learning: Multiplying Integers and Decimals, Part 1 [offline]

In the Book
Read pages 85–88 in *Pre-Algebra: A Reference Guide and Problem Sets*.

Problem Sets
Complete Problems 1–14 and 22–23 on page 88 of the Reference Guide.

Lesson Assessment: Multiplying Integers and Decimals, Part 1
Quiz [online]
Now go back online to complete the lesson quiz.

Student Guide

Multiplying Integers and Decimals, Part 2

In this lesson, you'll continue to build your skills with multiplying signed numbers. You'll learn to solve problems involving multiplication with addition, and multiplication with subtraction. You will also evaluate expressions involving positive and negative integers and decimals.

Goals for the Lesson

- Simplify an expression involving multiplication of positive and negative numbers.

- Evaluate an expression involving multiplication of signed integers and decimals.

Graded Activities in This Lesson

Lesson Quiz (computer-scored)

Materials

Pre-Algebra: A Reference Guide and Problem Sets, pages 85–88

Optional

Multiplying Integers and Decimals Solutions

Calculator

Keywords and Pronunciation

factors: two or more numbers that are multiplied to form a product

order of operations: the order in which operations must be computed when more than one operation is involved

Groundwork: Preparing for the Lesson [online]

In this groundwork, you will practice using the order of operations to evaluate expressions. Remember:

First, evaluate expressions inside grouping symbols.

Next, multiply and divide (from left to right).

Last, add and subtract (from left to right).

Notes

Learn: Simplifying Expressions [online]

There are lots of different things to keep in mind when simplifying expressions. It helps to think through the problem one step at a time.

First, decide which operation must be done first. Use the order of operations.

Next, execute the operation. Follow the rules you have learned for adding, subtracting, and multiplying signed numbers.

Then, rewrite the problem. Replace the small problem you just solved with its answer.

Repeat until the problem is simplified as much as possible.

Notes

Learn: Evaluating Expressions with Variables [online]
Notes

Mathcast: Evaluating Expressions [online]

View the video to see how to solve a typical problem.

Summary: Multiplying Integers and Decimals, Part 2 [online]

When evaluating and simplifying expressions, remember to use these important steps:

- Use the order of operations.

- Use the rules for multiplying positive and negative numbers.

- Use the rules for adding and subtracting positive and negative numbers.

Offline Learning: Multiplying Integers and Decimals, Part 2 [offline]

In the Book

Review pages 85–88 in the Reference Guide.

Problem Sets

Complete Problems 23–27 on page 88 of the Reference Guide.

Lesson Assessment: Multiplying Integers and Decimals, Part 2
Quiz [online]

Now go back online to complete the lesson quiz.

Student Guide

Dividing Integers and Decimals

Many situations involve division of positive and negative numbers. Calculating the average temperature in a city and splitting the cost of a pizza between several friends are two examples. In this lesson you will learn how to simplify expressions involving division of positive and negative numbers.

Goals for the Lesson

- Simplify an expression involving division of positive and negative numbers.

- Evaluate an expression involving division of positive and negative numbers.

- Find the mean of a set of signed values.

Graded Activities in This Lesson
Lesson Quiz (computer-scored)

Materials
Pre-Algebra: A Reference Guide and Problem Sets, pages 89–91

Optional
Dividing Integers and Decimals

Calculator

Keywords and Pronunciation
quotient: the answer to a division problem

inverse operations: mathematical operations that undo each other, such as addition and subtraction, or multiplication and division

order of operations: the order in which operations must be computed when more than one operation is involved

Groundwork: Preparing for the Lesson [online]
In this groundwork, you will review what you have learned about determining the sign of a product. Since products and quotients are closely related, this will help prepare you for dividing signed numbers.

Notes

Learn: Introduction to Dividing Signed Numbers [online]

Dividing signed numbers is easy!

Ignore the signs of the numbers and divide as usual.

Give the quotient a sign using the chart below:

Sign of the quotient $a \div b$

		a	
		Positive	Negative
b	Positive	+	-
	Negative	-	+

Notes

Worked Examples: Dividing Integers and Decimals [online]

Notes

Learn: Finding the Mean [online]

When finding the mean, the number of values you are averaging is always positive—so you will always be dividing by a positive number.

Notes

Mathcasts: Evaluate Expressions [online]

View the video to see how to solve a typical problem.

Summary: Dividing Integers and Decimals [online]

When evaluating an expression that includes the quotient of signed numbers, keep the following important facts in mind.

- Substitute in for variables, using parentheses.

- Use the order of operations correctly.

- Remember the rules for multiplying and dividing.

- Remember the rules for adding and subtracting.

Offline Learning: Dividing Integers and Decimals [offline]

In the Book

Review pages 89-90 in the Reference Guide.

Problem Sets

Complete Problems 1–29 odd on page 91 of the Reference Guide.

Lesson Assessment: Dividing Integers and Decimals Quiz [online]

Now go back online to complete the lesson quiz.

Student Guide

Multiplication and Division Properties

Previously, you've learned some properties of addition—rules that are always true for *any* addition sentence. In this lesson you will learn some properties of multiplication and division.

In algebra, it's important to know these properties so you can easily rearrange an expression to create other, equivalent expressions that make an equation easier to solve.

Goals for the Lesson
- Identify properties of equality.

- Use a property of equality to simplify an expression.

- Use a property of equality to solve an equation.

Graded Activities in This Lesson
Lesson Quiz (computer-scored)

Materials
Pre-Algebra: A Reference Guide and Problem Sets, pages 92—95

Optional
Multiplication and Division Properties Solutions

Calculator

Keywords and Pronunciation
reciprocals: two numbers whose product is 1

Groundwork: Preparing for the Lesson [online]
In this groundwork, you will revisit some addition and subtraction properties. In this lesson, you will learn rules for rearranging multiplication and division expressions into new, equivalent expressions.

Notes

Learn Mult. and Div. Properties Involving 0, 1, and –1 [online]

These properties probably seem pretty obvious to you! In order to succeed as you progress in your study of mathematics, you'll need to have vocabulary that accurately and precisely describes what steps you take to solve a problem. Naming the properties helps us agree on a common language to talk about mathematics.

Notes

Learn: The Reciprocal Property of Multiplication [online]

To convert a number into a fraction, you can always put the number in the numerator with 1 in the denominator. This is because of the identity property of division: Any number divided by 1 is itself.

$$6 = \frac{6}{1} \qquad -9 = \frac{-9}{1} = -\frac{9}{1} \qquad 3.14 = \frac{3.14}{1}$$

If you use this strategy, you only need to remember one definition of a reciprocal: The reciprocal of $\frac{a}{b}$ is $\frac{b}{a}$.

Notes

Learn: Commutative and Associative Properties [online]

Remember, *commutative* is a word that is similar to *commute*, *commuter*, or *commuting*. When you commute to work or school, you follow the same route in each direction—you just change the **order** in which you see things along the way.

Associative is a word that is similar to *associate*. When you associate with someone, you spend time with them in a **group**.

Notes

Learn: Simplifying Expressions [online]

Keep these tips handy as you try the simplifying problems on the homework!

Notes

Learn: Solving Equations [online]

Remember to check your answer in the original equation once you've found your answer. The equation should always be a true statement if you've correctly solved for the variable.

Notes

Summary: Multiplication and Division Properties [online]

In this lesson, you have learned about several properties of multiplication and division and their applications.

Knowing how to use these properties is an important step in being able to solve equations using algebra.

Offline Learning: Multiplication and Division Properties [offline]

In the Book
Review pages 92–95 in the Reference Guide.

Problem Sets
Complete Problems 1–19 odd and 21–26 on page 96 of the Reference Guide.

Lesson Assessment: Multiplication and Division Properties Quiz

[online]
Now go back online to complete the lesson quiz.

Student Guide

Rounding and Estimation

About how much does that basketball cost? Approximately how many people will be attending the parade? Sometimes questions do not need exact answers. Instead, you can give a rounded answer. Today you will practice rounding decimals to a given place and then use rounding to check calculations.

Goals for the Lesson
- Round a number to a specified place.

- Use rounding to estimate the value of an expression.

- Identify a reasonable answer to a given problem.

- Determine whether or not an answer to an equation or word problem is reasonable.

Graded Activities in This Lesson
Mid-Unit Test (computer-scored)

Materials
Pre-Algebra: A Reference Guide and Problem Sets, pages 97–101

Optional
Rounding and Estimation Solutions

Keywords and Pronunciation
none

Groundwork: Preparing for the Lesson [online]
In this groundwork, you will practice rounding whole numbers to a specified place.

Notes

Learn: Rules for Rounding [online]

One of the hardest things about rounding is remembering the names for each of the decimal places. One common way to remember the names is by thinking about the places as paired up on either side of the decimal point.

tens/tenths

hundreds/hundredths

thousands/thousandths

Be careful, though—the first place to the right of the decimal place is the tenths place, but the first place to the left of the decimal place isn't the tens place—it's the unit or ones place.

Notes

Learn: Using Rounding to Estimate [online]

You might be wondering why to bother learning about estimation. Isn't it better to get an exact answer if you can? And can't you always use a calculator to easily get the exact answer? It might be easier, but most people don't always have a calculator at the ready. You might be standing in the aisle at the grocery store and want to figure out how many packages of paper cups to buy for your picnic; or you might be driving and trying to figure out when you'll arrive at your destination. Estimation is a skill that most people use every day.

Notes

Mathcasts: Product Estimation [online]

View the video to see how to solve a typical problem.

Summary: Rounding and Estimation [online]

- When you round a decimal number to a given place, you are finding a specific number it is close to.

- When you round a decimal number to a decimal place, change every digit to the right of the one you are rounding to zero. Zeros after the decimal place can be dropped.

- When you estimate a calculation, round each number in the expression to the same place, then perform the operations as indicated.

Offline Learning: Rounding and Estimation [offline]

In the Book
Review pages 97–100 in the Reference Guide.

Problem Sets
Complete Problems 1–10 and 13–21 odd on pages 100–101 of the Reference Guide.

Mid-Unit Assessment: Multiplication and Division Rounding and Estimation Test [online]

Now go back online to complete the mid-unit test.

Student Guide

Equations Involving Multiplication and Division

As you know, adding or subtracting the same number on both sides of an equation can help solve certain equations. Similarly, other equations can be solved by multiplying or dividing both sides of an equation by the same number. The inverse operation is the correct operation to use when solving an equation.

Goals for the Lesson
- Use transformation by multiplication or division to solve an equation.

Graded Activities in This Lesson
Lesson Quiz (computer-scored)

Materials
Pre-Algebra: A Reference Guide and Problem Sets, pages 103–106

Optional
Equations Involving Multiplication and Division Solutions

Calculator

Keywords and Pronunciation
equivalent equations: equations that have the same solution

Groundwork: Preparing for the Lesson [online]
In this groundwork, you will review what you know about inverse operations.

Notes

Learn: Properties of Equality [online]
In this activity, you will learn how to transform and solve simple equations using the multiplication and division properties of equality.

Use a property of equality to transform each equation. What is the solution for each equation?

$$\frac{x}{5} = 10 \qquad\qquad\qquad 5x = 10$$

Learn: Transformations [online]

It's important to show your work clearly. Here are some things you should always remember when showing your work:

- Always begin by writing the original equation.

- For each transformation, rewrite the equation on a new line, below your previous work.

- Make sure that the expressions on either side of the equals symbol are truly equivalent.

- Clearly show how each side of the equation is simplified in each step.

- Check your work. You might want to tell the reader you're doing a check by using a check mark.

Correct:	Incorrect:
$\dfrac{x}{3} = 8$	$\dfrac{x}{3} = 8 \cdot 3 = 24$
$\dfrac{x}{3} \cdot 3 = 8 \cdot 3$	* The above work is not shown vertically. Even though the answer is correct, the solution does not show that the multiplication property of equality was used. The answer has also not been checked.
$x = 24$	
Check:	
$\dfrac{24}{3} \overset{?}{=} 8$	
$8 = 8$	

Notes

Mathcasts: Transformations [online]

View the video to see how to solve a typical problem.

Summary: Equations Involving Multiplication and Division [online]

Applying a transformation to an equation results in a new equation that is equivalent to the first equation. The transformed equation has the same solution.

When you transform an equation, the goal is to arrive at the simplest equation: the equation where the variable is alone on one side of the equals symbol.

Offline Learning: Equations Involving Multiplication and Division
[offline]

In the Book
Review pages 103–105 in the Reference Guide.

Problem Sets
Complete Problems 1–29 odd on page 106 of the Reference Guide.

Lesson Assessment: Equations Involving Multiplication and Division Quiz [online]
Now go back online to complete the lesson quiz.

Student Guide

Multiplication and Division Applications, Part 1

Are you interested in sports? In cooking? In art? No matter what your interests are, there is probably a formula that relates to it. You might want to figure out how to calculate a baseball player's on-base percentage, how to convert between tablespoons and teaspoons, or how to find the amount of paint you need to finish a project. In this lesson, you will learn how to use formulas to find solutions to word problems.

Goals for the Lesson
* Use a formula to solve a word problem.

Graded Activities in This Lesson
Lesson Quiz (computer-scored)

Materials
Pre-Algebra: A Reference Guide and Problem Sets, pages 107–111

Optional
Multiplication and Division Applications Solutions

Calculator

Keywords and Pronunciation
none

Groundwork: Preparing for the Lesson [online]
In this Groundwork, you will review what you know about evaluating expressions.

Notes

Learn: Using Formulas [online]

When substituting in for variables in an equation, make sure you use parentheses or other multiplication symbols when appropriate. Always be sure to read the problem all the way through so you know what letters are being used to represent what variables. It is common to use the first letter of a quantity as the variable (for example, *d* for distance, etc.), but sometimes it can be unclear—is *C* total cost, or cost per person? Is *m* minutes or miles?

Notes

Learn: Properties of Equality and Formulas [online]

Notice that there can be multiple forms of an equation relating the same quantities. For example, you have seen the formula $d = rt$ relate distance (*d*), rate (*r*), and time (*t*).

In this lesson, you also see the formula $s = \dfrac{d}{t}$ relate distance (*d*), speed (*s*), and time (*t*).

These formulas say the same thing about how the three quantities are related; they are *equivalent forms* of the same equation, since rate and speed are the same.

Notes

MathCast: Using Formulas Involving Multiplication and Division [online]

View the video to see how to solve a typical problem.

Summary: Multiplication and Division Applications, Part 1 [online]

In this lesson, you have learned about how formulas can be used to solve problems.

These steps are used to solve problems that involve a formula:

- Read the problem.
- Write the formula.
- Substitute known values of variables into the formula.
- Solve for the unknown variable to get the answer.

Offline Learning: Multiplication and Division Applications, Part 1 [offline]

In the Book
Review pages 107-109 in the Reference Guide.

Problem Sets
Complete Problems 1–15 odd and 25–28 on pages 110–111 of the Reference Guide.

Lesson Assessment: Multiplication and Division Applications, Part 1 Quiz [online]

Now go back online to complete the lesson quiz.

Student Guide

Multiplication and Division Applications, Part 2

You have learned that a formula can be transformed to solve for a variable. But what if you want to solve a formula for a certain variable, but you don't yet know the values of the other variables in the formula? A literal equation is an equation that has one or more variables; in this lesson, you will learn to rewrite literal equations into different, equivalent forms.

Goals for the Lesson

- Solve a literal equation for a given variable.

Graded Activities in This Lesson

Lesson Quiz (computer-scored)

Materials

Pre-Algebra: A Reference Guide and Problem Sets, pages 107–110

Optional
Multiplication and Division Applications Solutions

Calculator

Keywords and Pronunciation

Groundwork: Preparing for the Lesson [online]

In this Groundwork, you will try your hand at determining if two equations are equivalent.

Notes

Learn: Literal Equations [online]

To solve a literal equation, you will use the same strategies you used when writing equivalent equations for formulas in the previous lesson. If you don't know how to get started solving a literal equation, you can always try to substitute actual numbers for the variables—just don't substitute a value in a variable you are solving. Choose numbers that will be easy to recognize if you simplify the expression—prime numbers like 2, 3, 5, 7, or 11 are generally good choices.

Here's an example:

Solve for b: $Q = \dfrac{abc}{2}$

If you don't know how to get started, choose numbers for every variable except b and substitute them. You can choose whatever numbers you want!

Let: $Q = 11$, $a = 5$, $c = 3$.

$11 = \dfrac{5 \cdot b \cdot 3}{2}$. Now, solve this equation. Try *not* to simplify. Pay attention to what steps you take. Once you have solved for b, repeat the process with the variables instead.

$11 = \dfrac{5 \cdot b \cdot 3}{2}$	$Q = \dfrac{abc}{2}$
$11 \cdot 2 = 5 \cdot b \cdot 3$	$Q \cdot 2 = a \cdot b \cdot c$
$11 \cdot 2 = 5 \cdot 3 \cdot b$	$Q \cdot 2 = ac \cdot b$
$\dfrac{11 \cdot 2}{5 \cdot 3} = b$	$\dfrac{Q \cdot 2}{ac} = b$

Notes

Worked Examples: Multiplication and Division Applications, Part 2 [online]
Notes

Mathcasts: Solve Variable Equations [online]

View the video to see how to solve a typical problem.

Summary: Multiplication and Division Applications, Part 2 [online]

Now you know how to transform a literal equation into equivalent equations. Remember that you can treat all variables in the equation—other than the one you are trying to solve for—as if they were actual numbers. That can make it easier to solve for the specified variable. Use the properties of equality to solve the equation for the desired variable.

Offline Learning: Multiplication and Division Applications, Part 2

[offline]

In the Book

Review pages 107–109 in the Reference Guide.

Problem Sets

Complete Problems 17–23 on page 110 of the Reference Guide.

Lesson Assessment: Multiplication and Division Applications, Part 2 Quiz [online]

Now go back online to complete the lesson quiz.

Student Guide

Multiplication and Division Review

You have finished studying the multiplication and division unit, which includes multiplying integers and decimals, dividing integers and decimals, multiplication and division properties, rounding and estimation, equations involving multiplication and division, and multiplication and division applications. Now it's time to pull together what you have learned. Throughout the review, see how the skills you have learned relate to the pre-algebra big ideas.

Goals for the Lesson
* Review the concepts and skills learned in the unit.

Materials
"Multiplication and Division" in *Pre-Algebra: A Reference Guide and Problem Sets*

Multiplication and Division Practice Problems

Preparing for the Unit Test

Unit Review: Multiplication and Division Review [online]

In this activity, choose the topics you feel you need to review. Under Try These, you will find interactive problems that will test your understanding of each big idea. As you work through this lesson, take notes in the spaces provided.

Summary: Multiplication and Division Review [online]

In this unit you covered the following topics:

- Multiplying integers and decimals

- Dividing integers and decimals

- Multiplication and division properties

- Rounding and estimation

- Equations involving multiplication and division

- Multiplication and division applications

Offline Learning: Multiplication and Division Review [offline]

How well have you mastered the goals of this unit? Complete the Multiplication and Division Practice Problems. These problems are similar to the problems you will have on the Unit Test.

You can also:

- Review the Multiplication and Division unit in *Pre-Algebra: A Reference Guide and Problem Sets.*

- Review your notes in your Student Guide.

- Read and follow the instructions in Preparing for the Unit Test.

Practice Problems

Multiplication and Division

For questions 1–7, simplify the expressions.

1. $-3 \cdot 12$

2. $-9 \cdot (-4)$

3. $5 \cdot (-13)$

4. $14 \div (-7)$

5. $-24 \div (-3)$

6. $12 - 8 \div (-4)$

7. $14 + (-3) \cdot 5$

For questions 8–9, determine the signs of the products without doing the multiplication.

8. $(-4)(5)(-3)(12)(3)(-7)$

9. $(-2)(-8)(-7)(6)(10)(-4)$

10. Find the mean of the following numbers.

$$-3, 5, -12, 8, -9, -1$$

For questions 11–12, evaluate the expressions if $a = 6$ and $b = -4$.

11. $\dfrac{8a}{b}$

12. $\dfrac{3a}{-2b - 5}$

For questions 13–14, find the value of x that makes the equation true.

13. $(-4)(5)(x) = (2)(10)$

14. $(3)(-6)(x) = 0$

15. Round the number 12536.373259 to each of the following places.

    a)   nearest tenth:

    b)   nearest hundredth:

    c)   nearest ten thousandth:

16. Estimate the product by rounding each number to the nearest unit.

$$(0.54)(2.87)(4.03)$$

For questions 17–19, use transformations to solve the equations. State the property you used to transform each equation.

17. $-4x = -24$

18. $7y = -28$

19. $\dfrac{m}{-3} = 14$

20. Solve the equation for m.

$$4m = 5n$$

Answers

1. −36

2. 36

3. −65

4. −2

5. 8

6. 14

7. −1

8. Negative, because there are an odd number of negative factors

9. Positive, because there are an even number of negative factors

10. −2

11. −12

12. 6

13. −1

14. 0

15. a) 12536.4

    b) 12536.37

    c) 12536.3733

16. 12

17. $x = 6$: Division Property of Equality

18. $x = -4$: Division Property of Equality

19. $m = -42$: Multiplication Property of Equality

20. $m = \dfrac{5n}{4}$

Unit Assessment

Multiplication and Division Unit Test, Offline

(6 points)

1. At the grocery store checkout, you watch at the register as it rings up your purchases and coupons. The prices were as follows:

   $2.95
   $1.19
   $4.61
   $1.74
   $3.04
   $8.83
   $1.16
   − $0.75 (coupon)
   − $1.00 (coupon)

   The register gives your total bill as $21.77.

   A. Round each price to the nearest dollar, and then estimate the total amount of the bill.

   B. Use your estimate to determine whether the total on the register is reasonable.

(8 points)

2. The following formula relates three quantities: Force (F), mass (m), and acceleration (a).

$$F = ma$$

a. Solve this equation for a.

b. If the force is $F = -25$ units and the mass is $m = 10$ units, find the acceleration, a.

c. If the force is $F = 25$ units and the acceleration is $a = 5$ units, find the mass, m.

Answer:

Your Score	____ of 14

Student Guide

Equivalent Fractions, Part 1

What do the fractions $\frac{1}{3}$, $\frac{3}{9}$, and $\frac{8}{24}$ have in common? All three of them represent the same number. They are equivalent fractions. The word *equivalent* comes from a Latin word meaning "equal in value." So equivalent fractions are equal in value, even if the numbers in the numerator and denominator are different.

Goals for the Lesson
- Determine if two fractions are equivalent.
- Simplify a fraction that has a variable factor in the numerator or denominator.
- Write a proper fraction in lowest terms.

Graded Activities in This Lesson
Lesson Quiz (computer-scored)

Materials
Pre-Algebra: A Reference Guide and Problem Sets, pages 115–116 and 118

Optional
Equivalent Fractions Solutions

Calculator

Keywords and Pronunciation
equivalent fractions: fractions that name the same number

factor: any whole number multiplied with another to form a product

greatest common factor (GCF): the greatest integer that is a factor of two or more given integers

lowest terms: a fraction whose numerator and denominator have no common factor other than 1 or –1

Groundwork: Preparing for the Lesson [online]
The Groundwork reviews what was learned in a previous lesson. As you work through the activity online, use the spaces below to take notes and to answer the question.
Notes

Explain how to find all the factors of a whole number.

Learn: Divisibility Rules [online]

As you work through the activity online, use the spaces below to take notes and to answer the question.

Notes

How do you know if a fraction is in lowest terms?

Learn: Equivalent Fractions [online]

As you work through the activity online, use the spaces below to take notes and to answer the question.

Notes

Write two fractions equivalent to $\frac{1}{2}$.

Worked Examples: Equivalent Fractions, Part 1 [online]

Notes

MathCast: Equivalent Fractions [online]

View the video to see how to solve a typical problem.

Summary: Equivalent Fractions, Part 1 [online]

A fraction is in lowest terms when the numerator and denominator have no common factors other than 1.

Fractions with the same value are called equivalent fractions.

Offline Learning: Equivalent Fractions, Part 1 [offline]

Skills Update

1. Simplify: $\dfrac{6 + 3(5)}{11 - 8}$.

2. Which of the following statements is false?

    a. $-\dfrac{2}{7} = \dfrac{-2}{7}$

    b. $-\dfrac{2}{7} = \dfrac{2}{-7}$

    c. $-\dfrac{2}{7} = \dfrac{-2}{-7}$

    d. $\dfrac{-2}{7} = \dfrac{2}{-7}$

3. What is the value of the expression $(5a - 1) \cdot (3b)$ when $a = 2$ and $b = 1$?

4. Write an inequality for the following phrase:
   The sum of 3 and x is greater than the sum of 16 and y.

In the Book

Review pages 115–116 in the reference guide.

Complete the Skills Update in the student guide.

Do the Math

More on Equivalent Fractions

Can you think of another way to determine if $\frac{6}{9}$ and $\frac{8}{12}$ are equivalent fractions?

You can find the cross products of the fractions. Multiply the numerator of the first fraction by the denominator of the second fraction. Then multiply the numerator of the second fraction by the denominator of the first fraction. Set the products equal to each other in an equation.

$12 \cdot 6 = 9 \cdot 8$

$72 = 72$

Simplify. If the statement is true, the fractions are equivalent.

The products are equal. Thus, $\frac{6}{9}$ and $\frac{8}{12}$ are equivalent fractions.

Prime Factorization

When you write 84 as $2 \cdot 2 \cdot 3 \cdot 7$, you are writing the prime factorization of 84. Look at the two methods for finding the prime factorization of 84.

Method 1: A factor tree	Method 2: Repeated division
84 ╱ ╲ 4 21 ╱╲ ╱╲ ② ② ③ ⑦	$\begin{array}{r}42\\2\overline{)84}\end{array}$ $\begin{array}{r}21\\2\overline{)42}\end{array}$ $\begin{array}{r}7\\3\overline{)21}\end{array}$

Problem Sets

Complete Problems 1–23 odd on page 118 of the Reference Guide.

Extra Practice (optional)

Complete Problems 1–24 even on page 118 of the Reference Guide.

Lesson Assessment: Equivalent Fractions, Part 1 Quiz [online]

Now go back online to complete the lesson quiz.

Answers

Skills Update

1. 7

2. Statement C is false.

3. 27

4. $3 + x > 16 + y$

Student Guide

Equivalent Fractions, Part 2

In mathematics, one skill builds on another. You have already learned how to determine whether two fractions are equivalent by writing each fraction in lowest terms. Now you will use that skill to solve equations and real-world problems involving fractions.

Goals for the Lesson
*   Solve a word problem involving fractions.

*   Solve an equation involving fractions.

Graded Activities in This Lesson
Lesson Quiz (computer-scored)

Materials
Pre-Algebra: A Reference Guide and Problem Sets, pages 117–118

Optional
Equivalent Fractions Solutions

Calculator

Keywords and Pronunciation
equivalent fractions: fractions that name the same number

Groundwork: Preparing for the Lesson [online]
The Groundwork reviews what was learned in the previous lesson. As you work through the activity online, use the space below to take notes and answer the question.

Notes

Explain how to simplify an algebraic fraction.

Learn: Using Equivalent Fractions [online]

As you work through the activity online, use the space below to take notes and answer the question.

Notes

Show two different ways to solve the equation $\frac{20}{60} = \frac{x}{3}$.

Worked Examples: Equivalent Fractions, Part 2 [online]

Notes

MathCast: Solve an Equation [online]

View the video to see how to solve a typical problem.

Summary: Equivalent Fractions, Part 2 [online]

Equivalent fractions can be used to solve equations and real-world problems.

You can find a fraction that is equivalent to another fraction by multiplying by or dividing out the same number in the numerator and denominator in one or both of the fractions.

Offline Learning: Equivalent Fractions, Part 2 [offline]

Skills Update

1. Which is **NOT** a factor of 45?

    a. 1

    b. 3

    c. 5

    d. 7

2. What is the value of the expression |8| + |−3|?

3. What is the value of the expression −12 − (−5)?

4. Which statement is true?

    a. −2.5 > −1.5

    b. −8.7 < −8.75

    c. −3.27 < 2

    d. 3.7 = − 3.7

In the Book

Review page 117–118 in the Reference Guide.

Complete the Skills Update in the Student Guide.

Do the Math

Another Real-World Example

Gene saves 5 cents of every dollar he earns. Jim saves $\frac{1}{20}$ of his earnings. Do they save equivalent fractions of their earnings?

One way to compare Gene's 5 cents of every dollar and $\frac{1}{20}$ of Jim's earnings is to write them as equivalent fractions with the same denominator.

Fraction Gene saves: $\qquad \frac{5}{100} = \frac{5 \div 5}{100 \div 5} = \frac{1}{20}$

Fraction Jim saves: $\qquad \frac{1}{20}$

Yes, Gene and Jim save equivalent amounts.

Problem Sets

Complete Problems 25–39 odd on page 118 of the Reference Guide.

Lesson Assessment: Equivalent Fractions, Part 2 Quiz [online]

Now go back online to complete the lesson quiz.

Answers

Skills Update

1. Answer D
2. 11
3. −7
4. Answer C

Student Guide

Multiplying Fractions

You and your friend want to share last night's leftover pizza equally. One-half of the pizza was left over. How can you determine how much of the original pizza each of you should get? You can find the answer by multiplying fractions.

Goals for the Lesson
*   Multiply fractions.

Graded Activities in This Lesson
Lesson Quiz (computer-scored)

Materials
Pre-Algebra: A Reference Guide and Problem Sets, pages 119–122

Optional
Multiplying Fractions Solutions

Calculator

Groundwork: Preparing for the Lesson [online]
Review your knowledge of finding equivalent fractions. As you work through this activity, record any notes and answer the question below.

Notes

Explain how to find fractions that are equivalent to $\frac{4}{8}$.

Learn: Multiplying Fractions [online]

As you work through this activity, record any notes and answer the questions below.

Notes

Why is it a good idea to divide out common factors before you multiply two fractions?

How is multiplying fractions like multiplying integers?

Worked Examples: Multiplying Fractions [online]

Notes

MathCast: Multiply Fractions to Solve a Problem [online]

View the video to see how to solve a typical problem.

Summary: Multiplying Fractions [online]

- To multiply two fractions, multiply the numerators and denominators. Write the product in lowest terms.

- Remember, you can multiply first and then write the product in lowest terms, or you can divide out common factors first and then multiply. Either method will result in the same product, though by dividing out common factors first you will have smaller numbers to work with for the remainder of the problem.

Offline Learning: Multiplying Fractions [offline]

In the Book
Review pages 119–121 in the Reference Guide.

Do the Math
Solve the problem presented in the opener:

You and your friend want to share last night's leftover pizza equally. One-half of the pizza was left over. How can you determine how much of the original pizza each of you should get?

The problem tells you that $\frac{1}{2}$ of the pizza was left over. Since you are sharing the remaining pizza equally, you each get $\frac{1}{2}$ of the leftover pizza. (Remember that the word *of* tells you to "multiply.") Multiply to find how much of the original pizza you will get.

$$\frac{1}{2} \cdot \frac{1}{2} = \frac{1 \cdot 1}{2 \cdot 2} = \frac{1}{4}$$

You each get $\frac{1}{4}$ of the original pizza.

Problem Sets
Complete Problems 1–8, 13–25 odd, and 31–34 on pages 121–122 of the Reference Guide.

Extra Practice (optional)
Complete Problems 14–24 even on page 121 of the Reference Guide.

Lesson Assessment: Multiplying Fractions Quiz [online]
Now go back online to complete the lesson quiz.

Student Guide

Dividing Fractions

Multiplication and division are inverse operations—one undoes the other. This relationship allows you to use multiplication to divide fractions. Dividing a number by a fraction is the same as multiplying the number by the reciprocal of the fraction. In this lesson, you will learn about reciprocals and learn how to divide fractions.

Goals for the Lesson

- Find the reciprocals of fractions.

- Divide fractions.

Graded Activities in This Lesson
Lesson Quiz (computer-scored)

Materials
Pre-Algebra: A Reference Guide and Problem Sets, pages 123–126

Optional
Dividing Fractions Solutions

Calculator

Keywords and Pronunciation
multiplicative inverse: two numbers whose product is 1, also known as *reciprocals*

reciprocals: two numbers whose product is 1

Groundwork: Preparing for the Lesson [online]

The Groundwork reviews what you learned in a previous lesson. As you work through this activity, record any notes and answer the question below.
Notes

How do you multiply two fractions?

Learn: Finding Reciprocals   [online]

As you work through this activity, record any notes and answer the question below.

Notes

How do you find the reciprocal of a fraction?

Learn: Dividing Fractions [online]

As you work through this activity, record any notes below.

Notes

Bror was asked to find the quotient of $\frac{5}{12} \div \frac{1}{3}$. He said the solution was $\frac{12}{15}$. Was he correct?

Bror's Solution:

$$\frac{5}{12} \div \frac{1}{3} = \frac{12}{5} \cdot \frac{1}{3}$$

$$= \frac{12 \cdot 1}{5 \cdot 3}$$

$$= \frac{12}{15}$$

Is Bror's solution correct or incorrect? Explain.

Worked Examples: Dividing Fractions [online]

As you work through this activity, record any notes and answer the question below.

Notes

How do you divide a whole number by a fraction?

MathCast: Divide Fractions [online]

View the video to see how to solve a typical problem.

Summary: Dividing Fractions [online]

In this lesson, you have learned how to find the reciprocal of a number and to divide fractions using the reciprocal.

Two numbers are reciprocals of each other if their product is 1.

To divide by a fraction, multiply by the reciprocal of the fraction.

Offline Learning: Dividing Fractions [offline]

In the Book

Review pages 123–125 in the Reference Guide.

Do the Math

Think About This

For a series of subtractions, it is possible to change each difference into the sum of its opposite *before* simplifying. For example: $-4 - 6 - 2 - 11 - 8 = -4 + (-6) + (-2) + (-11) + (-8) = -31$.

For a series of divisions, is it possible to multiply by the reciprocal of each fraction before simplifying?

For instance, would $\frac{2}{3} \div \frac{5}{12} \div \frac{9}{10}$ give the same result as $\frac{2}{3} \cdot \frac{12}{5} \cdot \frac{10}{9}$, or must you compute the quotients one at a time?

Problem Sets
Complete Problems 1–4, 9–15, and 35–36 on pages 125–126 of the Reference Guide.

Extra Practice (optional)
Complete Problems 5–6 and 17–21 odd on page 125 of the Reference Guide.

Lesson Assessment: Dividing Fractions Quiz [online]
Now go back online to complete the lesson quiz.

Student Guide

Common Denominators

You've learned to determine if two fractions are equivalent fractions. Knowing how to write equivalent fractions will help you express fractions using the same denominator. Finding the least common denominator (LCD) of a set of fractions is a skill you will use repeatedly. In this lesson, you learn how to find the LCD.

Goals for the Lesson

- Find the LCD of a pair of fractions.

- Find equivalent fractions with a common denominator for a set of fractions.

- Compare fractions.

Graded Activities in This Lesson
Lesson Quiz (computer-scored)

Materials
Pre-Algebra: A Reference Guide and Problem Sets, pages 127–131

Optional
Common Denominators Solutions

Calculator

Keywords and Pronunciation
least common multiple (LCM): the least common nonzero number that is a multiple of two or more nonzero given numbers

least common denominator (LCD): the least common multiple of two or more denominators

equivalent fractions: fractions that name the same number

Groundwork: Preparing for the Lesson [online]
Review material about least common multiples (LCMs). As you work through this activity, record any notes and answer the question below.

Notes

How would you find the LCM of three numbers?

Learn: Finding the LCD [online]

As you work through this activity, record any notes and answer the questions below.

Notes

If one denominator is a factor of the second denominator, what is the LCD of the two fractions?

If two denominators share no common factors other than 1, what is the LCD of the two fractions?

For any pair of fractions, is the LCD always greater than either denominator?

Learn: Using the LCD [online]

As you work through this activity, record any notes and answer the question below.

Notes

Bror was asked to express $\frac{1}{7}$ and $\frac{3}{14}$ using the same denominator. This is his solution.

> Bror's Solution:
>
> The LCD is 14.
>
> The fraction $\frac{3}{14}$ already has the LCD.
>
> To rename $\frac{1}{7}$:
> $$\frac{1}{7} = \frac{1}{7} \bullet \frac{1}{2}$$
> $$= \frac{1}{14}$$
>
> The fractions are $\frac{1}{14}$ and $\frac{3}{14}$.

Is Bror's solution correct or incorrect? Explain.

Learn: Comparing Fractions [online]

As you work through this activity, record any notes and answer the question below.

Notes

How is comparing two fractions like comparing two whole numbers?

Worked Examples: Common Denominators [online]

As you work through this activity, record any notes below.

Notes

MathCast: Comparing Fractions with Unlike Denominators [online]

View the video to see how to solve a typical problem.

Summary: Common Denominators [online]

In this lesson, you learned how to write equivalent fractions with a common denominator by finding the LCD of a given pair of fractions. You also learned how to compare two fractions.

Notes

Offline Learning: Common Denominators [offline]

In the Book
Review pages 127–130 in the Reference Guide.

Do the Math

How Are LCD and LCM Related?

The least common denominator (LCD) of two or more fractions is the least common multiple (LCM) of their denominators. You can write equivalent fractions by renaming the fractions using the LCM as the denominators.

What is the LCM of 6 and 15? What is the LCD of $\frac{5}{6}$ and $\frac{4}{15}$?

Problem Sets
Complete Problems 1–31 odd on page 131 of the Reference Guide.

Lesson Assessment: Common Denominators Quiz [online]
Now go back online to complete the lesson quiz.

Student Guide
Adding and Subtracting Fractions, Part 1

You may have heard the expression, "It's like comparing apples and oranges." The expression means that you can't compare two things that are essentially different and expect your comparison to make any sense. Similarly, you can't add or subtract two fractions whose denominators are different. It would be like comparing apples and oranges. In this lesson, you will learn how to add and subtract fractions.

Goals for the Lesson
- Add proper fractions.
- Subtract proper fractions.

Graded Activities in This Lesson
Lesson Quiz (computer-scored)

Materials
Pre-Algebra: A Reference Guide and Problem Sets, pages 132–135
Calculator

Optional
Adding and Subtracting Fractions Solutions

Keywords and Pronunciation
like denominators: fractions have like denominators when the denominators are the same

unlike denominators: fractions have unlike denominators when the denominators are different

Groundwork: Preparing for the Lesson [online]
Review the addition and subtraction of integers. As you work through this activity, record any notes and answer the questions below.

Notes

How do you add two integers with the same sign? How do you subtract two integers with the same sign?

How do you add two integers with different signs? How do you subtract two integers with different signs?

Learn: Adding and Subtracting Like Fractions [online]

As you work through this activity, record any notes and answer the question below.

Notes

How are adding and subtracting like fractions similar to adding and subtracting integers?

Learn: Adding and Subtracting Unlike Fractions [online]

As you work through this activity, record any notes and answer the question below.

Notes

What is the first step when you add unlike fractions?

Worked Examples: Adding and Subtracting Fractions, Part 1 [online]

As you work through this activity, record any notes below.

Notes

Summary: Adding and Subtracting Fractions, Part 1 [online]

In this lesson, you learned how to add and subtract fractions.

To add or subtract like fractions:

*   Add or subtract the numerators and keep the same denominator.

*   Simplify if possible.

To add or subtract unlike fractions:

*   Write equivalent fractions so that the fractions have the same denominator.

*   Add or subtract the fractions.

Skills Update: Practice Your Math Skills [online]

Complete the Skills Update online.

Offline Learning: Adding and Subtracting Fractions, Part 1 [offline]

In the Book

Review pages 132–134 in the Reference Guide.

Do the Math
Adding and Subtracting Fractions

Use the addition and subtraction skills you have developed with integers to add and subtract fractions.

Adding and subtracting fractions with the same denominator is fairly straightforward: Add or subtract the numerators, and then write the sum or difference over the denominator.

$$-\frac{3}{4} + \left(-\frac{1}{4}\right) = -\frac{4}{4} = -1$$

The least common denominator (LCD) is the least common multiple of the denominators. The LCD is helpful when you rename fractions for adding and subtracting. For example, you would want to find the LCD for the following expression before adding.

$$\frac{1}{2} + \left(-\frac{1}{8}\right)$$

Add $\frac{1}{2} + \left(-\frac{1}{8}\right)$.

Multiples of 2: 2, 4, 6, ⑧ ...　　　List the multiples of 2 and 8 to find the LCD.

Multiples of 8: ⑧ 16, 24, 32 ...　　　The LCD is 8.

$\frac{1}{2} = \frac{1 \cdot 4}{2 \cdot 4} = \frac{4}{8}$　　　Create an equivalent fraction by using the LCD.

$\frac{4}{8} + \left(-\frac{1}{8}\right) = \frac{3}{8}$　　　Add.

So $\frac{1}{2} + \left(-\frac{1}{8}\right) = \frac{3}{8}$

Now here's a chance to practice adding fractions. Complete the addition table.

+	$\frac{1}{4}$	$-\frac{2}{3}$	$-\frac{7}{8}$
$-\frac{5}{12}$			
$\frac{1}{3}$			
$\frac{4}{5}$			

Problem Sets

Complete Problems 1–19 on page 135 of the Reference Guide.

Lesson Assessment: Adding and Subtracting Fractions, Part 1
Quiz [online]
Now go back online to complete the lesson quiz.

Answers

Addition Table

+	$\dfrac{1}{4}$	$-\dfrac{2}{3}$	$-\dfrac{7}{8}$
$-\dfrac{5}{12}$	$\dfrac{-1}{6}$	$-1\dfrac{1}{12}$	$-1\dfrac{7}{24}$
$\dfrac{1}{3}$	$\dfrac{7}{12}$	$-\dfrac{1}{3}$	$-\dfrac{13}{24}$
$\dfrac{4}{5}$	$1\dfrac{1}{20}$	$\dfrac{2}{15}$	$-\dfrac{3}{40}$

Student Guide

Adding and Subtracting Fractions, Part 2

The ability to add and subtract fractions has many applications in everyday life. Recipes, measurements, time, and money are just some examples where these skills are needed. In this lesson you will learn how to solve word problems involving addition and subtraction of fractions.

Goals for the Lesson
- Solve a word problem involving addition and subtraction of fractions.

Graded Activities in This Lesson
Lesson Quiz (computer-scored)

Materials
Pre-Algebra: A Reference Guide and Problem Sets, pages 132–136

Optional
Adding and Subtracting Fractions Solutions

Calculator

Keywords and Pronunciation
none

Groundwork: Preparing for the Lesson [online]
Review the steps for finding the LCD of two fractions. As you work through this activity, record any notes and answer the question below.

Notes

How do you find the LCD of two fractions?

Learn: Solving a Word Problem [online]

As you work through this activity, record any notes and answer the question below.

Notes

What are the five steps in the problem-solving plan?

Worked Example: Adding and Subtracting Fractions, Part 2 [online]

As you work through this activity, record any notes below.

Notes

MathCast: Solve a Word Problem [online]

View the video to see how to solve a typical problem.

Summary: Adding and Subtracting Fractions, Part 2 [online]

In this lesson, you have learned to solve word problems involving addition and subtraction of fractions using the five-step problem-solving plan.

Notes

Offline Learning: Adding and Subtracting Fractions, Part 2 [offline]

Skills Update

1. Subtract: $-21.18 - (-16.37)$.

2. Solve the equation $-14x = -42$.

3. Write an expression for this word phrase: *four less than the product of two and a number.*

4. Evaluate $x - 5$ when $x = -2$.

In the Book

Review pages 132–134 in the Reference Guide.

Do the Math

Addition and subtraction of fractions can help you solve real-world situations such as the following one.

When Bryan left his home to go to his mother's house, he had $\frac{1}{2}$ of a tank of gas. When he arrived, he had $\frac{1}{8}$ of a tank of gas. How much gas did Bryan use on his trip?

To solve the problem, subtract the amount he arrived with from the amount he started with.

$$\frac{1}{2} - \frac{1}{8} = \frac{1}{2} + \left(-\frac{1}{8}\right)$$
$$= \frac{4}{8} + \left(-\frac{1}{8}\right)$$
$$= \frac{3}{8}$$

Bryan used $\frac{3}{8}$ of a tank of gas during his trip.

Problem Sets

Complete Problems 42–44 on page 136 of the Reference Guide.

Extra Practice (optional)

Complete Problem 45 on page 136 of the Reference Guide.

Lesson Assessment: Adding and Subtracting Fractions, Part 2
Quiz [online]

Now go back online to complete the lesson quiz.

Answers

Skills Update

1. −4.81
2. $x = 3$
3. $2n - 4$
4. −7

Student Guide

Working with Improper Fractions and Mixed Numbers

Sometimes amounts of things are greater than 1, so not all fractions are proper fractions. You might need $2\frac{1}{2}$ cups of sugar to bake a cake or $4\frac{1}{4}$ gallons of gas to fill your gas tank. In this lesson, you will learn to add and subtract mixed numbers and improper fractions.

Goals for the Lesson

*   Convert a mixed number to an improper fraction.

*   Add or subtract mixed numbers and improper fractions.

Graded Activities in This Lesson
Mid-Unit Test (computer-scored)

Materials
Pre-Algebra: A Reference Guide and Problem Sets, pages 137–141

Optional
Working with Mixed Numbers Solutions

Calculator

Keywords and Pronunciation
mixed number: a whole number plus a proper fraction

improper fraction: a positive fraction whose numerator is greater than or equal to its denominator, or the opposite of such a fraction

Groundwork: Preparing for the Lesson [online]
Review converting improper fractions to mixed numbers. As you work through this activity, record any notes and answer the question below.

Notes

How do you convert an improper fraction to a mixed number?

Learn: Converting Mixed Numbers to Improper Fractions [online]

As you work through this activity, record any notes and answer the question below.

Notes

How do you convert a mixed number to an improper fraction?

Learn: Adding and Subtracting Mixed Numbers [online]

As you work through this activity, record any notes and answer the question below.

Notes

In your own words, what are the two methods for adding and subtracting mixed numbers?

Worked Examples: Working with Improper Fractions and Mixed Numbers [online]

As you work through this activity, record any notes below.

Notes

MathCast: Add Mixed Numbers [online]

View the video to see how to solve a typical problem.

Summary: Working with Improper Fractions and Mixed Numbers

[online]

In this lesson, you learned how to add and subtract mixed numbers.

Method 1:

- Add or subtract the integer parts.

- Add or subtract the fraction parts.

- Simplify.

Method 2:
- Write each mixed number as an improper fraction.

- Add or subtract the fractions.

- Simplify.

Offline Learning: Working with Improper Fractions and Mixed Numbers [offline]

In the Book

Review pages 137–140 in the Reference Guide.

Problem Sets

Complete Problems 1–15 odd and 32–35 on pages 140–141 of the Reference Guide.

Mid-Unit Assessment: Fractions Test [online]

Now go back online to complete the Mid-Unit Assessment.

Student Guide
Multiplying and Dividing Mixed Numbers

Think of some real-world examples of mixed numbers. Maybe you walked $5\frac{1}{2}$ miles this week, used a recipe that called for $1\frac{3}{4}$ cups of kidney beans, or watched a movie that was $2\frac{1}{4}$ hours long. There are times when you need to perform multiplication and division using mixed numbers. You might want to find your average walking distance per day or the amount of kidney beans to use if you make $1\frac{1}{2}$ times the recipe. In this lesson, you will learn how to multiply and divide mixed numbers.

Goals for the Lesson
* Multiply fractions, mixed numbers, and integers.
* Divide fractions, mixed numbers, and integers.

Graded Activities in This Lesson
Lesson Quiz (computer-scored)

Materials
Pre-Algebra: A Reference Guide and Problem Sets, pages 142–145

Optional
Multiplying and Dividing Mixed Numbers

Calculator

Keywords and Pronunciation
reciprocals: two numbers whose product is 1

Groundwork: Preparing for the Lesson [online]
Review the skills needed to multiply and divide proper fractions. As you work through this activity, record any notes in the space below.

Notes

Learn: Multiplying Mixed Numbers   [online]

As you work through this activity, record any notes and answer the question below.

Notes

How is multiplying mixed numbers similar to multiplying proper fractions?

Learn: Dividing Mixed Numbers   [online]

As you work through this activity, record any notes and answer the question below.

Notes

How is dividing mixed numbers similar to dividing proper fractions?

Worked Examples: Multiplying and Dividing Mixed Numbers [online]

As you work through this activity, record any notes below.

Notes

MathCast: Dividing Mixed Numbers [online]

View the video to see how to solve a typical problem.

Summary: Multiplying and Dividing Mixed Numbers [online]

In this lesson, you have learned how to multiply and divide mixed numbers.

- To multiply mixed numbers, rewrite the mixed numbers as improper fractions and multiply. You can use mental math and the distributive property to multiply a fraction by a mixed number.

- To divide mixed numbers, rewrite the mixed numbers as improper fractions and change the problem to multiplication by multiplying by the reciprocal.

Offline Learning: Multiplying and Dividing Mixed Numbers [offline]

In the Book
Review pages 142–144 in the Reference Guide.

Problem Sets
Complete Problems 1–31 odd on page 145 of the Reference Guide.

Lesson Assessment: Multiplying and Dividing Mixed Numbers
Quiz [online]
Now go back online to complete the lesson quiz.

Student Guide

Equations with Fractions and Mixed Numbers

Once you know how to add, subtract, multiply, and divide fractions, you're ready to solve equations that involve fractions. In this lesson, you will learn to do just that.

Goals for the Lesson

- Use transformations to solve an addition or subtraction equation with mixed numbers or fractions.
- Use transformations to solve a multiplication equation with mixed numbers or fractions.

Graded Activities in This Lesson

Lesson Quiz (computer-scored)

Materials

Pre-Algebra: A Reference Guide and Problem Sets, pages 146–149

Optional

Equations with Fractions Solutions
Calculator

Keywords and Pronunciation

Groundwork: Preparing for the Lesson [online]

As you read through the lesson online, use the spaces below to take notes on each screen.

Notes

Learn: Transformations [online]

In this activity, you will apply your knowledge of adding and subtracting fractions and mixed numbers to solve equations. Use the space below to follow along with the example provided online.

Notes

Learn: Fractions as Coefficients [online]

In this lesson, you will learn to solve multiplication equations that involve fractions. Use the space provided here to follow along with the example online.

Notes

Worked Examples: Equations with Fractions and Mixed Numbers [online]

Notes

Summary: Equations with Fractions and Mixed Numbers [online]

The ultimate goal of performing a series of transformations is to develop an equivalent equation with the *variable* on one side and a *number* on the other. Reaching that goal may take many steps.

Simplify both sides of an equation before solving it; simplification is a transformation.

When a fraction is multiplied by the variable in an equation, you must divide both sides of the equation by the fraction, and then follow the rules for dividing fractions.

Offline Learning: Equations with Fractions and Mixed Numbers

[offline]

In the Book

Review pages 146–148 in the Reference Guide.

Problem Sets

Complete Problems 1–21 odd and 25–28 on page 149 of the Reference Guide.

Lesson Assessment: Equations with Fractions and Mixed Numbers Quiz [online]

Now go back online to complete the lesson quiz.

Student Guide

Fractions Review

You have finished studying the Fractions unit, which includes equivalent fractions, multiplying and dividing fractions, common denominators, adding and subtracting fractions, and working with improper fractions and mixed numbers. Now it's time to pull together what you have learned. Throughout the review, see how the skills you have learned relate to the Pre-Algebra big ideas.

Goals for the Lesson
- Review the concepts and skills learned in the unit.

Materials

"Fractions" in *Pre-Algebra: A Reference Guide and Problem Sets*
Preparing for the Unit Test

Unit Review: Fractions [online]

This is your chance to review the big ideas of Pre-Algebra you have learned in this unit of this course. Under Review These Activities, you will find activities that will review each big idea. Choose the topics you feel you need to review. Under Try These, you will find interactive problems that will test your understanding of each big idea. As you work through this lesson, take notes in the spaces provided.

Big Idea

A number is any entity that obeys the laws of arithmetic; all numbers obey the laws of arithmetic. The laws of arithmetic can be used to simplify algebraic expressions.

Big Idea

Expressions, equations, and inequalities express relationships between different entities.

Big Idea
The laws of arithmetic can be used to simplify algebraic expressions and equations. Solving an equation means finding values for the variable or variables that make the equation a true statement.

Big Idea
If you can create a mathematical model for a situation, you can use the model to solve other problems that you might not be able to solve otherwise. Algebraic equations can capture key relationships among quantities in the world.

Summary: Fractions Review [online]

In this unit, you covered the following topics:

- equivalent fractions
- multiplying fractions
- dividing fractions
- common denominators
- adding and subtracting fractions
- improper fractions and mixed numbers
- multiplying and dividing mixed numbers
- solving equations with fractions and mixed numbers

Offline Learning: Fractions Review [offline]

How well have you mastered the goals of this unit? Complete the Fractions Practice Problems. These problems are similar to the problems you will have on the Unit Test.

You can also

- Review the Fractions unit in *Pre-Algebra: A Reference Guide and Problem Sets*
- Review the notes in your Student Guide.
- Read and follow the instructions in Preparing for the Unit Test.

Practice Problems

Fractions

1. Which of the following fractions is *not* equivalent to $\frac{5}{12}$?

$\dfrac{10}{24}$ $\dfrac{20}{48}$ $\dfrac{15}{60}$ $\dfrac{15}{36}$

For questions 2–4, write the fractions in lowest terms.

2. $\dfrac{12}{54}$

3. $\dfrac{14}{36}$

4. $\dfrac{24}{32}$

For questions 5–6, find the value of *x* that makes the equation true.

5. $\dfrac{4}{13} = \dfrac{x}{39}$

6. $\dfrac{5}{14} = \dfrac{25}{x}$

For questions 7–14, simplify the expressions.

7. $\dfrac{2}{5} \bullet \dfrac{15}{16}$

8. $\dfrac{9}{14} \div \dfrac{3}{4}$

9. $-4\dfrac{4}{5} \bullet \left(-3\dfrac{3}{4}\right)$

10. $\dfrac{4}{15} + \left(-\dfrac{2}{5}\right)$

11. $3\dfrac{3}{4} - \dfrac{1}{2}$

12. $-5\dfrac{5}{6} \div 7$

13. $2\dfrac{4}{7} \div 12$

14. $-2\dfrac{1}{2} + \dfrac{1}{6}$

For questions 15–16, solve the equations.

15. $\dfrac{2}{3}x = 10$

16. $\dfrac{4}{5}y = 16$

For questions 17–18, compare the fractions using < , >, or =.

17. $-\dfrac{5}{7}$ _____ $-\dfrac{4}{5}$

18. $-\dfrac{3}{14}$ _____ $-\dfrac{1}{4}$

19. A recipe that makes 6 servings calls for $\dfrac{3}{4}$ cup of oil. Angela wants to reduce the number of servings, so she decides to use $\dfrac{1}{3}$ the amount of oil. How much oil does she use?

Answers

1. $\dfrac{15}{60}$

2. $\dfrac{2}{9}$

3. $\dfrac{7}{18}$

4. $\dfrac{3}{4}$

5. 12

6. 70

7. $\dfrac{3}{8}$

8. $\dfrac{6}{7}$

9. 18

10. $-\dfrac{2}{15}$

11. $3\dfrac{1}{4}$

12. $-\dfrac{5}{6}$

13. $\dfrac{3}{14}$

14. $-2\dfrac{1}{3}$

15. 15

16. 20

17. >

18. >

19. $\frac{1}{4}$ cup

Unit Assessment

Fractions Unit Test, Offline

Answer each question in the space provided.

(10 points)

1. Milo bought $2\frac{1}{2}$ pounds of red apples and $3\frac{3}{4}$ pounds of green apples to make applesauce. How many pounds of apples did he buy in all?

    A. Write an expression that models the problem.

    B. What is the Least Common Denominator of the fractions in your expression?

    C. Evaluate the expression.

    D. Answer the question asked in the problem.

Score

Score	___ of 10

Student Guide

The Distributive Property

If you have 3 packages of 8 chocolates, and 3 packages of 12 caramels, there are a few different ways you can calculate that you have 60 total pieces of candy. You could calculate that you have 24 chocolates and 36 caramels and then add. Or you could calculate that 1 package of chocolates and 1 package of caramels have 20 total pieces of candy, then multiply by 3. In this lesson, you'll learn how the distributive property allows you to calculate certain expressions.

Goals for the Lesson

- Use the distributive property and mental math to evaluate an expression.

- Use the distributive property to solve an equation.

Graded Activities in This Lesson

Lesson Quiz (computer-scored)

Materials

Pre-Algebra: A Reference Guide and Problem Sets, pages 153–156

Optional
The Distributive Property Solutions

Keywords and Pronunciation

Groundwork: Preparing for the Lesson [online]

Try to do the multiplication problems mentally. If you need to, use pencil and paper. Don't use a calculator!

Notes

Learn: Introduction to the Distributive Property [online]

Note that the distributive property works *only* when multiplication is distributed over addition. Try evaluating the following expressions—you will see that the two sides are unequal.

Addition does not distribute over addition: $3 + (4 + 6) \neq 3 + 4 + 3 + 6$.

Addition does not distribute over multiplication: $3 + (4 \cdot 6) \neq 3 + 4 \cdot 3 + 6$.

Multiplication does not distribute over multiplication: $3(4 \cdot 6) \neq 3 \cdot 4 \cdot 3 \cdot 6$.

Notes

Learn: Mental Math with Multiplication [online]

A sum of a factor of 10 and a remainder is often the most useful way to rewrite a number, but it is not the only way. When you are working with money, factors of 25 might be helpful. When you are working with time, factors of 12 or 60 might be useful.

Example: $3 \cdot 27 = 3 \cdot 25 + 3 \cdot 2 = 75 + 6 = 81$

Notes

Worked Examples: The Distributive Property [online]
Notes

MathCast: The Distributive Property [online]

View the video to see how to solve a typical problem.

Summary: The Distributive Property [online]

In this lesson, you learned about the distributive property.

Like all the properties of addition and multiplication you have learned, the distributive property can be used to rewrite a mathematical expression in an equivalent form. This skill is very important in solving equations.

One application of the distributive property is to aid in mental multiplication of large numbers.

Skills Update: Practice Your Math Skills [online]

Complete the Skills Update online.

Offline Learning: The Distributive Property [offline]

In the Book

Review pages 153–155 in the Reference Guide.

Do the Math

Solving Equations by Recognizing the Distributive Property

Sometimes you can use the distributive property to solve an equation. Here are some examples.

Example 1:

Solve $c(7 - 2) = 3 \cdot 7 - 3 \cdot 2$.

Apply the distributive property on the expression on the left side of the equation.

$c(7 - 2) = c \cdot 7 - c \cdot 2$

Now you can write the equation as follows:

$c \cdot 7 - c \cdot 2 = 3 \cdot 7 - 3 \cdot 2$

So, $c = 3$.

Example 2:

Solve $4 \cdot 10 + 4 \cdot y = 4(10 + 9)$

Apply the distributive property on the expression on the right side of the equation.

$4(10 + 9) = 4 \cdot 10 + 4 \cdot 9$

Now you can write the equation as follows:

$4 \cdot 10 + 4 \cdot y = 4 \cdot 10 + 4 \cdot 9$

So, $y = 9$.

Problem Sets

Complete Problems 1–27 odd and 31–39 odd on pages 156–157 of the Reference Guide.

Lesson Assessment: The Distributive Property Quiz [online]

Now go back online to complete the lesson quiz.

Student Guide

Like Terms

A messy closet might look like a jumble of all different types of things—soccer cleats, T-shirts, musical instruments, textbooks, games, and more. But if someone organized that closet, all the things that are alike would be together—all the sports equipment might be together, all the clothing, and all the school supplies. Similarly, in this lesson, you will learn how to simplify mathematical expressions by combining parts of the expression that are alike.

Goals for the Lesson
- Identify like terms.
- Combine like terms.

Graded Activities in This Lesson
Lesson Quiz (computer-scored)

Materials
Pre-Algebra: A Reference Guide and Problem Sets, pages 158–160

Optional
Like Terms Solutions

Keywords and Pronunciation
coefficient: a number that is multiplied by a variable in a variable expression; in an expression such as $3ab$, the numerical coefficient of ab is 3

like terms: terms in which only the numerical coefficients are different

Groundwork: Preparing for the Lesson [online]

Expressions are equivalent if they simplify to the same number, regardless of what number you substitute for the variable. For instance, the expressions $3x$ and $2x + x$ are equivalent because no matter what value of x is substituted, they simplify to the same number.

Notes

Learn: Identifying Like Terms [online]

A *term* is a word used only with addition and/or subtraction problems. Note that in the expression $20x \cdot 4$, $20x$ and 4 are not terms—they are factors.

Notes

Learn: Combining Like Terms [online]

Combining like terms is easy, and it can be easy to get carried away! Remember to simplify only *like* terms. Unlike terms cannot be combined.

For instance, $9x + 8y$ is fully simplified. You cannot make this expression any more compact.

Notes

Summary: Like Terms [online]

In this lesson, you have learned how to identify and combine **like terms**.

Like terms have the same combination of variables, but may have different **coefficients**.

If an expression contains one or more sets of like terms, simplify by **combining like terms**.

To **combine like terms**, just add the coefficients and keep the same variables.

Offline Learning: Like Terms [offline]

In the Book
Review pages 158–160 in the Reference Guide.

Problem Sets
Complete Problems 1–6, 15–39 odd, and 41–42 on pages 160–161 of the Reference Guide.

Lesson Assessment: Like Terms Quiz [online]

Now go back online to complete the lesson quiz.

Student Guide

Expressions with Mixed Operations

In this lesson, you will use the order of operations to evaluate expressions with mixed operations.

Goals for the Lesson
*   Simplify an expression with mixed operations.

*   Evaluate an expression with mixed operations.

Graded Activities in This Lesson
Mid-Unit Test (computer-scored)

Materials
Pre-Algebra: A Reference Guide and Problem Sets, pages 162–164

Optional
Expressions with Mixed Operations Solutions

Calculator

Keywords and Pronunciation
order of operations: the order in which operations must be computed when more than one operation is involved

Groundwork: Preparing for the Lesson [online]

In this groundwork, you will identify the first operation to do in simplifying an expression. Use what you remember about the order of operations!

Notes

Learn: The Order of Operations [online]

You may have already learned a *mnemonic device* for learning the order of operations. A mnemonic device (the *m* is silent; the word is pronounced "nemonic") is a tool that can help you remember something. Here is a device you might remember learning:

My – Multiplication

Dear – Division

Aunt – Addition

Sally – Subtraction

"My Dear Aunt Sally" is one way to help you remember the order of operations, but this mnemonic device has its limitations. For example, "My Dear" makes it sound as though multiplication always comes before division, and that isn't true. Remember that you perform operations inside grouping symbols first, followed by multiplication and division—from left to right—and finally addition and subtraction, again from left to right.

Can you come up with your own mnemonic device to help you remember the order of operations?

Notes

Learn: Evaluating Expressions [online]

You've had lots of practice evaluating expressions. Now is a good time to reflect: What types of problems are difficult for you? Are there mistakes you make often, or steps you sometimes forget? Identifying the concepts that you have problems with will allow you to correct the mistakes.
Notes

Worked Examples: Expressions with Mixed Operations [online]

Make sure you write out each step of each problem to show your work completely. It's okay to do more than one simplification in a single step, as long as you still are using the order of operations.

Notes

MathCast: Evaluate an Expression [online]

View the video to see how to solve a typical problem.

Summary: Expressions with Mixed Operations [online]

In this lesson you have reviewed and practiced using the order of operations.

To simplify expressions, use the correct order of operations:

Step 1: Perform operations inside grouping symbols.

Step 2. Multiply and divide from left to right.

Step 3: Add and subtract from left to right.

Offline Learning: Expressions with Mixed Operations [offline]

In the Book

Review pages 162–164 in the Reference Guide.

Problem Sets

Complete Problems 1–10 and 19–25 on page 165 of the Reference Guide.

Mid-Unit Assessment: Combined Operations Test [online]

Now go back online to complete the mid-unit test.

Student Guide
Equations With Mixed Operations

If you misplace something important, you might retrace your steps to find out where you left it. Solving an equation with multiple transformations is like retracing your steps. You mathematically work through the steps of evaluating and simplifying expressions to get to the important thing—the solution of the equation.

Goals for the Lesson
- Solve equations with mixed operations.

- Solve an equation that involves simplification.

- Solve an equation with variables on both sides.

Graded Activities in This Lesson
Lesson Quiz (computer-scored)

Materials
Pre-Algebra: A Reference Guide and Problem Sets, pages 167–171

Optional
Equations With Mixed Operations Solutions

Keywords and Pronunciation
coefficient: a number that is multiplied by a variable in a variable expression; in an expression such as $3ab$, the numerical coefficient of ab is 3

inverse operations: mathematical operations that undo each other, such as addition and subtraction, or multiplication and division

order of operations: the order in which operations must be computed when more than one operation is involved

Groundwork: Preparing for the Lesson [online]
In this groundwork, you will practice your skills solving equations involving multiplication and division. Remember that any operation you use to transform the equation must be applied to both sides of the equation.

Notes

Learn: Reversing the Order of Operations [online]

When solving an equation by reversing the order of operations, you will usually use addition or subtraction as the first operation. This is because addition and subtraction come after multiplication and division in the order of operations. However, sometimes grouping symbols can change the order of operations. Consider the following two equations:

$3(x - 5) = -12$	$\dfrac{x - 5}{3} = -12$

In both cases, the grouping symbols tell you that subtraction is the first operation performed when evaluating the expression for a particular value of x. The last operation you would perform in evaluating the expression is the first operation you would use when solving the equation—so here, you would use multiplication or division first.

$3(x - 5) = -12$

$\dfrac{3(x - 5)}{3} = \dfrac{-12}{3}$

$x - 5 = -4$

$x - 5 + 5 = -4 + 5$

$x = 1$

$\dfrac{x - 5}{3} = -12 = -12$

$\dfrac{x - 5}{3} \cdot 3 = -12 \cdot 3$

$x - 5 = -36$

$x - 5 + 5 = -36 + 5$

$x = -31$

Notes

Learn: Solving More Complex Equations [online]

Remember the steps in combining like terms:

- Identify like terms. Like terms have the same combination of variables.

- Rearrange the expression so that like terms are next to each other.

- Combine like terms by adding their coefficients and keeping the same variables.

Notes

Learn: Variables on Both Sides [online]

Remember to isolate the variable on one side of the equation.

Notes

Worked Examples: Equations With Mixed Operations [online]

Remember the steps in combining like terms:

- Identify like terms. Like terms have the same combination of variables.

- Rearrange the expression so that like terms are next to each other.

- Combine like terms by adding their coefficients and keeping the same variables.

Notes

MathCast: Solve an Equation [online]

View the video to see how to solve a typical problem.

Summary: Equations With Mixed Operations [online]

In this lesson, you have learned how to solve equations with mixed operations.

- Before starting to solve the equation, simplify one or both sides of the equation by combining like terms or removing parentheses.

- Then, undo the operations by using the reverse order of operations.

Offline Learning: Equations With Mixed Operations [offline]

In the Book
Review pages 167–170 in the Reference Guide.

Problem Sets
Complete Problems 1–29 odd and 33–34 on page 171 of the Reference Guide.

Lesson Assessment: Equations With Mixed Operations Quiz [online]
Now go back online to complete the lesson quiz.

Student Guide

Error Analysis

Sometimes you make a mistake. Making mistakes is a normal part of learning. You can learn quite a bit from your mistakes and from other people's mistakes. The important thing is to try to learn from mistakes.

In this lesson, you will learn how to identify and correct mistakes in problem solving.

Goals for the Lesson
- Identify errors in a solution to an equation and a word problem.
- Correct errors in a solution to an equation and a word problem.

Graded Activities in This Lesson
Lesson Quiz (computer-scored)

Materials
Pre-Algebra: A Reference Guide and Problem Sets, pages 173–180

Optional
Error Analysis Solutions

Keywords and Pronunciation
none

Groundwork: Preparing for the Lesson [online]
In this groundwork, you will practice your skills solving equations. Remember to check your solution in the original equation.

Notes

Learn: Where Did Bror Go Wrong? [online]

You may see a mistake but have a hard time explaining exactly what went wrong. Here are some tips for explaining to someone else where the mistake is in a solution:

- Give each line of the solution a number, and then tell on what line the error occurs.

- Tell exactly what the student did that was incorrect. "He multiplied by 3 and shouldn't have," or "He added 7 to only the left side."

- Tell what the student *should* have done instead. "He should have divided by 3 instead.", or "He should have added 7 to both sides of the equation."

Notes

Learn: Finding Errors in Solutions to Word Problems [online]

Writing the correct equation for a word problem can be challenging. It takes a lot of practice to get good at writing equations correctly. Remember to define a variable for the unknown quantity, and carefully read the word problem to see what it says about the variable. Once you have your equation, read through the word problem again to make sure that your equation and the word problem agree.

Notes

Worked Examples: Error Analysis [online]
Notes

MathCast: Find and Correct Errors [online]
View the video to see how to solve a typical problem.

Summary: Error Analysis [online]
In this lesson, you have learned how to identify errors in the solutions to problems.

Checking the given solution in the original equation can let you know if there is a mistake to look for.

For word problems, pay special attention to deciding whether the equation written is a correct translation of the initial problem.

Skills Update: Practice Your Math Skills [online]
Complete the Skills Update online.

Offline Learning: Error Analysis [offline]

In the Book
Review pages 173–177 in the Reference Guide.

Problem Sets
Complete Problems 1–4 and 19–20 on pages 178–179 of the Reference Guide.

Lesson Assessment: Error Analysis Quiz [online]
Now go back online to complete the lesson quiz.

Student Guide

Inequalities

Your budget says you can spend *up to* $300 for the workshop. You need to study *at least* 2 hours for your test. Company A charges *less than* Company B for the job. These are just a few of examples of how inequalities might be used in real-world situations.

Goals for the Lesson
- Solve a simple inequality when given a replacement set.
- Solve an inequality in one variable.
- Graph the solution to an inequality in one variable on a number line.

Graded Activities in This Lesson
Lesson Quiz (computer-scored)

Materials
Pre-Algebra: A Reference Guide and Problem Sets, pages 182–187

Optional
Inequalities Solutions

Keywords and Pronunciation
inequality: a mathematical sentence formed by placing an inequality sign between two expressions

coefficient: a number that is multiplied by a variable in a variable expression; in an expression such as 3*ab*, the numerical coefficient of *ab* is 3

solution set: the set of all solutions of an open sentence

Groundwork: Inequalities [online]
In this groundwork, you will practice your skills solving equations. Remember to check your solution in the original equation.

Notes

Learn: Solution Sets [online]

Be careful when you're working with negative decimals and fractions. Remember that $-7.1 < -7$, and $-6.9 > -7$.

Notes

Learn: Solving Inequalities [online]

Fill in the chart below as you explore the inequality $2x + 3 \geq 11$ on the number line. Write in the value of $2x + 3$ for each value of x. Then, circle the symbol that correctly compares $2x + 3$ and 11.

x	0	1	2	3	4	5	6	7	8	9	10
$2x + 3$											
$2x + 3$ _?_ 11	 = >	 = >	 = >	 = >	 = >	 = >	 = >	 = >	 = >	 = >	 = >

Notes

Learn: Dividing or Multiplying by a Negative Number [online]

Notes

What happens to the inequality sign when you multiply or divide both sides of an inequality by a negative number? Give an example.

Worked Examples: Inequalities [online]
Notes

Summary: Inequalities [online]

When you're solving an inequality, simplify the inequality using transformations as you would when solving an equation.

Remember, when you're multiplying or dividing both sides of the inequality by a negative number, reverse the direction of the inequality.

Graph the solution to the inequality on a number line. Use open circles to indicate < or > relationships, and filled-in circles to indicate ≤ or ≥ relationships.

Offline Learning: Inequalities [offline]

In the Book
Read pages 182–186 in the Reference Guide.

Problem Sets
Complete Problems 1–21 odd and 27–28 on pages 186–187 of the Reference Guide.

Lesson Assessment: Inequalities Quiz [online]
Now go back online to complete the lesson quiz.

Student Guide

Combined Operations Review

You have finished studying the Combined Operations unit, which includes the distributive property, like terms, expressions with mixed operations, equations with mixed operations, error analysis, and inequalities. Now it's time to pull together what you have learned. Throughout the review, see how the skills you have learned relate to the Pre-Algebra big ideas.

Goals for the Lesson
* Review the concepts and skills learned in the unit.

Materials
"Combined Operations" in *Pre-Algebra: A Reference Guide and Problem Sets*
Preparing for the Unit Test

Unit Review: Combined Operations [online]

This is your chance to review the big ideas of Pre-Algebra you have learned in this unit. Under Review These Activities, you will find activities from previous lessons that will help you review each big idea. Choose the topics you feel you need to review. Under Try These, you will find interactive problems that will test your understanding of each big idea. As you work through this lesson, take notes in the spaces provided.

Big Idea
A number is any entity that obeys the laws of arithmetic; all numbers obey the laws of arithmetic. The laws of arithmetic can be used to simplify algebraic expressions.

Big Idea
Expressions, equations, and inequalities express relationships between different entities.

Big Idea

The laws of arithmetic can be used to simplify algebraic expressions and equations. Solving an equation means finding values for the variable or variables that make the equation a true statement.

Summary: Combined Operations Review [online]

In this unit, you covered the following topics:

- the distributive property

- like terms

- expressions with mixed operations

- equations with mixed operations

- error analysis

- inequalities

Offline Learning: Combined Operations Review [offline]

How well have you mastered the goals of this unit? Complete the Combined Operations Practice Problems. These problems are similar to the problems you will have on the Unit Test.

You can also

- Review the Combined Operations unit in *Pre-Algebra: A Reference Guide and Problem Sets*

- Review the notes in your Student Guide.

- Read and follow the instructions in Preparing for the Unit Test.

Practice Problems

Combined Operations

1. Rewrite the expression without using grouping symbols.

$$4(12 - x)$$

2. Rewrite the expression using grouping symbols.

$$8 \cdot y + 8 \cdot 10$$

3. Solve the equation.

$$8(5 - n) = 8 \cdot 5 - 8 \cdot 4$$

4. Combine like terms.

$$4y - 8 + 3y + 5$$

5. Evaluate the expression if $x = 4$ and $y = 2$.

$$16 \div x \bullet y - 3 \bullet y + 7$$

6. Solve the equations.

a. $3x - 4 = 11$

b. $\dfrac{x - 4}{3} = -6$

c. $5x - 8 - 3x = -12$

d. $6x - 7 = 2x + 9$

7. Write the solution set for the inequality if the replacement set is {−10, −8.4, −8, −5.2, −4.8, 4.4, 8}.

$$x < -5$$

8. Graph the following inequalities.

a. $x < -2$

b. $y \geq 1$

9. Solve the inequalities and graph the solutions.

a. $4x - 2 \leq -10$

b. $-5x + 4 > -6$

10. Find, explain, and correct the error in the solution given.

Steps:

(1) $\dfrac{2x + 4}{3} - 6 = -8$

(2) $\dfrac{2x + 4}{3} - 6 + 6 = -8 + 6$

(3) $\dfrac{2x + 4}{3} = -2$

(4) $\dfrac{2x + 4}{3} - 4 = -2 - 4$

(5) $\dfrac{2x}{3} = -6$

(6) $\dfrac{2x}{3} \bullet 3 = -6 \bullet 3$

(7) $2x = -18$

(8) $\dfrac{2x}{2} = \dfrac{-18}{2}$

(9) $x = -9$

Answers

1. $4 \cdot 12 - 4 \cdot x$

2. $8(y + 10)$

3. $n = 4$

4. $7y - 3$

5. 9

6. a. $x = 5$

    b. $x = -14$

    c. $x = -2$

    d. $x = 4$

7. $\{-10, -8.4, -8, -5.2\}$

8. a.

    b.

9. a. $x \leq -2$

    b. $x < 2$

10. Step 4 is incorrect. The student subtracted 4 from both sides, but he should have multiplied each side by 3.

Steps: (1) $\dfrac{2x + 4}{3} - 6 = -8$

(2) $\dfrac{2x + 4}{3} - 6 + 6 = -8 + 6$

(3) $\dfrac{2x + 4}{3} = -2$

(4) $\dfrac{2x + 4}{3} \bullet 3 = -2 \bullet 3$

(5) $2x + 4 = -6$

(6) $2x + 4 - 4 = -6 - 4$

(7) $2x = -10$

(8) $\dfrac{2x}{2} = \dfrac{-10}{2}$

(9) $x = -5$

Unit Assessment

Combined Operations Unit Test, Offline

Answer each question in the space provided.

(10 points)

1. Find, explain, and correct the error in the solution given.

Steps: (1) $\dfrac{3x-2}{4} + 1 = 5$

(2) $\dfrac{3x-2}{4} + 1 - 1 = 5 - 1$

(3) $\dfrac{3x-2}{4} = 4$

(4) $\dfrac{3x-2}{4} + 2 = 4 + 2$

(5) $\dfrac{3x}{4} = 6$

(6) $\dfrac{3x}{4} \cdot 4 = 6 \cdot 4$

(7) $3x = 24$

(8) $\dfrac{3x}{3} = \dfrac{24}{3}$

(9) $x = 8$

Score

(10 points)

2. Solve the given inequality and graph it on the number line.

$-3x + 9 \leq 15$

Score

Score	___ of 20

Student Guide

Positive Exponents

A shortcut is a way to do something more quickly and often more easily than the way it is usually done. Mathematics is full of shortcuts. For example, multiplication is a shortcut for repeated addition. In this lesson, you will use exponents as a shortcut for repeated multiplication.

Goals for the Lesson
* Simplify a numerical expression involving exponents.
* Evaluate a variable expression involving exponents.
* Write a number as a power of a given number.

Graded Activities in This Lesson
Lesson Quiz (computer-scored)

Materials
Pre-Algebra: A Reference Guide and Problem Sets, pages 191–195

Optional
Positive Exponents Solutions

Calculator

Beyond the Lesson: Calculator Activity sheet

Beyond the Lesson Answer Key

Keywords and Pronunciation
base: a number that is raised to some power (for example, in 5^3, 5 is the base)

exponent: a number that shows how many times the base is used as a factor

power of a number: the product when a number is multiplied by itself a given number of times (e.g., 5^3 or 5 • 5 • 5 is the third power of five)

factor: any of two or more numbers multiplied to form a product

Groundwork: Preparing for the Lesson [online]
The Groundwork reviews what was learned in a previous lesson. As you work through this activity, answer the question below and record any notes in the space provided.

Notes
What are the steps in the order of operations?

Learn: Working with Positive Exponents [online]

As you work through this activity, answer the question below and record any notes in the space provided.

Notes
How can you write 243 as a power of 3?

Worked Examples: Positive Exponents [online]

As you work through this activity, answer the question below and record any notes in the space provided.

Notes
Write another exponential expression that evaluates to the same number as -5^3.

Summary: Positive Exponents [online]

You can use exponents to simplify an expression that involves repeated multiplication. The exponent tells you how many times to use the base as a factor.

Any number to the zero power equals 1.

Any number to the first power equals the number.

Offline Learning: Positive Exponents [offline]

In the Book
Read pages 191–195 in the Reference Guide.

Do the Math

What Are Exponents?
When you need to multiply the same factor more than once, you can write a multiplication expression using an exponent.

When you write an expression using exponents, the repeated factor is the base, and the number of times the base is multiplied is the exponent.

Example:

$$2 \cdot 2 \cdot 2 = 2^3$$

2 is the base

3 is the exponent and indicates the number of times the base is multiplied.

Problem Sets
Complete 1–29 odd and 32 on pages 194–195 of the Reference Guide.

Beyond the Lesson: Calculator Activity (optional)
Print and complete the Calculator Activity sheet.

Lesson Assessment: Positive Exponents Quiz [online]
Now go back online to complete the lesson quiz.

More Practice: Optional Assignment [online]

For extra practice, print the Optional Assignment and complete one or more of the problems.

Name: _____   Date: _____

Optional Assignment
Positive Exponents

1. Write four hundred five and thirty-seven hundredths:

   a. as a decimal

   b. in expanded form

   c. rounded to the nearest tenth

Answer:

2. Simplify the following expressions. Show each step.

   a. $4^2 + 3(56 \div 2^3)$

   b. $5x + 8y + 4x + 3y$

Answer:

Name _____   Date _____

Beyond the Lesson
Calculator Activity

Calculators are useful when simplifying expressions with exponents. You could use repeated multiplication, or you may find an even quicker shortcut.

Scientific calculators often use a caret (^) key to represent the use of exponents. This method can save many steps, especially when the exponent is a large number.

Use a calculator to complete the activities below. Use a scientific calculator if you have one.

1.   To evaluate 5^4, you can use repeated multiplication.

     Press these buttons on your calculator:

     The result should be 625.

2.   If your calculator has a caret (^) key, you can use it as a shortcut. It tells the calculator to make the next digit you enter an exponent. Press these buttons on your calculator:

     The result should again be 625.

3.   Experiment with your calculator to evaluate the following.

     a. $6^3 =$

     b. $7^5 =$

     c. $2^{12} =$

     d. $1^{20} =$

     e. $1^{70} =$

Student Guide

Factors and Primes

You and a group of 6 friends want to buy tickets to a baseball game. If you all sit in one row, it will be hard for everyone to talk to each other. Is there any way to split up the people into equal-sized groups so that no one will be sitting alone? The answer is no because 7 is a prime number. In this lesson, you will learn about prime and composite numbers and how to find the prime factorization of a number.

Goals for the Lesson

- Find factors of a given number.

- Determine whether a number is prime or composite.

- Find the prime factorization of a number.

Graded Activities in This Lesson
Lesson Quiz (computer-scored)

Materials
Pre-Algebra: A Reference Guide and Problem Sets, pages 196–199

Optional
Factors and Primes Solutions
Calculator

Keywords and Pronunciation
factor: any of two or more numbers multiplied to form a product

prime number: a whole number greater than 1 that has only two whole-number factors, 1 and itself

composite number: a whole number greater than 1 that is not prime

prime factorization: expressing a positive integer as a product of primes

Groundwork: Preparing for the Lesson [online]
The Groundwork reviews what was learned in the previous lesson. As you work through this activity, answer the question below and record any notes in the space provided.

Notes
Explain the difference between the expression $-3x^2$ and the expression $(-3x)^2$.

Learn: Factors   [online]

As you work through this activity, answer the question below and record any notes in the space provided.

Notes

Explain how the divisibility rules can help you determine that 29 is a prime number.

Learn: Prime Factorization   [online]

As you work through this activity, answer the question below and record any notes in the space provided.

Notes

Construct a factor tree for 24 that is different from the one shown in this activity.

Worked Examples: Factors and Primes [online]

As you work through this activity, answer the question below and record any notes in the space provided.

Notes

How can you use the divisibility rules to help you find the factors of 75?

MathCast: Prime Factorization [online]
View the video to see how to solve a typical problem.

Summary: Factors and Primes [online]
In this lesson, you learned how to find factors of numbers.

You also learned how to determine whether a number is prime or composite.

You used this information to find the prime factorization of numbers.

Offline Learning: Factors and Primes [offline]

In the Book
Read pages 196–198 in the Reference Guide.

Do the Math
Eratosthenes (ehr-uh-TAHS-thuh-neez) of Cyrene was a Greek astronomer and mathematician who lived from 275 B.C. to 195 B.C. One of his major accomplishments was measuring the diameter of the earth within 1 percent of its actual measurement! One of his other accomplishments was an invention to list all of the prime numbers, known as the Sieve of Eratosthenes. You are going to use this sieve to find all of the prime numbers from 1 to 100, but this technique will work for all prime numbers up to any given number.

The object is to ring all prime numbers and draw a line through all nonprime numbers. Use the number below to reproduce the sieve.

1. Start with the number 1. Since 1 is neither prime nor composite, draw a line through it.

2. The next greater number is 2. Since 2 is prime, ring it.

3. Now count by 2s to find all of the multiples of 2 (4, 6, 8, and so on) and draw a line through each multiple.

4. The next greater number is 3. Since 3 is prime, ring it.

5. Now count by 3s to find all of the multiples of 3 (6, 9, 12, and so on) and draw a line through each multiple.

6. Continue the same steps, ringing the next greater prime number and then drawing a line through all of its multiples until you have no numbers left.

7. Finally, list all of the prime numbers from 1 to 100 in the space below the number table.

1	2	3	4	5	6	7	8	9	10
11	12	13	14	15	16	17	18	19	20
21	22	23	24	25	26	27	28	29	30
31	32	33	34	35	36	37	38	39	40
41	42	43	44	45	46	47	48	49	50
51	52	53	54	55	56	57	58	59	60
61	62	63	64	65	66	67	68	69	70
71	72	73	74	75	76	77	78	79	80
81	82	83	84	85	86	87	88	89	90
91	92	93	94	95	96	97	98	99	100

_____

_____

_____

Now that you have a list of all of the prime numbers from 1 to 100, let's explore two kinds of prime numbers: twin primes and Mersenne (mer-sen) primes.

Twin Primes
Twin primes are prime numbers that have a difference of 2.

Example:
3 and 5 are both prime numbers and 5 – 3 = 2. Therefore, 3 and 5 are called twin primes. We usually write twin primes in parentheses: (3, 5).

There are 8 pairs of twin primes from 1 to 100. Using the list of prime numbers you created using the Sieve of Eratosthenes, list all of the twin primes from 1 to 100.

Mersenne Primes
A Mersenne number is a number that can be written in the form $2^n - 1$. If this number is prime, it is called a *Mersenne prime*.

Examples:

$2^2 - 1 = 3$

Because 3 is prime, $2^2 - 1$ is a Mersenne prime.

$2^4 - 1 = 15$

Because 15 is not prime, $2^4 - 1$ is not a Mersenne prime.

There are three Mersenne primes from 1 to 100. List the Mersenne primes from 1 to 100.

Problem Sets
Complete Problems 1–23 odd and 24–29 on page 199 of the Reference Guide.

Lesson Assessment: Factors and Primes Quiz [online]
Now go back online to complete the lesson quiz.

Answers

Do the Math

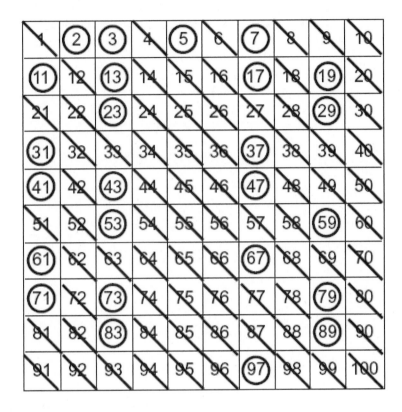

Prime Numbers

2, 3, 5, 7, 11, 13, 17, 19, 23, 29, 31, 37, 41, 43, 47, 53, 59, 61, 67, 71, 73, 79, 83, 89, 97

Twin Primes
(3, 5); (5, 7); (11, 13); (17, 19); (29, 31); (41, 43); (59, 61); (71, 73)

Mersenne Primes
3, 7, 31

Student Guide

GCF and Relative Primes

Suppose you are making snack bags to give out to runners during a marathon. There are 120 energy bars, 240 cookies, and 300 packs of peanut butter crackers. You want to divide the food evenly so that each snack bag has the same number of energy bars, cookies, and peanut butter crackers. How many snack bags can you make so that no food is left over? Knowing how to find the greatest common factor of a set of numbers can help you solve the problem.

Goals for the Lesson
- Find the common factors of two numbers.

- Find the GCF of two numbers.

- Determine whether two numbers are relatively prime or not.

Graded Activities in This Lesson
Mid-Unit Test (computer-scored)

Materials
Pre-Algebra: A Reference Guide and Problem Sets, pages 200–202

Optional
Problem Sets Answer Key

Calculator

GCF and Relative Primes Solutions

Keywords and Pronunciation
common factor: a factor that is the same for two or more integers

greatest common factor (GCF): the greatest integer that is a factor of two or more given integers

relatively prime numbers: two or more numbers that have no common factors other than 1

Groundwork: Preparing for the Lesson [online]
The Groundwork reviews what was learned in the Factors and Primes lesson. As you work through this activity, answer the question below and record any notes in the space provided. You can use divisibility rules to help you find the factors of a number:

Notes

Is 2 a factor of all even numbers? Explain.

A number is divisible by:

- 2 if the last digit has 2 as a factor
- 3 if the sum of the digits is a multiple of 3
- 4 if the last two digits are a multiple of 4
- 5 if the last digit is 5 or 0
- 9 if the sum of the digits is a multiple of 9
- 10 if the last digit is 0

Learn: Greatest Common Factors [online]

As you work through this activity, answer the question below and record any notes in the space provided.

Notes

Explain why 18 and 25 are relatively prime.

Worked Examples: GCF and Relative Primes [online]

As you work through this activity, record any notes in the space provided.

Notes

Summary: GCF and Relative Primes [online]

In this lesson, you learned how to find the GCF of two numbers. You also learned how to determine whether two numbers are relatively prime.

You can find the GCF by listing all the factors and selecting the greatest of the common factors.

You can also find the GCF by writing the prime factorization of each number. The GCF is the product of the least powers of the common bases.

Offline Learning: GCF and Relative Primes [offline]

In the Book
Read pages 200–202 in the Reference Guide.

Problem Sets
Complete Problems 1–4, 7–10, 15–18, and 23–25 on page 202 of the Reference Guide.

Extra Practice (optional)
Complete Problems 5–6, 11, 19–20, and 26–28 on page 202 of the Reference Guide.

Mid-Unit Assessment: Number Properties Test [online]

Now go back online to complete the mid-unit test.

Student Guide

Negative Exponents

It's one thing to evaluate expressions and solve equations containing *positive* exponents; in this lesson, you will learn to evaluate expressions and solve equations containing *negative* exponents. If you think negative exponents are like negative integers, you may be surprised!

Goals for the Lesson
- Simplify an expression involving negative exponents.
- Solve an equation involving negative exponents.

Graded Activities in This Lesson
Lesson Quiz (computer-scored)

Materials
Pre-Algebra: A Reference Guide and Problem Sets, pages 203–206

Optional
Calculator
Negative Exponents Solutions

Keywords and Pronunciation
base: a number that is raised to some power (for example, in 5^3, 5 is the base)

exponent: a number that shows how many times the base is used as a factor

Groundwork: Preparing for the Lesson [online]
Review the skills needed for working with positive exponents. As you work through this activity, answer the questions below and record any notes in the space provided.

Notes
Explain why the exponentiation is done before the multiplication in the expression $9^2 \cdot 3^4$.

Why does a positive exponent mean repeated multiplication?

Learn: Expressions with Negative Exponents [online]

As you work through this activity, answer the questions below and record any notes in the space provided.

Notes

How are a^n and a^{-n} related? What is the product of a^n and a^{-n}?

Learn: Equations with Negative Exponents [online]

As you work through this activity, answer the question below and record any notes in the space provided.

Notes

If $2^3 = 8$ and $2^x = 8$, what is the value of x? How do you know?

MathCast: Solve an Equation [online]

View the video to see how to solve a typical problem.

Summary: Negative Exponents [online]

In this lesson, you learned how to work with negative exponents. To simplify expressions or solve equations containing negative exponents, use the properties of negative exponents.

Offline Learning: Negative Exponents [offline]

In the Book

Read pages 203–205 in the Reference Guide.

Do the Math

What Does a Negative Exponent Mean?

Evaluating a number with a positive exponent requires repeated multiplication of the base. For example, $3^3 = 3 \cdot 3 \cdot 3 = 27$.

When you evaluate a power that has a whole number base raised to a positive exponent, you usually end up with a number that has a greater absolute value than the base. In this case, 27 has a greater absolute value than the base, 3.

The only exceptions occur when the base or exponent is 0 or 1.

$3^0 = 1$

$3^1 = 3$

$1^{14} = 1$

$0^{14} = 0$

What happens when the exponent is negative (for example, 3^{-3})?

When you evaluate a whole number with a negative exponent, you usually end up with a number that has a smaller absolute value than the base. You can find out why by reading pages 203–205 in your Reference Guide.

Problem Sets

Complete Problems 1–8 and 22–25 on pages 205–206 of the Reference Guide.

Extra Practice (optional)

Complete Problems 9–13 and 26–27 on pages 205–206 of the Reference Guide.

Lesson Assessment: Negative Exponents Quiz [online]

Now go back online to complete the lesson quiz.

Student Guide

Powers of Ten

How much does an ant weigh? How much does the earth weigh? Powers of ten can be used to represent very small or very large numbers, such as these. In this lesson, you will learn how to work with integer powers of ten.

Goals for the Lesson
- Write a power of ten in standard form.
- Write a number in standard form as a power of ten.
- Multiply a decimal by a power of ten.
- Divide a decimal by a power of ten.

Graded Activities in This Lesson
Lesson Quiz (computer-scored)

Materials
Pre-Algebra: A Reference Guide and Problem Sets, pages 207–211

Optional
Powers of Ten Solutions

Calculator

Keywords and Pronunciation
power of ten: any number that can be written in the form 10^n, where *n* is an integer

Groundwork: Preparing for the Lesson [online]
Review multiplication and division by 10. As you work through this activity, answer the question below and record any notes in the space provided.

Notes

Explain how you can multiply or divide a number by 10 using mental math.

Learn: Expressing Powers of Ten [online]

As you work through this activity, answer the questions below and record any notes in the space provided.

Notes

Explain how to write 10^{25} in standard form.

Explain how to write 10^{-35} in standard form.

Learn: Multiplying by Powers of Ten [online]

As you work through this activity, answer the questions below and record any notes in the space provided.

Notes

You want to multiply 7.82 by 10^{-7}. In what direction do you move the decimal point? How many decimal places are in the product?

Learn: Dividing by Powers of Ten [online]

As you work through this activity, answer the questions below and record any notes in the space provided.

Notes

You want to divide 7.82 by 10^{-7}. In what direction do you move the decimal point? How many decimal places are in the quotient?

Summary: Powers of Ten [online]

In this lesson, you learned how to convert an integer power of ten to standard form.

Powers of Ten in Standard Form

To write 10^n in standard form, start with 1.0:

- When $n \geq 0$, move the decimal point n places to the right.
- When $n < 0$, move the decimal point n places to the left.

You also learned how to multiply and divide numbers by integer powers of ten.

Multiplying by a Power of Ten
- To multiply a number by 10^n, where n is a **positive** integer, move the decimal point of the number exactly n places to the **right**.
- To multiply a number by 10^n, where n is a **negative** integer, move the decimal point of the number exactly $|n|$ places to the **left**.

Dividing by a Power of Ten
- To divide a number by 10^n, where n is a **positive** integer, move the decimal point of the number exactly n places to the **left**.
- To divide a number by 10^n, where n is a **negative** integer, move the decimal point of the number exactly $|n|$ places to the **right**.

Offline Learning: Powers of Ten [offline]

In the Book
Read pages 207–211 in the Reference Guide.

Problem Sets
Complete Problems 1–27 odd and 29–31 on page 211 of the Reference Guide.

Lesson Assessment: Powers of Ten Quiz [online]
Now go back online to complete the lesson quiz.

Student Guide

Scientific Notation

The average distance from the planet Neptune to the sun is approximately 4,540,000,000 km. To read this number, you need to count a lot of zeros. Scientists work with numbers like this every day. To make their work easier, they use scientific notation to represent very large and very small numbers. The number 4,540,000,000 can be written in scientific notation as 4.54×10^9. Now that's a little easier to read, isn't it?

Goals for the Lesson

- Convert a number from standard form to scientific notation.

- Convert a number from scientific notation to standard form.

- Multiply numbers in scientific notation.

Graded Activities in This Lesson

Lesson Quiz (computer-scored)

Materials

Pre-Algebra: A Reference Guide and Problem Sets, pages 212–215

Optional

Scientific Notation Solutions

Multiplying with Scientific Notation sheet

calculator

Keywords and Pronunciation

scientific notation: a representation of a number as the product of a number that is greater than or equal to 1 but less than 10 and an integer power of ten

Groundwork: Preparing for the Lesson [online]

Review writing numbers as powers of ten. As you work through this activity, answer the questions below and record any notes in the space provided.

Notes

How do you write 100,000 as a power of ten?

How do you write $\dfrac{1}{1,000,000}$ as a power of ten?

Learn: Scientific Notation and Standard Form [online]

As you work through this activity, answer the questions below and record any notes in the space provided.

Notes

Why is scientific notation used?

Learn: Multiplying Numbers in Scientific Notation [online]

As you work through this activity, answer the questions below and record any notes in the space provided.

Notes

Explain how the expression $(1.2 \times 10^{-2}) \times (5 \times 10^{4})$ can be transformed into the expression $1.2 \times 5 \times 10^{-2} \times 10^{4}$.

MathCast: Mutiplying Scientific Notation [online]

View the video to see how to solve a typical problem.

Summary: Scientific Notation [online]

- Scientific notation is a convenient way to represent very large and very small numbers.

- A number is written in scientific notation if it is expressed as the product of a number greater than or equal to 1 but less than 10 and an integer power of ten.

- You can multiply numbers written in scientific notation by using real-number properties to regroup the numbers.

Offline Learning: Scientific Notation [offline]

In the Book
Read pages 212–214 in the Reference Guide.

Do the Math

Try It
Many numbers in real life are very large or very small.

Example

Scientists estimate that there are about 100,000,000,000,000,000,000,000 stars in our universe.

Express 100,000,000,000,000,000,000,000 in scientific notation.

1.00000000000000000000000	Move the decimal point to the left to get a number greater than or equal to 1 but less than 10. Count the number of spaces the decimal point is moved.
1×10^{23}	Since the decimal point is moved 23 places to the left, you multiply 1 by 10^{23} to express the number in scientific notation.

100,000,000,000,000,000,000,000 = 1×10^{23} or 10^{23}

Example

The mass of an electron is about 0.000000000000000000000000000911 g.

00000000000000000000000009.11g	Move the decimal point to the right to get a number greater than or equal to 1 but less than 10. Count the number of spaces the decimal point is moved.
9.11×10^{-28}	Since the decimal point is moved 28 places to the right, you multiply 9.11 by 10^{-28} to express the number in scientific notation.

0.000000000000000000000000000911 g = 9.11×10^{-28} g

Problem Sets
Complete Problems 1–27 odd and 31–32 on page 215.

Extra Practice (optional)
Complete Problems 2–26 even and 33 on page 215.

Extension (optional)
If you have not already done so, print the Multiplying with Scientific Notation sheet and complete the activities.

Lesson Assessment: Scientific Notation Quiz [online]

Now go back online to complete the lesson quiz.

Answers

Extension

1. scientific notation form: 6.48×10^6
    standard form: 6,480,000

2. scientific notation form: 1.56×10^3
    standard form: 1560

3. scientific notation form: 4.2×10^{-6}
    standard form: 0.0000042

4. scientific notation form: 4.788×10^7
    standard form: 47,880,000

5. scientific notation form: 1.6×10^{-3}
    standard form: 0.0016

6. scientific notation form: 9.0×10^6
    standard form: 9,000,000

7. scientific notation form: 8.722×10^{-9}
    standard form: 0.000000008722

8. scientific notation form: 1.287×10^6
    standard form: 1,287,000

Name _____   Date _____

Extension

Multiplying with Scientific Notation

If you didn't have a calculator, it could take some time to find the product of numbers such as 4,400,000 and 1,200,000.

Example

$$\begin{array}{r} 4,400,000 \\ \times\,1,200,000 \\ \hline 880000000000 \\ 4400000000000 \\ \hline 5,280,000,000,000 \end{array}$$

If you wrote the numbers in scientific notation, would they be easier to multiply? Yes, they would.

You can multiply numbers expressed in scientific notation using the associative and commutative properties as well as the rules for multiplying powers with like bases.

Use scientific notation to multiply:

$4,400,000 \times 1,200,000$

$(4.4 \times 10^6) \times (1.2 \times 10^6) =$ Begin by writing the expression using scientific notation

$(4.4 \times 1.2) \times (10^6 \times 10^6) =$

$(4.4 \times 1.2) \times (10^6 \times 10^6)$ Use the associative and commutative properties to change the groupings of the factors.

5.28×10^{12} Multiply the decimal numbers and then multiply the powers of 10.

$5.28 \times 10^{12} = 5,280,000,000,000$ Write the number in decimal form.

Now, that's a lot faster than multiplying the numbers in standard form! Take a look at one more example.

Find the product. Write the result in scientific notation and in decimal form.

$(3.2 \times 10^{-3})(8.1 \times 10^{-1})$

$(3.2 \times 8.1)(10^{-3} \times 10^{-1})$ Use the associative and commutative properties to change the groupings of the factors

25.92×10^{-4} Multiply the decimal numbers and then multiply the powers of 10. (Remember to add the exponents.)

2.592×10^{-3} To write the product in scientific notation, move the decimal point one place to the left and add 1 to the exponent.

0.002592 Write the number in decimal form

Tip: If you move the decimal point to the left, you need to add to the exponent. If you move the decimal point to the right, you need to subtract from the exponent.

Find the product. Write the result in scientific notation and in decimal form.

1. $(7.2 \times 10^2)(9 \times 10^3)$

2. $(6.5 \times 10^{-3})(2.4 \times 10^5)$

3. $(0.6 \times 10^{-4})(0.7 \times 10^{-1})$

4. $(5.7 \times 10^4)(8.4 \times 10^2)$

5. $(5 \times 10^3)(3.2 \times 10^{-7})$

6. $(0.6 \times 10^5)(1.5 \times 10^2)$

7. $(8.9 \times 10^{-4})(9.8 \times 10^{-6})$

8. $(1.3 \times 10^{-2})(9.9 \times 10^7)$

Student Guide

Number Properties Review

You have finished studying the Number Properties unit, which includes positive exponents, factors and primes, GCF and relative primes, negative exponents, powers of ten, and scientific notation. Now it's time to pull together what you have learned. Throughout the review, see how the skills you have learned relate to the Pre-Algebra big ideas.

Goals for the Lesson
* Review the concepts and skills learned in the unit.

Materials
"Number Properties" in *Pre-Algebra: A Reference Guide and Problem Sets*
Preparing for the Unit Test

Unit Review: Number Properties [online]
This is your chance to review the big ideas of Pre-Algebra you have learned in this unit. Under Review These Activities, you will find activities from previous lessons that will review each big idea. Choose the topics you feel you need to review. Under Try These, you will find interactive problems that will test your understanding of each big idea. As you work through this lesson, take notes in the spaces provided.

Big Idea
A number is any entity that obeys the laws of arithmetic; all numbers obey the laws of arithmetic. The laws of arithmetic can be used to simplify algebraic expressions.

Big Idea
The laws of arithmetic can be used to simplify algebraic expressions and equations. Solving an equation means finding values for the variable or variables that make the equation a true statement.

Summary: Number Properties Review [online]

In this unit you covered the following topics:

- positive exponents
- factors and primes
- GCF and relative primes
- negative exponents
- powers of ten
- scientific notation

Offline Learning: Number Properties Review [offline]

How well have you mastered the goals of t his unit? Complete the Number Properties Practice Problems. These problems are similar to the problems you will have on the Unit Test.

You can also

- Review the Number Properties unit in *Pre-Algebra: A Reference Guide and Problem Sets*
- Review the notes in your Student Guide
- Read and follow the instructions in Preparing for the Unit Test

Practice Problems [offline]

1. Evaluate $4^3 - 3^2$.

2. Evaluate $2a^4 - 3b^3$ if $a = -2$ and $b = 3$.

3. Write the following powers in standard form:
   a. 4^3

   b. $(-3)^4$

   c. -2^3

   d. -2^4

4. List all of the factors of 84.

5. Identify each of the following numbers as prime or composite:
   a. 42

   b. 53

    c. 27

    d. 19

6. Find the prime factorization of 56.

7. Find the GCF of 36 and 48.

8. Find the GCF of 14 and 45.

9. Solve the following equations:

    a. $3^a = \dfrac{1}{81}$

    b. $b^{-5} = \dfrac{1}{32}$

10. Write the following powers in standard form:

    a. 10^5

    b. 10^{-6}

11. Write the following numbers as powers of ten:

    a. $10,000,000$

    b. 0.00000001

12. Find each of the following:

    a. 42.3×10^4

    b. $32 \div 10^5$

13. Write the following in standard form:

    a. 7.83×10^4

    b. 5.2×10^{-3}

14. Write the following numbers in scientific notation.

    a. 12,300,000

    b. 0.00036

15. Simplify $\left(1.4 \times 10^3\right) \times \left(2.1 \times 10^{-8}\right)$.

Answers

1. 55

2. −49

3. **a.** 64

   b. 81

   c. −8

   d. −16

4. 1, 2, 3, 4, 6, 7, 12, 14, 21, 28, 42, 84

5. **a.** composite

   b. prime

   c. composite

   d. prime

6. $2^3 \cdot 7$

7. 12

8. 1; 14 and 45 are relatively prime

9. **a.** $a = -4$

   b. $b = 2$

10. **a.** 100,000

    b. 0.000001

11. **a.** 10^7

    b. 10^{-8}

12. **a.** 423,000

    b. 0.00032

13. **a.** 78,300

    b. 0.0052

14. a. 1.23×10^7

    b. 3.6×10^{-4}

15. 2.94×10^{-5}

Unit Assessment

Number Properties Unit Test, Offline

Answer each question in the space provided.

(5 points)

1. Read each problem and give your answer.

    A) The average distance in kilometers (km) from the sun to the planet Mercury is about 58,000,000 km. Write this distance in scientific notation.

    B) The diameter in centimeters (cm) of a human hair is about 0.0025 cm. Write this diameter in scientific notation.

(5 points)

2. Evaluate the expression $a^2 - 4b^3$ if a = 3 and b = –2.

Score

Score	___ of 10

Student Guide

Points, Lines, and Planes

You can *point* at the sun, *line* up to buy concert tickets, and take a *plane* to Africa. In mathematics, however, these terms have very different meanings. In this lesson, you will learn about geometric points, lines, and planes—the three most fundamental geometric objects.

Goals for the Lesson
- Name a point.
- Name a line.
- Name a plane.

Graded Activities in This Lesson
Lesson Quiz (computer-scored)

Materials
Pre-Algebra: A Reference Guide and Problem Sets, pages 219–223

Points, Lines, and Planes Solutions

compass

straightedge

Keywords and Pronunciation
collinear: three or more points are collinear if a straight line can be drawn through the given points

line: a collection of points arranged in a straight path that extends without end in both directions

line segment: part of a line; it includes any two points on the line and all the points in between those two points

point: a location in space with no length, width, or depth

plane: a flat surface with infinite length and width but no thickness

Groundwork: Preparing for the Lesson [online]

In this activity, you will pick out and describe at least 10 different shapes from the photograph. Use the space below to list and describe the shapes that you see.

Notes

Learn: Introduction to Points, Lines, and Planes [online]

Draw and label a point.

Draw and label a line.

Draw and label a plane.

Notes

Worked Examples: Points, Lines, and Planes [online]
Notes

Summary: Points, Lines, and Planes [online]

In this lesson, you have learned about three essential ideas in geometry: *point, line,* and *plane*.

You have learned how to draw and name a point, a line segment, a line, and a plane.

These essential skills form the basis of most of the geometric concepts you will learn throughout this unit.

Offline Learning: Points, Lines, and Planes [offline]

Skills Update

1. Express 81 as a power of 3.

2. Insert <, =, or > into the space to make the statement true. $\frac{8}{9}$ ___ $\frac{10}{11}$

3. Round 347.0537 to the nearest hundredth.

4. Solve the inequality $4x - 16 < -20$.

5. Simplify $2 + 3 \cdot 4 - 15 \div 5$.

In the Book
Read pages 219–221 in the Reference Guide.

Problem Sets
Complete Problems 1–4, 7–10, and 17–18 on pages 222–223 of the Reference Guide.

Lesson Assessment: Points, Lines, and Planes Quiz [online]
Now go back online to complete the lesson quiz.

Answers

Skills Update

1. 3^4

2. $<$

3. 347.05

4. $x < -1$

5. 11

Student Guide

Rays and Angles

A ray of sunshine starts at the sun and continues shining along a straight path forever—unless it runs into something along the way! Rays are very similar to lines and line segments; in this lesson, you will learn why. You will also learn how they relate to angles.

Goals for the Lesson

- Name a ray.

- Name an angle.

- Determine whether an angle is acute, right, or obtuse.

Graded Activities in This Lesson

Lesson Quiz (computer-scored)

Materials

Pre-Algebra: A Reference Guide and Problem Sets, pages 224–227

straightedge

Optional

Rays and Angles Solutions

protractor

Keywords and Pronunciation

acute angle: an angle that measures less than 90°

angle: the figure formed by two rays, called sides, that share the same endpoint

line: a collection of points arranged in a straight path that extends without ends in both directions

line segment: a part of a line; it includes any two points on the line and all the points in between those two points

obtuse angle: an angle that measures greater than 90° and less than 180°

point: a location in space with no length, width, or depth

ray: a part of a line that begins from an endpoint and extends infinitely in one direction

right angle: an angle that measures 90°

vertex: a point common to two sides of an angle or polygon; the plural of vertex is vertices

Groundwork: Preparing for the Lesson [online]

You will practice naming points, lines, and segments.

Notes

Learn: Introduction to Rays and Angles [online]

Notes

Draw and label a ray:

Draw and label an angle:

Learn: Classifying Angles [online]

If an angle might be a right angle, you can always compare the angle to an object that has a right angle—like the corner of a piece of paper. One of the angles drawn below is right, one is acute, and one is obtuse. Identify which one is which.

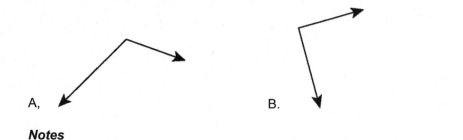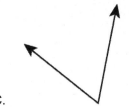

A,

B.

C.

Notes

Worked Examples: Rays and Angles [online]
Notes

MathCast: Identifying Angles [online]

View the video to see how to solve a typical problem.

Summary: Rays and Angles [online]

In this lesson, you have learned about two important geometric figures, the ray and the angle. You have learned how to identify and label both.

You have also learned to classify an angle as acute, right, or obtuse, depending on its degree measure.

Offline Learning: Rays and Angles [offline]

Skills Update [offline]

1. Simplify. $9\frac{1}{3} \div [(2\frac{1}{3} + 1\frac{2}{3}) \bullet 3\frac{1}{2}]$

2. Write an expression for the word phrase: four less than the product of two and a number a.

3. Solve for x. $4x - 7 = 15$

4. Express $\frac{7}{11}$ as a decimal.

In the Book
Read pages 224–227 in the Reference Guide.

Problem Sets
Complete Problems 1–4, 7–10, and 17–18 on pages 227-228 of the Reference Guide.

Lesson Assessment: Rays and Angles Quiz [online]

Now go back online to complete the lesson quiz.

Answers

Classifying Angles

    A. Obtuse

    B. Right

    C. Acute

Skills Update

    1. $\dfrac{2}{3}$

    2. $2a - 4$

    3. $x = 5\dfrac{1}{2}$

    4. $0.\overline{63}$

Student Guide

Parallel Lines and Transversals

When you look at a street map, you will see many streets intersecting other streets. You will also see various angles that are formed when the streets intersect. In this lesson, you will learn about the angles formed when a line intersects other lines.

Goals for the Lesson

- Identify a pair of alternate interior angles associated with a transversal that intersects parallel lines.

- Identify a pair of corresponding angles associated with a transversal that intersects parallel lines.

- Use properties to determine unknown angle measures associated with a transversal that intersects two parallel lines.

- Use properties to determine unknown angle measures associated with a transversal that intersects two parallel lines in a complex figure.

Graded Activities in This Lesson

Lesson Quiz (computer-scored)

Materials

Pre-Algebra: A Reference Guide and Problem Sets, pages 229–232

straightedge

Optional

Parallel Lines and Transversals Solutions

Keywords and Pronunciation

adjacent angles: two angles in the same plane that have a common side and a common vertex, but no common interior points

alternate interior angles: the inside angles on opposite diagonal sides of a transversal crossing two parallel lines

alternate exterior angles: the outside angles on opposite diagonal sides of a transversal crossing two parallel lines

corresponding angles: the angles that lie in the same position or "match up" when a transversal crosses two parallel lines

line: a collection of points arranged in a straight path that extends without end in both directions

parallel lines: coplanar lines that never intersect

transversal: a line that intersects two or more lines in a plane

Groundwork: Preparing for the Lesson [online]

In this activity, you will learn about adjacent angles.

Draw and label two adjacent angles below:

Notes

Learn: Pairs of Angles Around a Transversal [online]

Draw and label two parallel lines crossed by a transversal.

Number the angles formed 1–8.

Write all the pairs of corresponding angles (there should be four pairs).

Write all the pairs of alternate interior angles (there should be two pairs).

Write all the pairs of adjacent angles (there should be eight pairs).

Notes

Learn: Finding Angle Measures [online]

Draw two parallel lines with a transversal crossing them at 90°. Notice that all eight angles formed are equal to 90°.

Strategy for finding angles:

There is more than one way to approach this problem. One approach is to find the measures of angles 1, 3, and 4 first, since you know that the measure of angle 2 is 65°. Once you have those, you will see that they correspond to angles 9–12. You can repeat this strategy to find the measures of angles 5–8 and 13–16.

Notes

MathCast: Finding Angle Measures [online]

View the video to see how to solve a typical problem.

Summary: Parallel Lines and Transversals [online]

In this lesson, you have learned how to identify some of the special angle pairs created when a transversal intersects two lines.

You have also learned that when the lines are parallel, the corresponding angles and the alternate interior angles have equal measure. And you have learned that adjacent angles are supplementary.

Offline Learning: Parallel Lines and Transversals [offline]

Skills Update [offline]

1. Convert $-\dfrac{7}{8}$ to a decimal.

2. Evaluate $|2.1 - x|$ when $x = 5.8$.

3. What is the GCF of 42 and 28?

4. Solve for x: $5(3 + x) = 75$.

In the Book
Read pages 229–231 in the Reference Guide.

Problem Sets
Complete Problems 1–17 odd and 23–26 on page 232 of the Reference Guide.

Lesson Assessment: Parallel Lines and Transversals Quiz [online]
Now go back online to complete the lesson quiz.

Answers

Skills Update

1. −0.875
2. 3.7
3. 14
4. $x = 12$

Student Guide

Triangles

Everyone knows what a triangle is, but how much do you know about triangles? In this lesson, you will learn how to name different types of triangles; you will also learn about an important property that relates the angle measures of a triangle.

Goals for the Lesson

- Use triangle properties to find missing angle measures in a triangle.

- Determine whether a triangle is acute, obtuse, or right.

Graded Activities in This Lesson

Mid-Unit Test (computer-scored)

Materials

Pre-Algebra: A Reference Guide and Problem Sets, pages 234–239

Straightedge

Optional

Triangles Solutions

Keywords and Pronunciation

acute angle: an angle that measures less than 90°

acute triangle: a triangle with three acute angles

obtuse angle: an angle that measures greater than 90° and less than 180°

right angle: an angle that measures 90°

right triangle: a triangle with a right angle

obtuse triangle: a triangle with an obtuse angle

vertex: a point common to two sides of an angle or polygon; the plural of vertex is *vertices*

Groundwork: Preparing for the Lesson [online]

Review how to classify angles by their measure.

Notes

Learn: Finding Angle Measures [online]

When you find missing angle measures, you might end up solving an equation. These reminders may help you as you solve:

- If possible, combine like terms on one or both sides of the equation before solving the equation.
- Determine the correct transformation to use in order to solve the equation.

Notes

Learn: Classifying Triangles by Angle Measure [online]

Draw the following triangles by using a straightedge:

Acute triangle *TRI*

Obtuse triangle *ANG*

Right triangle *LES*

Notes

MathCast: Classify a Triangle [online]

View the video to see how to solve a typical problem.

Summary: Triangles [online]

In this lesson, you have learned several facts about triangles.

- You have learned how to identify an acute triangle, obtuse triangle, or right triangle.

- You have also learned that the triangle angle sum property can be used to find the unknown measure of an angle of a triangle.

Offline Learning: Triangles [offline]

Skills Update [offline]

1. Insert the symbol <, =, or > to make the statement true: $\frac{11}{20}$? $\frac{9}{15}$

2. Evaluate the expression $8n + 4 - 4n \div 2$ when $n = 7$.

3. Find the sum: $-5.7 + (-4.2) + 3.1$

In the Book

Read pages 234–239 in the Reference Guide.

Problem Sets

Complete Problems 1–19 odd and 26–29 on pages 237–239.

Mid-Unit Assessment: Geometry Basics Test [online]

Now go back online to complete the mid-unit test.

Answers

Skills Update

1. <

2. 46

3. −6.8

Student Guide

Polygons

A polygon is a closed figure made up of segments joined at their endpoints. The prefix *poly* is of Greek origin and means "many." That same prefix is in other words, such as *poly*anthus (a primrose with many flowers), *poly*glot (a person who speaks many languages), and *poly*nomial (a math expression with one or more terms). In this lesson, you will learn how to identify and classify polygons.

Goals for the Lesson
- Determine whether a figure is a polygon.
- Determine whether a polygon is regular.
- Identify a polygon by the number of its sides.

Graded Activities in This Lesson
Lesson Quiz (computer-scored)

Materials
Pre-Algebra: A Reference Guide and Problem Sets, pages 240–244

Optional
calculator

High-Flying Challenge sheet

High-Flying Challenge Answer Key

Polygons Solutions

Keywords and Pronunciation
equiangular polygon: a polygon with all angles congruent

equilateral polygon: a polygon with all sides congruent

polygon: a closed plane figure made up of line segments

regular polygon: a polygon in which all sides are congruent and all angles are congruent

Groundwork: Preparing for the Lesson [online]
As you read through the lesson online, use the spaces below to take notes on each screen.

Notes

Learn: Properties of Polygons [online]

In this activity, you will learn how to determine whether a figure is a polygon. You will also learn to identify types of polygons.

Notes

What is a polygon?

Draw two different polygons. Identify the sides and vertices of each.

What characteristics must a figure have to be considered a polygon?

Complete the following table.

Number of Sides	Polygon Name
3	
4	
5	
6	
7	
8	
9	
10	
n	

Learn: Classification of Polygons [online]

In this activity you will learn to classify polygons as regular.

Notes

What is a regular polygon?

Worked Examples: Polygons [online]

Notes

MathCast: Classifying Polygons [online]

View the video to see how to solve a typical problem.

Summary: Polygons [online]

In this lesson, you have learned about polygons.

- A **polygon** is a closed plane figure formed by three or more line segments, such that each line segment intersects exactly two other line segments at their endpoints.

- The line segments form the sides of the polygon. Any point where the line segments intersect is a vertex.

- A **regular polygon** has both congruent sides and congruent angles.

- A polygon can be named according to the number of sides it has.

Skills Update: Practice Your Math Skills
Complete the Skills Update online.

Offline Learning: Polygons [offline]

In the Book
Read pages 240–242 in the Reference Guide.

Problem Sets
Complete Problems 1–4 and 9–23 odd on pages 243–244 of the Reference Guide.

Lesson Assessment: Polygons Quiz [online]
Now go back online to complete the lesson quiz.

Name _____   Date _____

Extension
High-Flying Geometry

Earle Newton works for a company that designs kites. At the right is one of his newest designs.

1. Name a line segment parallel to $\overline{DF}$.

   _____

2. Name a right triangle that has $\overline{DF}$ as one of its sides.

   _____

3. What kind of figure is *XLPK*?

   _____

4. If $\overline{BA}$ is congruent to $\overline{AY}$, what kind of triangle is *BAY*?

   _____

5. $\overline{UZ} \parallel \overline{PF}$. What is $\overline{LP}$ called?

   _____

6. $\overline{AE} \parallel \overline{YF}$. $\angle UKP$ is congruent to $\angle KPY$ because _____

7. What is the most specific name you can give figure *LQPU*? _____

8. Name the trapezoid with one right angle. _____

9. Can you find a trapezoid with no right angles on the kite? _____

10. Can you find a parallelogram that is not a rectangle on the kite? _____

11. In $\triangle IVJ$, $m\angle I = m\angle V = 60°$. What is $m\angle J$? _____

12. What kind of triangle is $\triangle IVJ$? _____

13. Name an obtuse isosceles triangle. _____

14. Name a regular octagon in the kite. _____

15. Figure *XRLMWNZD* is an octagon. Name another octagon. _____

16. Name any pentagon. _____

Student Guide

Circles

At first glance, a circle might look as though it has nothing in common with a straight line. But many different lines and line segments are associated with a circle, such as a radius, a diameter, and a chord. In this lesson, you will explore the different types of line segments that are commonly associated with circles.

Goals for the Lesson
- Name radii.
- Name chords.
- Name diameters.
- Find the radius or diameter when given the other.

Graded Activities in This Lesson
Lesson Quiz (computer-scored)

Materials
Pre-Algebra: A Reference Guide and Problem Sets, pages 245–247

Optional

Circles Solutions

calculator

Optional Assignment

Keywords and Pronunciation
chord: a line segment that connects any two points on a circle

circle: the set of all points in a plane that are equidistant from a given point in the plane, called the *center*

diameter: a chord that contains the center of a circle; the length of this chord is also called the diameter

radius: a line segment that connects the center of the circle to a point on the circle; the length of that segment is also called the radius

Groundwork: Preparing for the Lesson [online]
You will see a compass being used to draw a circle. Why are compasses good for drawing circles?

Notes

Learn: What Is a Circle? [online]

A circle is always named by using the capital letter that represents its center. The order of the letters does not matter when you are naming a radius of a circle. For example, radius $\overline{AB}$ can also be called radius $\overline{BA}$.

Notes

Learn: Chords [online]

The words *diameter* and *radius* refer to both the segment and the length of the segment. Typically, when we say "the radius of circle A," we are asking for the length of the segment, but when we say "a radius of circle A," we are referring to the segment itself.

Notes

MathCast: Chords, Radii, and Diameter [online]

View the video to see how to solve a typical problem.

Summary: Circles [online]

A circle is named by using the capital letter that represents the center of the circle.

You can name a radius, chord, and diameter in the same way you name a line segment. You can do that because all three are line segments.

The diameter of a circle is twice the radius, as shown in the equation $d = 2r$.

Offline Learning: Circles [offline]

Skills Update

1. Simplify: $\dfrac{1}{2^{-3}}$

2. Solve the equation: $3x - 7 = 23$.

3. Write an equation for this sentence: *The product of three and a number is four less than the number*.

4. Find the least common denominator for $\dfrac{3}{10}$ and $\dfrac{2}{35}$.

5. How would you read the notation $\overrightarrow{AB}$?

In the Book
Read pages 245–247 in the Reference Guide.

Problem Sets
Complete Problems 1–6 and 13–19 odd on pages 248–249 of the Reference Guide.

More Practice: Optional Assignment [offline, optional]

For extra practice, print the Optional Assignment and complete one or more of the problems. Submit the assignment to your teacher on or before the due date to receive feedback on your work.

Lesson Assessment: Circles Quiz [online]

Now go back online to complete the lesson quiz.

Answers

Skills Update

1. 8

2. $x = 10$

3. $3x = x - 4$

4. 70

5. Ray AB

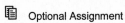
Name: _____   Date: _____

Optional Assignment

Parallel Lines and Circles

1. Lines *m* and *n* are parallel and $m\angle 1 = 100°$.

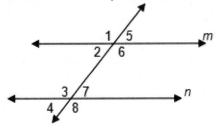

Find each measure and describe how you found each answer.

    a. $m\angle 6$

    b. $m\angle 3$

    c. $m\angle 2$

    d. $m\angle 7$

    e. $m\angle 7$

Answer:

2. A circle has a diameter of 12 cm. What is the radius of the circle?

Answer:

Student Guide

Transformations

If you pick up an apple, you can flip it over, turn it around, or move it somewhere else—and you still have the same apple you started with. Mathematically, these kinds of motions are called transformations. In this lesson, you will learn about two kinds of transformations—reflections and rotations.

Goals for the Lesson

- Draw a reflection when given a figure and a line of reflection.

- Draw a rotation of 90 or 180 degrees when given a figure and a center of rotation.

- Identify a reflection or rotation for a given image and preimage.

Graded Activities in This Lesson
Lesson Quiz

Materials
Pre-Algebra: A Reference Guide and Problem Sets, pages 250–255

Optional

Transformations Solutions

straightedge

protractor

Keywords and Pronunciation
center of rotation: the point about which a figure is rotated

image: in a transformation, the new figure that results from the transformation

line of reflection: the line that a figure is reflected across

preimage: the original figure in a transformation

reflection: a transformation of a figure by flipping it across a line or line segment, creating a mirror image of the figure

rotation: a transformation of a figure by turning it about a given point

Groundwork: Preparing for the Lesson [online]

Describe how the letter **b** can be moved around to make the letter **d**.

Describe how the letter **n** can be moved around to make the letter **u**.

Notes

Learn: Reflections [online]

For the problems given, draw your predicted result on the figure below.

Notes

Learn: Rotations [online]

Perform the specified rotation of **B** about the point.

90° counterclockwise	90° clockwise	180° counterclockwise
B ·	·B	B ·

Notes

Worked Examples: Transformations [online]

Work through the transformations.

Notes

Summary: Transformations [online]

A transformation is called a—

- *reflection* when a figure is reflected, or flipped, over a line.

- *rotation* when a figure is rotated, or turned, about a point.

The figure before a transformation happens is called the *preimage*. After the transformation, it is called the *image*.

Offline Learning: Transformations [offline]

In the Book
Read pages 250–254 in the Reference Guide.

Problem Sets
Complete Problems 1–11 on pages 254–255 of the Reference Guide.

Lesson Assessment: Transformations Quiz [online]
Now go back online to complete the lesson quiz.

Student Guide

Congruence

Congruence is often seen in real-world situations. For example, some parts of a house have standard (or congruent) sizes that are the same in different houses. Doors, windows, floors, walls, and stairs are just some of the parts that may be congruent from house to house. Think about how difficult it would be for manufacturers if every house had parts of different sizes. In this lesson, you will learn what it means for two figures to be congruent.

Goals for the Lesson
* Identify congruent parts of congruent figures.

* Determine whether given figures are congruent.

* Find an angle measure or side length when given two congruent polygons.

Graded Activities in This Lesson
Lesson Quiz (computer-scored)

Materials
Pre-Algebra: A Reference Guide and Problem Sets, pages 257–261

Optional

Congruence Solutions

Keywords and Pronunciation
congruent figures: figures that have the same size and shape

Groundwork: Preparing for the Lesson [online]
Review the definition of a polygon and identify sides and vertices of different polygons. As you work through this activity, answer the questions below and record any notes in the space provided.

Notes
How many vertices does a quadrilateral have? A pentagon? An octagon?

Learn: Congruent Figures [online]

As you work through this activity, answer the question below and record any notes in the space provided.

Notes

If two triangles have the same area, must they be congruent? Explain.

Worked Examples: Congruence [online]

As you work through this activity, record any notes in the space provided.

Notes

MathCast: Congruence [online]

View the video to see how to solve a typical problem.

Summary: Congruence [online]

Congruent polygons have the same size and shape, though they may or may not have the same orientation.

You can use a congruence statement to determine which sides and angles of a polygon are congruent. The order of the letters in a congruence statement tells you which vertices of one polygon match up to the vertices of the other.

Offline Learning: Congruence [offline]

In the Book
Read pages 257–259 in the Reference Guide.

Problem Sets
Complete Problems 1–7 odd and 9–25 on pages 260–261 of the Reference Guide.

Lesson Assessment: Congruence Quiz [online]
Now go back online to complete the lesson quiz.

Student Guide

Geometry Basics Review

You have finished studying the Geometry Basics unit, which includes points, lines, and planes; rays and angles; parallel lines and transversals; triangles; polygons; circles; transformations; and congruence. Now it's time to pull together what you have learned. Throughout the review, see how the skills you have learned relate to the Pre-Algebra big ideas.

Goals for the Lesson
* Review the concepts and skills learned in the unit.

Materials
"Geometry Basics" in *Pre-Algebra: A Reference Guide and Problem Sets*
Preparing for the Unit Test

Unit Review: Geometry Basics [online]

This is your chance to review the big ideas of Pre-Algebra you have learned in this unit. Under Review These Activities, you will find activities from previous lessons that will review each big idea. Choose the topics you feel you need to review. Under Try These Activities, you will find interactive problems that will test your understanding of each big idea. As you work through this lesson, take notes in the spaces provided.

Big Idea
Euclidean geometry uses five basic axioms to model real-world geometry and derives an amazing array of true results that apply extremely well to real-world geometry.

Summary: Geometry Basics Review [online]

In this unit, you have covered the following topics:

- points, lines, and planes

- rays and angles

- parallel lines and transversals

- triangles

- polygons

- circles

- transformations

- congruence

Offline Learning: Geometry Basics Review [offline]

How well have you mastered the goals of this unit? Complete the Geometry Basics Practice Problems. These problems are similar to the problems you will have on the Unit Test.

You can also—

- Review the Geometry Basics unit in *Pre-Algebra: A Reference Guide and Problem Sets*.

- Review the notes in your Student Guide.

- Read and follow the instructions in Preparing for the Unit Test.

Practice Problems

Geometry Basics

1. Use the figure to answer each of the questions.

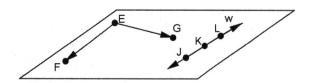

   a. Write three other names for line *w*.

   b. Write two names for the angle shown in the figure.

2. State whether each angle appears to be acute, right or obtuse.

   a.

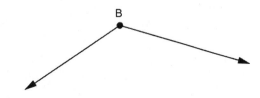

   b.

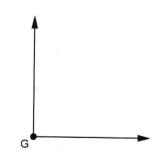

c.

Use the figure below to answer questions 3–6.

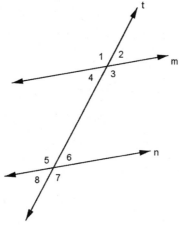

m‖n

3. Name the alternate interior angles.

4. Name the alternate exterior angles.

5. Name the corresponding angles.

6. If $m\angle 4 = 36°$, find the measures of the following angles.

      a. $m\angle 6$

      b. $m\angle 2$

7. Find the measure of the missing angle.

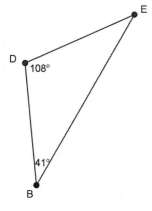

8. State whether each of the triangles appears to be acute, right, or obtuse.

a.

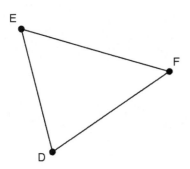

b.

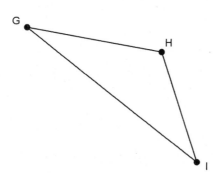

c.

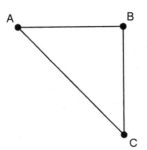

9. Is the following figure a polygon? If not, explain why not.

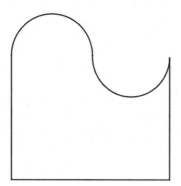

10. Name each of the following polygons, and state whether they appear to be regular or nonregular.

    a.

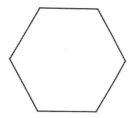

    b.

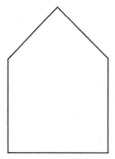

c.

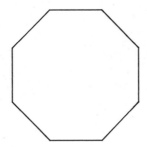

Use the circle to answer questions 11–12.

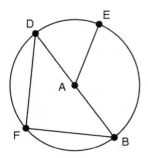

11. Name three radii shown in this circle.

12. Find the measure of $\overline{DB}$ if $AE = 8$ cm.

13. Draw the reflection of the figure above the line.

14. Draw the figure if it is rotated 90° around point C in a clockwise direction.

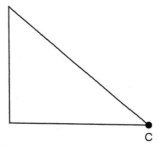

15. If $ABCD \cong RSTU$, what angle is congruent to $\angle C$?

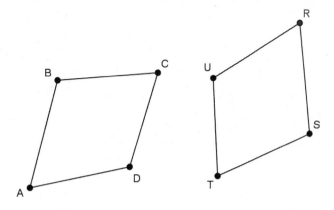

16. If $\lor ABC \cong \lor DEF$, $m\angle B = 47°$, and $m\angle C = 87°$, then find $m\angle D$.

Answers

1. **a.** Any 3 of the following: $\overleftrightarrow{JL}, \overleftrightarrow{LJ}, \overleftrightarrow{KJ}, \overleftrightarrow{JK}, \overleftrightarrow{KL}, \overleftrightarrow{LK}$
    b. Any 2 of the following: $\angle FEG, \angle GEF, \angle E$

2. **a.** obtuse
    b. right
    c. acute

3. $\angle 4$ and $\angle 6$, $\angle 3$ and $\angle 5$
4. $\angle 1$ and $\angle 7$, $\angle 2$ and $\angle 8$

5. $\angle 1$ and $\angle 5$, $\angle 2$ and $\angle 6$, $\angle 4$ and $\angle 8$, $\angle 3$ and $\angle 7$

6. **a.** $36°$

    b. $36°$

7. $31°$

8. **a.** acute

    b. obtuse

    c. right

9. No, this figure is not a polygon. A polygon is a closed figure whose sides are all line segments. This figure has curved sides, so it cannot be a polygon.

10. **a.** regular hexagon

    b. nonregular pentagon

    c. regular octagon

11. $\overline{AD}, \overline{AB}, \overline{AE}$

12. 16 cm

13.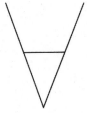

14.

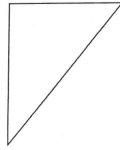

15. ∠*T*

16. 46°

Unit Assessment

Geometry Basics Unit Test, Offline

Answer each question in the space provided.

(6 points)

1. Use the figure shown here to answer the questions listed below.

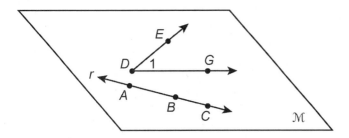

   A. Name all of the points shown in the figure.

   B. Write three other possible names for line *r*.

   C. Name all of the rays shown in the figure.

   D. What does ᴍ name?

   E. Write two other possible names for ∠1.

☼
(6 points)

2. Use the figure below to answer the questions that follow.

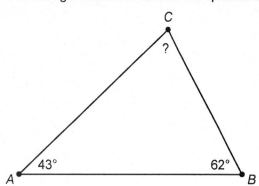

A. Find the missing angle measure.

B. Identify the triangle as acute, right, or obtuse.

Student Guide

Semester Review

You have finished the first semester of Pre-Algebra. You started with the basics, addition and subtraction, and multiplication and division; then built on these with fractions, combined operations, and number properties; and finished with geometry basics. You have covered a lot of material in this semester. This is your opportunity to review before the Semester Test.

Goals for the Lesson

*   Review the concepts and skills learned in the semester.

Materials

Pre-Algebra: A Reference Guide and Problem Sets

Semester Review: Preparing for the Assessment [online]

This is your chance to review the Big Ideas of Pre-Algebra that you have studied in this course. Under Review These Activities, you will find pieces from previous lessons that will help you review each Big Idea. Choose the topics that you feel you need to review. Under Try These, you will find interactive problems that will test your understanding of each Big Idea. As you work through this lesson, take notes in the spaces provided.

Big Idea

A number is any entity that obeys the laws of arithmetic; all numbers obey the laws of arithmetic. The laws of arithmetic can be used to simplify algebraic expressions.

Big Idea

A set is a well-defined collection of numbers or objects. Sets and operations defined on sets provide a clear way to communicate about collections of numbers or objects.

Big Idea

Expressions, equations, and inequalities express relationships between different entities.

Big Idea

The laws of arithmetic can be used to simplify algebraic expressions and equations. Solving an equation means finding values for the variable or variables that make the equation a true statement.

Big Idea

If you can create a mathematical model for a situation, you can use the model to solve other problems that you might not be able to solve otherwise. Algebraic equations and inequalities can capture key relationships among quantities in the world.

Big Idea

Euclidean geometry uses five basic axioms to model real-world geometry and derives an amazing array of true results that apply extremely well to real-world geometry.

Summary: Semester Review [online]

In this semester, you have covered the following topics:

- The basics: order of operations, variable expressions, translating words into variable expressions, comparing expressions, replacement sets, related equations, solving equations, and problem solving

- Addition and subtraction: integers on a number line, adding integers, subtracting integers, decimals on a number line, adding decimals, subtracting decimals, addition and subtraction properties, equations involving addition and subtraction, and addition and subtraction applications

- Multiplication and division: multiplying integers and decimals, dividing integers and decimals, multiplication and division properties, rounding and estimation, equations involving multiplication and division, multiplication and division applications

- Fractions: equivalent fractions, multiplying fractions, dividing fractions, common denominators, adding and subtracting fractions, improper fractions and mixed numbers, multiplying and dividing mixed numbers, solving equations with fractions and mixed numbers

- Combined operations: the distributive property, like terms, expressions with mixed operations, equations with mixed operations, error analysis, inequalities

- Number properties: positive exponents, factors and primes, GCF and relative primes, negative exponents, powers of ten, scientific notation

- Geometry basics: points, lines, and planes; rays and angles; parallel lines and transversals; triangles; polygons; circles; transformations; congruence

Offline Learning: Semester Review [offline]

To prepare for the semester test, you can also review the following:

- Units 1 through 7 of the Reference Guide

- Previous Unit Tests

- Previous Problem Sets sections of your Student Guides

- The notes in your Student Guide for each lesson in Units 1–7

Name: _____   Date: _____

Graded Assignment

Semester Test, Part 2

(10 points)

1. The diagram shows the intersection of streets in the downtown area of a city. The measure of angle 1 is 90°. Second Avenue and First Avenue are parallel.

Score

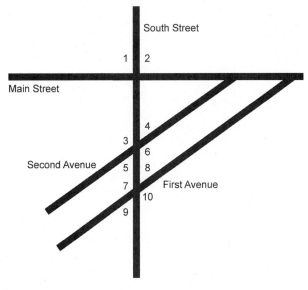

a. What kinds of angles are formed by the intersection of Main Street and South Street? Explain your answer.

b. Name a pair of alternate interior angles formed by the intersection of South Street with First and Second Avenues.

c. Name a pair of corresponding angles formed by the intersection of South Street with First and Second Avenues.

d. If the measure of angle 4 is 65°, what is the measure of angle 6? Explain how you know.

e. If the measure of angle 3 is 115°, what is the measure of angle 7? Explain how you know.

(5 points)

2. Don designed a triangular-shaped garden. Use the diagram to answer each question.

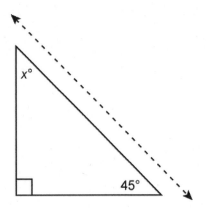

a. What kind of triangle is formed by the sides of the garden?

b. What is the measure of angle *x*?

c. Don wants to design another garden that is the reflection of the original garden over the dotted line. Draw the reflection of the triangular garden across the dotted line. Show your work on the diagram above.

Score	____ of 15

Student Guide

Ratio, Part 1

A ratio is a comparison of two quantities. Ratios are used frequently in everyday life as a way to compare quantities. For example, a ratio can be used to compare the number of cups of nuts to the number of cups of dried fruit in a trail mix recipe. If a bag of mix has 1 cup of dried fruit and 2 cups of nuts, then the ratio of dried fruit to nuts in the bag is 1 to 2. In this lesson, you will explore how to write and simplify ratios, and how to use ratios to represent real-world situations.

Goals for the Lesson
* Write a ratio as a fraction in lowest terms.
* Write a simplified ratio for a word problem.

Graded Activities in This Lesson
Lesson Quiz (computer-scored)

Materials
Pre-Algebra: A Reference Guide and Problem Sets, pages 265–268

Optional
calculator
Ratio Solutions

Keywords and Pronunciation
lowest terms: a fraction whose numerator and denominator have no common factor other than 1 or –1

ratio: a comparison of two quantities using division

Groundwork: Preparing for the Lesson [online]
Review writing fractions in lowest terms. As you work through this activity, answer the question below and record any notes in the space provided.

Notes
In your own words, explain how to write a fraction in lowest terms.

Learn: Writing and Simplifying Ratios [online]

As you work through this activity, answer the question below and record any notes in the space provided.

Notes

In what three ways can you write a ratio?

Learn: Comparing Parts and Wholes [online]

As you work through this activity, answer the question below and record any notes in the space provided.

Notes

A fruit bowl contains 5 apples, 3 peaches, and 6 bananas. What numbers represent the parts and what number represents the whole?

Worked Examples: Ratio, Part 1 [online]

Notes

Summary: Ratio, Part 1 [online]

In this lesson, you learned how to write and simplify ratios.

- A ratio is a comparison of two quantities by division.

- You can use a ratio to compare parts and wholes.

Offline Learning: Ratio, Part 1 [offline]

In the Book
Read page 265 and Comparing Parts and Wholes on page 267 in the Reference Guide.

Problem Sets
Complete Problems 1–10, 23, and 25 on page 268 of the Reference Guide.

Extra Practice (optional)
Complete Problems 11–16, 22, and 24 on page 211.

Try It
Suppose a baseball player has 210 hits in 525 at bats. The ratio of hits to at bats is 210 : 525, which reduces to 2 : 5. Now rewrite the ratio as a fraction: $\frac{2}{5}$. The fraction can then be converted to a decimal: 0.4. In baseball terminology this player would be "batting four hundred [.400]," which is an excellent batting average.

Extension (optional)

Visit the website http://www.thehitters.com/. This website lists the 36 Major League Baseball players with the highest batting averages of all time. It tells you each player's career batting average and total number of hits. Choose one or two players and try to determine the total number of at bats each player had in his career. Remember, the ratio of the number of hits to the number of at bats equals a player's lifetime batting average.

You can check your results (as well as learn more about the players) by clicking the link for each player's name, then clicking the "Full Stats" link to the right.

Lesson Assessment: Ratio, Part 1 Quiz [online]

Now go back online to complete the lesson quiz.

Student Guide

Ratio, Part 2

Unit rates can help you become a wise consumer. Suppose one store sells a 32-fluid-ounce container of lemonade for $2.89 and another sells a 64-fluid-ounce container of lemonade for $5.25. How do you know which is the better buy? Finding the unit rate of each container will give you the answer.

Goals for the Lesson

- Write a ratio as a rate.

- Write a ratio as a unit rate.

Graded Activities in This Lesson
Lesson Quiz (computer-scored)

Materials
Pre-Algebra: A Reference Guide and Problem Sets, pages 265–268

Optional
calculator
Ratio Solutions

Keywords and Pronunciation

rate: a ratio that compares quantities of different kinds of units

ratio: a comparison of two quantities using division

unit rate: a rate that has a denominator of 1

Groundwork: Preparing for the Lesson [online]
As you work through this activity, answer the question below and record any notes in the space provided.

Notes
How is simplifying a ratio similar to simplifying a fraction? How is it different?

Learn: Writing Rates [online]

As you work through this activity, answer the question below and record any notes in the space provided.

Notes

Is every ratio a rate? Explain.

Learn: Finding Unit Rates [online]

As you work through this activity, answer the question below and record any notes in the space provided.

Notes

Is $\dfrac{\$24}{3 \text{ tickets}}$ a unit rate? Explain.

Worked Examples: Ratio, Part 2 [online]

As you work through this activity, record any notes in the space provided.

Notes

MathCast: Unit Rate [online]

View the video to see how to solve a typical problem.

Summary: Ratio, Part 2 [online]

In this lesson, you learned how to write rates and find unit rates.

A rate is a ratio of quantities with different units.

A unit rate is a rate with a denominator of 1.

Offline Learning: Ratio, Part 2 [offline]

In the Book

Read page 266 and the Application sections on page 267 in the Reference Guide.

Do the Math

Best Buys

You can determine the best buy among different items by finding the unit rate or unit price for each item. The item with the lowest unit price is the best buy.

In the lesson opener, you were told of one store that sells a 32-fluid-ounce container of lemonade for $2.89 and another that sells a 64-fluid-ounce container of lemonade for $5.25. To determine the better buy, find the unit rate for each container of lemonade.

Container 1: $\dfrac{2.89}{32} \cdot \dfrac{\text{dollars}}{\text{fluid ounces}} = \dfrac{2.89 \div 32}{32 \div 32} \cdot \dfrac{\text{dollars}}{\text{fluid ounces}} \approx \dfrac{0.090}{1} \cdot \dfrac{\text{dollars}}{\text{fluid ounces}}$, or about 9 cents per fluid ounce

Container 2: $\dfrac{5.25}{64} \cdot \dfrac{\text{dollars}}{\text{fluid ounces}} = \dfrac{5.25 \div 64}{64 \div 64} \cdot \dfrac{\text{dollars}}{\text{fluid ounces}} \approx \dfrac{0.082}{1} \cdot \dfrac{\text{dollars}}{\text{fluid ounces}}$, or about 8 cents per fluid ounce

The second container of lemonade is the better buy.

Problem Sets

Complete Problems 17–21 odd and 27 on page 268 of the reference guide.

Extra Practice (optional)

Complete Problems 18–20 even and 26 on page 268 of the reference guide.

Lesson Assessment: Ratio, Part 2 Quiz [online]

Now go back online to complete the lesson quiz.

Student Guide

Proportion, Part 1

Suppose you are in a veterinarian's waiting room and notice that 4 of the 6 animals in the room are cats. When you return a month later, you notice that 6 of the 9 animals in the waiting room are cats. Is the ratio of cats to other animals the same during the two visits? In this lesson, you will learn ways to determine whether ratios are equivalent.

Goals for the Lesson
- Find equivalent ratios for a given ratio.

- Determine whether two ratios are proportional.

Graded Activities in This Lesson
Lesson Quiz (computer-scored)

Materials
Pre-Algebra: A Reference Guide and Problem Sets, pages 269–273

Optional
calculator

Proportion Solutions

Keywords and Pronunciation
cross products: the products obtained by multiplying the numerator of one fraction by the denominator of a second fraction and the denominator of the first fraction by the numerator of the second fraction

equivalent ratios: ratios that describe the same numerical relationship

extremes: in a proportion, the first and last numbers or variables; in $a : b = c : d$ or $\frac{a}{b} = \frac{c}{d}$, a and d are the extremes

means: in a proportion, the second and third numbers or variables; in $a : b = c : d$ or $\frac{a}{b} = \frac{c}{d}$, b and c are the means

proportion: an equation stating that two ratios are equal

Groundwork: Preparing for the Lesson [online]

This activity reviews the skills needed to compare fractions. As you work through it, answer the question below and record any notes in the space provided.

Notes

Explain how to compare two fractions.

Learn: Finding Equivalent Ratios [online]

As you work through this activity, answer the question below and record any notes in the space provided.

Notes

How many ratios can you find that are equivalent to $\frac{1}{2}$?

Learn: Proportional Ratios [online]

As you work through this activity, answer the question below and record any notes in the space provided.

Notes

Describe two ways to determine whether two ratios are proportional.

MathCast: Proportions [online]

View the video to see how to solve a typical problem.

Summary: Proportion, Part 1 [online]

In this lesson, you learned to write equivalent ratios and to determine whether ratios are proportional.

To find an equivalent ratio, multiply or divide the numerator and denominator of the ratio by the same nonzero number.

Two ratios form a proportion if the product of the means is equal to the product of the extremes.

Skills Update: Practice Your Math Skills [online]

Complete the Skills Update online.

Offline Learning: Proportion, Part 1 [offline]

In the Book

Read pages 269–271 up to the Solving Proportions section in the Reference Guide.

Problem Sets

Complete Problems 1–18 all and 33–36 on pages 272–273 of the Reference Guide.

Lesson Assessment: Proportion, Part 1 Quiz [online]

Now go back online to complete the lesson quiz.

Student Guide

Proportion, Part 2

A proportion is an equation stating that two ratios are equal. You can use proportions to solve many kinds of real-world problems, such as finding the correct amount of an ingredient in a recipe or the unit price of an item at the grocery store. In this lesson, you will learn to write and solve proportions.

Goals for the Lesson

- Solve a proportion.

- Solve a word problem involving proportions.

Graded Activities in This Lesson

Lesson Quiz (computer-scored)

Materials

Pre-Algebra: A Reference Guide and Problem Sets, pages 271–273

Optional
calculator
Proption Solutions

Keywords and Pronunciation

proportion: an equation stating that two ratios are equal

Groundwork: Preparing for the Lesson [online]

This activity reviews solving multiplication equations. As you work through it, answer the question below and record any notes in the space provided.

Notes
Explain how to solve a multiplication equation.

Learn: Proportions [online]

As you work through this activity, answer the question below and record any notes in the space provided.

Notes

What are two methods you can use to solve a proportion? Please describe each method.

Worked Examples: Proportion, Part 2 [online]

As you work through this activity, record any notes in the space provided.

Notes

MathCast: Solve a Proportion [online]

View the video to see how to solve a typical problem.

Summary: Proportion, Part 2 [online]

A proportion is an equation stating that two ratios are equal.

Proportions are useful for solving everyday problems.

Offline Learning: Proportion, Part 2 [offline]

In the Book

Read pages 271–272 in the Reference Guide.

Do the Math

What Is a Proportion?

A proportion is an equation stating that two ratios are equal. Proportions can help you solve everyday problems such as this one:

> A kennel will hire 2 groomers for every 7 dogs boarded there. If the kennel expects to receive 42 more dogs, how many additional groomers will the kennel need to hire?

Solution:

Write ratios comparing the number of groomers to the number of dogs. Let x = number of groomers	
$\dfrac{2}{7}$	2 groomers for every 7 dogs
$\dfrac{x}{42}$	x groomers for 42 dogs
groomers $\dfrac{2}{7} = \dfrac{x}{42}$ groomers dogs dogs	Write a proportion comparing the two ratios. Note that both ratios compare groomers to dogs.
$\dfrac{2}{7} = \dfrac{x}{42}$ $2 \cdot 42 = 7x$ $\dfrac{84}{7} = x$ $12 = x$	Find the product of the extremes and the product of the means, and then solve for x.
$\dfrac{2}{7} = \dfrac{12}{42}$ $2 \cdot 42 = 7 \cdot 12$ $84 = 84$	Substitute the value of x into the original proportion to check your answer.
The kennel will need to hire 12 additional groomers for the 42 dogs.	

Problem Sets

Complete Problems 19–35 odd on page 273 of the Reference Guide.

Extra Practice (optional)

Complete Problems 20–38 even on page 273 of the Reference Guide.

Extension (optional)

Ratios and proportions can be found in art (da Vinci's *Vitruvian Man*), science (the golden ratio), and many other fields. Today, many industries use computers to determine the proper proportions for creating everything from furniture that can be used in dollhouses to scale models of cities that can be used in motion pictures.

Choose a room in your home and measure its length, width, and height. Suppose you wanted to create a model of the room that had a scale of 1 : 4 (that is, every foot in your model would correspond to 4 feet in the actual room). What would be the dimensions for your model room?

Vitruvian Man

Lesson Assessment: Proportion, Part 2 Quiz [online]

Now go back online to complete the lesson quiz.

Student Guide

Percents, Fractions, and Decimals, Part 1

If you earned $10.00 per hour as a sales clerk, would you rather receive a $1.00-per-hour raise or a 12% raise? Knowing how to work with percents and decimals can help you make a good decision. This lesson will help you understand how to convert between percents, fractions, and decimals.

Goals for the Lesson

- Express a fraction as a decimal.

- Express a decimal as a fraction or a mixed number.

- Convert a decimal to a percent.

- Convert a percent to a decimal.

Graded Activities in This Lesson

Lesson Quiz (computer-scored)

Materials

Pre-Algebra: A Reference Guide and Problem Sets, pages 274–278

Optional

calculator
Percents, Fractions, and Decimals Solutions

Keywords and Pronunciation

percent: a ratio that compares a number to 100

Groundwork: Preparing for the Lesson [online]

This activity reviews essential skills. As you work through it, record any notes in the space provided.

Notes

Learn: Converting Between Fractions and Decimals [online]

As you work through this activity, answer the questions below and record any notes in the space provided.

Notes

Explain how to convert a fraction to a decimal.

Explain how to convert a decimal to a fraction.

Learn: Converting Between Decimals and Percents [online]

As you work through this activity, answer the questions below and record any notes in the space provided.

Notes

Explain how to convert a decimal to a percent.

Explain how to convert a percent to a decimal.

Summary: Percents, Fractions, and Decimals, Part 1 [online]

In this lesson, you have learned how to convert between decimals and fractions and between decimals and percents.

- To convert a fraction to a decimal, divide the numerator by the denominator.

- To convert a decimal to a fraction, write the decimal as a fraction and then simplify.

- To write a decimal as a percent, move the decimal point two places to the right and add a percent sign.

- To write a percent as a decimal, divide the percent by 100 and drop the percent sign. This is the same as moving the decimal point two places to the left.

Skills Update: Practice Your Math Skills [online]

Complete the Skills Update online.

Offline Learning: Percents, Fractions, and Decimals, Part 1 [offline]

In the Book

Read pages 274–276 in the Reference Guide.

Problem Set

Complete Problems 1–23 on page 278 of the Reference Guide.

Lesson Assessment: Percents, Fractions, and Decimals, Part 1

Quiz [online]

Now go back online to complete the lesson quiz.

Student Guide

Percents, Fractions, and Decimals, Part 2

Suppose an assignment has 24 questions, and you have finished 15 questions so far. What percent of the assignment have you finished? Questions such as this require an understanding of the relationship between percents, fractions, and decimals. In this lesson, you will learn how to express fractions as percents and percents as fractions. You will then use the skills you have learned to solve word problems involving decimals, fractions, and percents.

Goals for the Lesson
- Convert a fraction to a percent.
- Convert a percent to a fraction.
- Solve word problems involving percents.

Graded Activities in This Lesson
Lesson Quiz (computer-scored)

Materials
Pre-Algebra: A Reference Guide and Problem Sets, pages 274–278

Optional
calculator
Percents, Fractions, and Decimals Solutions

Groundwork: Preparing for the Lesson [online]
This activity reviews skills that are essential for this lesson. As you work through the activity, answer the question below and record any notes in the space provided.

Notes
Explain how to convert a fraction to a decimal.

Learn: Converting Between Fractions and Percents [online]

As you work through this activity, answer the questions below and record any notes in the space provided.

Notes

Explain how to convert a fraction to a percent.

Explain how to convert a percent to a fraction.

Learn: Solving a Word Problem Involving Percents [online]

As you work through this activity, answer the question below and record any notes in the space provided.

Notes

How can you determine whether an answer is reasonable?

MathCast: Percents [online]

View the video to see how to solve a typical problem.

Summary: Percents, Fractions, and Decimals, Part 2 [online]

In this lesson, you learned how to convert between fractions and percents and to solve word problems involving percents.

- To convert a fraction to a percent, first write the fraction as a decimal. Then write the decimal as a percent.

- To convert a percent to a fraction, first write the percent as a fraction with a denominator of 100. Then simplify.

Offline Learning: Percents, Fractions, and Decimals, Part 2 [offline]

In the Book
Read page 277 in the Reference Guide.

Problem Set
Complete Problems 25–35 odd and 37–38 on page 278 of the Reference Guide.

Extra Practice (optional)
Complete Problems 26–36 even and 39–40 on page 278 of the Reference Guide.

Extension (optional)
If you flipped a coin 40 times, how many times do you think the coin would come up "heads"?

Flip a coin 40 times. Express as a fraction, decimal, and percent the number of times the coin comes up "heads" compared to the total number of times you flip the coin.

Lesson Assessment: Percents, Fractions, and Decimals, Part 2
Quiz [online]
Now go back online to complete the lesson quiz.

Student Guide

Similarity and Scale

Think about how you would measure the height of a tall building. It would probably be too difficult using a ruler or some other measuring device. This kind of measurement can be made by using what are called similar figures. In this lesson, you will learn about similar figures and how to make use of their properties.

Goals for the Lesson

- Determine whether two figures are similar.

- Find a missing length in a pair of similar figures when given known corresponding pairs of lengths.

- Find the scale factor for a pair of similar figures with at least one known pair of corresponding side lengths.

Graded Activities in This Lesson
Mid-Unit Test (computer-scored)

Materials
Pre-Algebra: A Reference Guide and Problem Sets, pages 279–283

Optional
calculator
Similarity and Scale Solutions

Keywords and Pronunciation
congruent angles: angles that have the same measure

scale factor: a ratio of one measure to another, where both measures are the same unit of measure

similar figures: figures that have the same shape but not necessarily the same size

Groundwork: Preparing for the Lesson [online]
This activity reviews solving proportions. As you work through it, answer the question below and record any notes in the space provided.

Notes
How does the means-extremes product property help you solve a proportion?

Learn: Similar Figures [online]

As you work through this activity, answer the question below and record any notes in the space provided.

Notes

What two things are true about similar figures?

Learn: Finding Missing Lengths [online]

As you work through this activity, answer the question below and record any notes in the space provided.

Notes

Explain how to use the properties of similar figures to find the length of a missing side.

Learn: Scale Factors [online]

As you work through this activity, answer the question below and record any notes in the space provided.

Notes

Explain how you know whether a figure is a reduction or an enlargement of the original figure.

MathCast: Similar Figures [online]

View the video to see how to solve a typical problem.

Summary: Similarity and Scale [online]

Two figures are similar if all corresponding angles are congruent and all corresponding sides are proportional.

You can use properties of similar figures to find the length of a missing side.

A scale factor is a ratio of one measure to another. You can find the scale factor of a figure by writing the ratio of its corresponding sides.

Offline Learning: Similarity and Scale [offline]

In the Book
Read pages 279–280 in the Reference Guide.

Do the Math
The Lesson Opener suggested that similar figures can be used to find indirect measurements. Here is an example of an indirect measurement.

James wants to know how many feet a tree in his neighborhood grows in one year. He needs to know the current height of the tree, but it is too tall for him to measure directly. James is 6 feet tall. He stands by the tree and casts a shadow that is 8 feet long. The tree casts a shadow that is 14 feet long. How can he use this information to find the height of the tree?

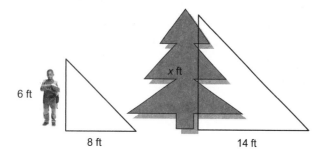

The triangles formed are similar. James can set up a proportion to find the height of the tree.

$$\frac{\text{James's height}}{\text{tree's height}} = \frac{\text{length of the James's shadow}}{\text{length of tree's shadow}}$$

$$\frac{6}{x} = \frac{8}{14}$$

$$8x = 84$$

$$x = 10.5$$

The tree is 10.5 feet tall.

Problem Set

Complete Problems 1–6 on pages 282–283 of the Reference Guide.

Mid-Unit Assessment: Ratio, Proportion, and Percent Test [online]

Now go back online to complete the Mid-Unit Assessment.

Student Guide

Working with Percent

Parts of wholes can be expressed as fractions, decimals, or percents. In this lesson, you will learn how to solve percent problems that involve parts of wholes. Baseball averages, discounts, and commissions are a few examples of parts of wholes that are commonly expressed as percents.

Goals for the Lesson

- Solve a percent of a whole problem.

- Solve word problems involving a percent of a whole.

Graded Activities in This Lesson

Lesson Quiz (computer-scored)

Materials

Pre-Algebra: A Reference Guide and Problem Sets, pages 284–286

Optional

calculator
Working with Percent Solutions

Keywords and Pronunciation

percent: a ratio that compares a number to 100

Groundwork: Preparing for the Lesson [online]

This activity reviews essential skills involving proportions. As you work through the activity, record any notes in the space provided.

Notes

Learn: The Percent Proportion [online]

As you work through this activity, answer the question below and record any notes in the space provided.

Notes

Explain how you know which value is the unknown when you use the percent proportion to solve a percent of a whole problem.

Learn: Solving Word Problems [online]

As you work through this activity, answer the question below and record any notes in the space provided.

Notes

How can you determine whether your answer to a percent of a whole problem is reasonable?

Worked Examples: Working with Percent [online]

As you work through this activity, record any notes in the space provided.

Notes

MathCast: Solving Percent Problems [online]

View the video to see how to solve a typical problem.

Summary: Working with Percent [online]

Percent problems that involve parts of whole amounts can be solved using the percent proportion.

There are three types of percent problems that involve parts of whole amounts.

1. You know the part and the whole, and you want to find the percent.

2. You know the percent and the whole, and you want to find the part.

3. You know the percent and the part, and you want to find the whole.

Offline Learning: Working with Percent [offline]

In the Book

Read pages 284–285 in the Reference Guide.

Problem Set

Complete Problems 1–25 odd and 31–34 on page 286 of the Reference Guide.

Lesson Assessment: Working with Percent Quiz [online]

Now go back online to complete the lesson quiz.

Student Guide

Percent of Increase or Decrease

Sometimes a store will mark down the prices on its merchandise. For example, suppose a sweater that originally cost $40 is now on sale for $30. It has been marked down $10 below its original price. This decrease in price represents a percent of change of 25%, because $10 is 25% of $40. In this lesson, you will learn how to solve problems that involve percents of change.

Goals for the Lesson
- Solve a word problem involving percent of increase or decrease.
- Find a percent of increase or decrease.

Graded Activities in This Lesson
Lesson Quiz (computer-scored)

Materials
Pre-Algebra: A Reference Guide and Problem Sets, pages 287–291

Optional
calculator
Percent of Increase of Decrease Solutions

Keywords and Pronunciation
percent of change: ratio of the amount of change to the original amount, expressed in percent form

Groundwork: Preparing for the Lesson [online]
This activity reviews skills that are essential for this lesson. As you work through the activity, answer the questions and record any notes in the space provided.

Notes
Explain how to write a fraction as a percent.

Explain how to find the amount of increase or decrease between two values.

Learn: Percent of Change [online]

As you work through this activity, answer the question below and record any notes in the space provided.

Notes

Compare and contrast a percent of increase problem and a percent of decrease problem.

Learn: Exploring Percent of Increase and Decrease [online]

As you work through this activity, answer the question below and record any notes in the space provided.

Notes

How do you know whether a problem is a percent of increase or a percent of decrease?

MathCast: Percent of Increase or Decrease [online]

View the video to see how to solve a typical problem.

Summary: Percent of Increase or Decrease [online]

In this lesson, you have learned how to solve problems that involve percents of increase and decrease.

* A percent of change shows how much an amount increases or decreases.

* When the new amount is greater than the original amount, the percent of change is a percent of increase.

* When the new amount is less than the original amount, the percent of change is a percent of decrease.

Offline Learning: Percent of Increase or Decrease [offline]

In the Book
Read pages 287–289 in the Reference Guide.

Problem Set
Complete Problems 1–9 odd, 16–21, and 25–28 on pages 290–291 of the Reference Guide.

Extension (optional)

The U.S. Budget Deficit
The amount of the government's money in the U.S. Treasury has not been enough to keep up with the government's spending. As a result, the United States has a large deficit (the difference between an amount spent and an amount taken in each year).

History of U.S. Federal Deficit 1950–2000	
2000	$5674 billion
1990	$3233 billion
1980	$907 billion
1970	$370 billion
1960	$286 billion
1950	$257 billion

Source: http://www.treasurydirect.gov/govt/reports/pd/histdebt/histdebt.htm

Calculate the percent increase of the federal deficit data for each decade. Round to the nearest percent, if necessary.

1. 1950 to 1960

2. 1960 to 1970

3. 1970 to 1980

4. 1980 to 1990

5. 1990 to 2000

Lesson Assessment: Percent of Increase or Decrease Quiz [online]
Now go back online to complete the lesson quiz.

Answers

Extension

1. 11%

2. 29%

3. 145%

4. 256%

5. 76%

Student Guide

Simple Interest

Bank accounts often pay interest. When you keep your money in an account, you are, in a sense, lending the bank your money. In turn, the bank agrees to give you back your original amount of money (called the principal) plus a fee (called the interest). Similarly, if you borrow money to pay for a house or a car, you eventually pay the bank the original amount of money you borrowed, plus interest. In this lesson, you will learn about simple interest and how to solve word problems involving this type of interest.

Goals for the Lesson
* Solve a word problem involving simple interest.

Graded Activities in This Lesson
Lesson Quiz (computer-scored)

Materials
Pre-Algebra: A Reference Guide and Problem Sets, pages 292–295

Optional
calculator
Simple Interest Solutions

Keywords and Pronunciation
interest: the cost to borrow money or the amount earned by lending money

interest rate: the percentage of the original amount of money that the interest is based on

principal: money that earns interest at a given rate over time; the principal is the original amount of money that interest is based on

simple interest: interest earned or paid only on the principal, or interest deposit

Groundwork: Preparing for the Lesson [online]
This activity reviews what was learned in a previous lesson. As you work through the activity, answer the question below and record any notes in the space provided.

Notes
Explain how to write a fraction as a percent.

Learn: Simple Interest [online]

As you work through this activity, answer the question below and record any notes in the space provided.

Notes

What does each of the variables represent in the equation $I = Prt$?

Worked Examples: Simple Interest [online]

As you work through this activity, answer the question and record any notes in the space provided.

Notes

Explain how to solve the equation $I = Prt$ for t.

Summary: Simple Interest [online]

In this lesson, you learned how to solve word problems involving simple interest. Simple interest is interest computed only on the principal.

To solve simple-interest problems, use the formula $I = Prt$, where

I = interest earned

P = principal

r = annual interest rate (usually a percent that can be rewritten as a decimal)

t = time (expressed in years)

Skills Update: Practice Your Math Skills [online]

Complete the Skills Update online.

Offline Learning: Simple Interest [offline]

In the Book
Read pages 292–294 in the Reference Guide.

Problem Sets
Complete Problems 1–17 odd on page 294 of the Reference Guide.

Extra Practice (optional)
Complete Problems 2–6 even and 14–16 on page 294 of the Reference Guide.

Lesson Assessment: Simple Interest Quiz [online]
Now go back online to complete the lesson quiz.

Student Guide

Ratio, Proportion, and Percent Review

You have finished studying the Ratio, Proportion, and Percent unit, which includes ratio; proportion; percents, fractions, and decimals; similarity and scale; working with percent; percent of increase or decrease; and simple interest. Now it's time to pull together what you have learned. Throughout the review, see how the skills you have learned relate to the Pre-Algebra big ideas.

Goals for the Lesson
*   Review the concepts and skills learned in the unit.

Materials
"Ratio, Proportion, and Percent" in *Pre-Algebra: A Reference Guide and Problem Sets*
Preparing for the Unit Test
Ratio, Proportion, and Percent Practice Problems

Unit Review: Ratio, Proportion, and Percent [online]

This is your chance to review the big ideas of Pre-Algebra you have learned in this unit. Under Review These Activities, you will find activities from previous lessons that will review each big idea. Choose the topics you feel you need to review. Under Try These, you will find interactive problems that will test your understanding of each big idea. As you work through this lesson, take notes in the spaces provided.

Big Idea
A number is any entity that obeys the laws of arithmetic; all numbers obey the laws of arithmetic. The laws of arithmetic can be used to simplify algebraic expressions.

Big Idea

If you can create a mathematical model for a situation, you can use the model to solve other problems that you might not be able to solve otherwise. Algebraic equations can capture key relationships among quantities in the world.

Big Idea

Euclidean geometry uses five basic axioms to model real-world geometry and derives an amazing array of true results that apply extremely well to real-world geometry.

Summary: Ratio, Proportion, and Percent Review [online]

In this unit, you have covered the following topics:

- ratio

- proportion

- percents, fractions, and decimals

- similarity and scale

- working with percent

- percent of increase or decrease

- simple interest

Offline Learning: Ratio, Proportion, and Percent Review [offline]

How well hae you mastered the goals of this unit? Complete the Ratio, Proportion, and Percent Practice Problems. These problems are similar to the problems you will have on the Unit Test.

You can also

- Review the Ratio, Proportion, and Percent unit in *Pre-Algebra: A Reference Guide and Problem Sets*

- Review the notes in your Student Guide.

- Read and follow the instructions in Preparing for the Unit Test

Practice Problems

Ratio, Proportion, and Percent Review

1. Write each ratio in lowest terms.

   A. $\dfrac{9}{12}$

   B. 6 : 15

   C. 4 to 18

2. Write the rate $\dfrac{280 \text{ miles}}{14 \text{ gallons}}$ as a unit rate.

3. Find the percent change in price.
   A. A price increases from $12 to $15.
   B. A price decreases from $20 to $12.

4. In a new car lot, 40 out of 180 cars are black cars. About what percent of the cars are black cars? Round to the nearest percent, if necessary.

5. On a test, a student got 85% of the questions correct. There were 40 questions on the test. How many questions did the student get right?

6. In a class, 48% of the students are girls. There are 24 girls. How many students are in the class?

7. Solve each proportion.

   A. $\dfrac{4}{x} = \dfrac{6}{15}$

   B. $\dfrac{8}{12} = \dfrac{x}{9}$

8. The triangles shown are similar. What is the value of x?

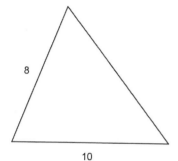 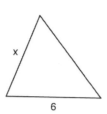

9. What is the scale factor of the triangles in question 8?

10. Write the following numbers as decimals.

    A. $\dfrac{12}{15}$

    B. 4.3%

11. Write the following numbers as fractions.

    A. 0.44

    B. 64%

12. Write the following numbers as percents.

    A. $\dfrac{14}{20}$

    B. 0.078

13. If an 18-ounce box of cereal costs $4.50, how much does a 12-ounce box cost?

14. If $14,500 is invested at 8% simple interest, how much interest will be earned after 5 years?

Answers

1. **A.** $\dfrac{3}{4}$

   B. $2 : 5$

   C. 2 to 9

2. $\dfrac{20 \text{ miles}}{1 \text{ gallon}}$

3. **A.** 25% increase

   B. 40% decrease

4. about 22%

5. 34 questions

6. 50 students

7. **A.** $x = 10$

   B. $x = 6$

8. $x = 4.8$

9. 0.6

10. **A.** 0.8

    B. 0.043

11. **A.** $\dfrac{11}{25}$

    B. $\dfrac{16}{25}$

12. **A.** 70%

    B. 7.8%

13. $3.00

14. $5,800

Unit Assessment Answer Key

Ratio, Proportion, and Percent Unit Test, Offline

(10 points)

1. Wanda took out a personal loan for $16,000 at 9% simple interest.

   A. How much interest will she pay after 5 years?

Score

   B. Suppose she pays off the loan in 3 years instead of 5 years. How much money will she save in interest?

(8 points)

2. The following formula relates three quantities: Force (*F*), mass (*m*), and acceleration (*a*).

   $$F = ma$$

   A. Solve this equation for *a*.

Score

   B. If the force is $F = -25$ units and the mass is $m = 10$ units, find the acceleration, *a*.

   C. If the force is $F = 25$ units and the acceleration is $a = 5$ units, find the mass, *m*.

Score	____ of 18

Student Guide

Points on the Plane

On a map, city streets are sometimes drawn on a grid, which makes it easy to follow directions. For example, if you are told to go to the corner of C Street and 4th Avenue, and the streets are laid out in a grid, you can easily see how to get to the corner from where you are. In mathematics, you also use a grid, known as a *coordinate plane*, to describe the location of points in the plane.

Goals for the Lesson
- Find coordinates for a point in the plane.
- Determine the axis or quadrant for a given point.
- Graph an ordered pair in a coordinate plane.

Graded Activities in This Lesson
Lesson Quiz (computer-scored)

Materials
Pre-Algebra: A Reference Guide and Problem Sets, pages 303–308

Optional
Points on the Plane Solutions

calculator

graph paper

Keywords and Pronunciation
axes: two perpendicular number lines intersecting at the origin

coordinate: the number associated with a point on a number line

coordinate plane: a plane in which the coordinates of a point are its distances from two intersecting perpendicular lines called *axes*

ordered pair: a pair of numbers in which the first number is the *x*-coordinate and the second number is the *y*-coordinate of the location of a point

origin: the point on a number line whose coordinate is zero

quadrant: one of the four regions into which the coordinate axes separate the coordinate plane

x-axis: the horizontal number line in the coordinate plane

x-coordinate: the first number in an ordered pair of numbers that designates the location of a point in the coordinate plane; also called the *abscissa* (ab-SIH-suh)

y-axis: the vertical number line in the coordinate plane

y-coordinate: the second number in an ordered pair of numbers that designates the location of a point in the coordinate plane; also called the *ordinate* (OR-duh-nuht)

Groundwork: Preparing for the Lesson [online]

The Groundwork reviews essential skills involving identifying coordinates of points on a number line. As you work through this activity, answer the question below and record any notes in the space provided.

Notes

Explain how to name the coordinate of a point on a number line.

Learn: The Coordinate Plane [online]

As you work through this activity, answer the questions below and record any notes in the space provided.

Notes

Explain how to graph a point in the coordinate plane.

Learn: Coordinating Points in a Plane [online]

As you work through this activity, answer the question below and record any notes in the space provided.

Notes

Draw a coordinate plane. Label each of the following in the plane:

origin   Quadrant I   Quadrant II   Quadrant III

Quadrant IV   x-axis   y-axis

Explain how to name the ordered pair for a point in the coordinate plane.

Summary: Points on the Plane [online]

A coordinate plane is made up of two perpendicular number lines called axes. The intersection of the axes is called the origin. The horizontal line is called the *x*-axis, and the vertical line is called the *y*-axis. The axes separate the plane into four quadrants.

You can describe the position of a point on a plane with an ordered pair of numbers.

You can find the *x*-coordinate of a point by moving right or left along the *x*-axis. Then find the *y*-coordinate by moving up or down along the *y*-axis.

Skills Update: Practice Your Math Skills [online]

Complete the Skills Update online.

Offline Learning: Points on the Plane [offline]

In the Book
Read pages 303–306 in the Reference Guide.

Problem Sets
Complete Problems 1–5 and 11–15 on page 307 of the Reference Guide.

Extra Practice (optional)
Complete Problems 6–10 even and 16–20 on page 307.

Extension (optional)
On graph paper, draw and label the coordinate plane, and graph the following ordered pairs: (2, 2), (4, 0), (4, –3), (0, –3), (0, 0), (2, 2).

Draw line segments to connect the points in the order listed.

Name the figure as specifically as you can.

Try creating a picture puzzle of your own.

Lesson Assessment: Points on the Plane Quiz [online]

Now go back online to complete the lesson quiz.

Student Guide

Two-Variable Equations

A solution to an equation is the value of the variable that makes the equation a true statement. Many equations, such as $x + 1 = 9$, have only one variable. But what if an equation has *two* variables, as in $x + y = 9$? You can easily find values of x and y so that their sum is equal to 9, such as $x = 4$ and $y = 5$. In this lesson, you will learn how to determine whether an ordered pair is a solution to a two-variable equation and to identify independent and dependent variables in two-variable equations.

Goals for the Lesson
- Determine whether an ordered pair is a solution of a linear equation in two variables.

- Identify the dependent and independent variables for a problem situation.

Graded Activities in This Lesson
Lesson Quiz (computer-scored)

Materials
Pre-Algebra: A Reference Guide and Problem Sets, pages 308–312

Optional
Two-Variable Equations Solutions
calculator

Keywords and Pronunciation
dependent variable: the output variable

independent variable: the input variable

Groundwork: Preparing for the Lesson [online]
The Groundwork reviews skills related to graphing points and identifying coordinates of points. As you work through this activity, answer the question below and record any notes in the space provided.

Notes
Explain how to graph an ordered pair on a coordinate plane.

Learn: Solutions to Equations in Two Variables [online]

As you work through this activity, answer the question below and record any notes in the space provided.

Notes

How do you know whether a particular ordered pair is a solution to an equation in two variables?

Learn: Equations in Two Variables: One Approach [online]

As you work through this activity, answer the question below and record any notes in the space provided.

Notes

Suppose you choose a value for x and then find the corresponding value for y. Is this ordered pair the only solution to the equation? Explain.

Learn: Equations in Two Variables: Another Approach [online]

As you work through this activity, record any notes in the space provided.

Notes

Bror was asked to solve the equation $8f - 4g = 28$ for g. He said the solution is $g = -2f - 7$.

> Bror's Solution:
>
> $8f - 4g = 28$
> $-4g = -8f + 28$
> $g = -2f - 7$

Is Bror's solution correct? Explain.

Learn: Independent and Dependent Variables [online]

As you work through this activity, answer the questions below and record any notes in the space provided.

Notes

How can you identify the dependent variable?

How can you identify the independent variable?

Worked Examples: Two-Variable Equations [online]

As you work through this activity, record any notes in the space provided.

Notes

MathCast: Solve a Two-Variable Equation [online]

View the video to see how to solve a typical problem.

Summary: Two-Variable Equations [online]

An ordered pair is a solution to an equation in two variables if substituting the coordinates into the equation results in a true statement.

You can find a solution to an equation in two variables by choosing any value for one of the variables. Then substitute the value into the equation and solve to find the value of the other variable.

In this lesson, you also learned to identify independent and dependent variables in real-world problems.

In a two-variable equation, the input variable is called the independent variable and the output variable is called the dependent variable.

Offline Learning: Two-Variable Equations [offline]

In the Book
Read pages 308–311 in the Reference Guide.

Problem Sets
Complete Problems 1–6, 13–16, and 28–29 on pages 311–312 of the Reference Guide.

Extra Practice (optional)
Complete Problems 7–12, 17–18, and 30–31 on pages 311–312 of the Reference Guide.

Lesson Assessment: Two-Variable Equations Quiz [online]

Now go back online to complete the lesson quiz.

Student Guide

Linear Equations and Intercepts, Part 1

You've probably heard the word *intercept* used in different ways. In football, one player can *intercept* a ball thrown by a member of the opposing team. A message can be *intercepted* before it reaches its destination. In algebra, the word has its own unique meaning: An *intercept* is the point where a graph intersects the *x*- or *y*-axis. In this lesson, you will learn to find the intercepts of a line.

Goals for the Lesson
- Find intercepts of a given linear graph.

- Find intercepts for a linear equation.

Graded Activities in This Lesson
Lesson Quiz (computer-scored)

Materials
Pre-Algebra: A Reference Guide and Problem Sets, pages 313–314, 317

Optional
Linear Equations and Intercepts Solutions
calculator

Keywords and Pronunciation
line: a collection of points arranged in a straight path that extends without end in both directions

linear equation: an equation whose graph is a line

standard form for a linear equation: an equation of the form $Ax + By = C$, where A, B, and C are integers and A and B are not both zero

x-intercept: the *x*-coordinate of a point where a graph intersects the *x*-axis

y-intercept: the *y*-coordinate of a point where a graph intersects the *y*-axis

Groundwork: Preparing for the Lesson [online]
This activity reviews essential skills. As you work through this it, record any notes in the space provided.

Notes

Learn: Identifying Intercepts [online]

As you work through this activity, answer the question below and record any notes in the space provided.

Notes
Does every line have both an *x*-intercept and a *y*-intercept? Explain.

Learn: Finding Intercepts [online]

As you work through this activity, answer the question below and record any notes in the space provided.

Notes
Explain how to find the *x*- and *y*-intercepts of the line $7x + 2y = 28$.

MathCast: Finding x- and y-Intercepts [online]

View the video to see how to solve a typical problem.

Summary: Linear Equations and Intercepts, Part 1 [online]

In this lesson, you learned about intercepts of a line.

- The *x*-intercept of a line is the *x*-coordinate of the point where the line intersects the *x*-axis.

- The *y*-intercept of a line is the *y*-coordinate of the point where the line intersects the *y*-axis.

- Most vertical lines have an *x*-intercept, but no *y*-intercept.

- Most horizontal lines have an *y*-intercept, but no *x*-intercept.

The standard form for a linear equation is

$$Ax + By = C$$

where A, B, and C are integers and A and B are not both zero.

- You can find the x-intercept of the line by setting y equal to zero and solving the equation for x.

- You can find the y-intercept of the line by setting x equal to zero and solving the equation for y.

Offline Learning: Linear Equations and Intercepts, Part 1 [offline]

In the Book
Read pages 313–314 in the Reference Guide.

Problem Sets
Complete Problems 1–12 on page 317 of the Reference Guide.

Lesson Assessment: Linear Equations and Intercepts, Part 1 Quiz

[online]
Now go back online to complete the lesson quiz.

Student Guide

Linear Equations and Intercepts, Part 2

The graph of a line can provide useful information about a real-world situation. For example, when the graph of a line crosses the *x*- or *y*-axis, it tells us that one of the variables is equal to zero. In this lesson, you will learn how to use intercepts to graph and write the equation of a line.

Goals for the Lesson
- Use intercepts to graph a linear equation.
- Use intercepts to write an equation for a given linear graph.

Graded Activities in This Lesson
Lesson Quiz (computer-scored)

Materials
Pre-Algebra: A Reference Guide and Problem Sets, pages 313–318

graph paper

straightedge

Optional
Linear Equations and Intercepts Solutions

calculator

Optional Assignment

Keywords and Pronunciation
intercept: the value at which a graph crosses one of the coordinate axes

x-intercept: the *x*-coordinate of the point where a graph intersects the *x*-axis

y-intercept: the *y*-coordinate of the point where a graph intersects the *y*-axis

Groundwork: Preparing for the Lesson [online]
This activity reviews skills that are essential for this lesson. As you work through it, record any notes in the space provided.

Notes

Learn: Using Intercepts to Graph a Line [online]

As you work through this activity, answer the questions below and record any notes in the space provided.

Notes

What is the equation of a horizontal line whose intercept is 11?

What is the equation of a vertical line whose intercept is –8?

Learn: Writing the Equation of a Line [online]

As you work through this activity, answer the question below and record any notes in the space provided.

Notes

How can you check that the equation you wrote is correct?

Worked Examples: Linear Equations and Intercepts, Part 2 [online]

As you work through this activity, record any notes in the space provided.

Notes

MathCast: Write the Equation of a Line [online]

View the video to see how to solve a typical problem.

Summary: Linear Equations and Intercepts, Part 2 [online]

To graph the equation of a line, follow these steps:

1. Find the *x*-intercept of the line.

2. Find the *y*-intercept of the line.

3. Graph the intercepts and draw the line connecting both points.

The graph of any equation in the form of $x = a$, where a is a constant, is a vertical line. The graph of any equation in the form of $y = b$, where b is a constant, is a horizontal line.

Use the intercepts to write the equation of a line by doing this:

1. Let C equal the product of the intercepts.

2. Substitute the ordered pairs that contain the intercepts into $Ax + By = C$ to find the values of A and B.

3. Substitute the values of A, B, and C into $Ax + By = C$.

Offline Learning: Linear Equations and Intercepts, Part 2 [offline]

In the Book
Read pages 313–318 in the Reference Guide.

Do the Math
Consider this example of a linear equation that is definitely not in standard form. You can write it in standard form to more easily draw its graph.

Graph this equation:	
$$\dfrac{x}{8} - \dfrac{y}{2} = \dfrac{1}{4}$$	
Rewrite the equation in standard form.	
$\dfrac{x}{8} - \dfrac{y}{2} = \dfrac{1}{4}$	Original equation
$x - 4y = 2$	Multiply by the least common denominator, 8.
Find the line's intercepts.	
$(0) - 4y = 2$ $\quad y = -\dfrac{2}{4} = -\dfrac{1}{2}$	Substitute 0 for *x*, and solve for *y*.
$x - 4(0) = 2$ $\quad x = 2$	Substitute 0 for *y*, and solve for *x*.

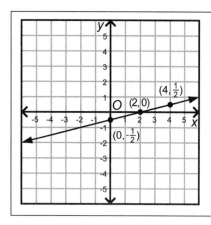

Graph the equation using the points you have identified: $\left(0, -\dfrac{1}{2}\right)$ and $(2, 0)$.

Problem Sets
Complete Problems 13–29 odd on page 318 of the Reference Guide.

Extra Practice (optional)
Complete Problems 14–20 even and 30–32 on page 318 of the Reference Guide.

More Practice: Optional Assignment [offline, optional]
For extra practice, print the Optional Assignment and complete one or more of the problems. Submit the assignment to your teacher on or before the due date to receive feedback on your work.

Lesson Assessment: Linear Equations and Intercepts, Part 2 Quiz

[online]
Now go back online to complete the lesson quiz.

Name: _____   Date: _____

Optional Assignment

Linear Equations and Intercepts

1. Henry found the following ordered pairs as solutions of the equation $-2x + y = 7$. Check his work to determine which ordered pairs are correct solutions. Show your work.

    A. $(1, 9)$

    B. $(-2, 3)$

    C. $(3, -1)$

Answer:

Student Guide

Slope, Part 1

Think about different ramps you have seen. Some ramps are steeper than others, depending on how they are used. For example, a skateboard ramp has a different steepness than a ramp used to load a horse into a trailer. The steepness of a ramp is called the slope of the ramp and can be calculated by using the algebraic formula for the slope of a line. In this lesson, you will learn to calculate the slope of a line.

Goals for the Lesson
* Find the slope of a line when given two points on the line.

Graded Activities in This Lesson
Lesson Quiz (computer-scored)

Materials
Pre-Algebra: A Reference Guide and Problem Sets, pages 319–325

Optional
Slope Solutions

graph paper

straightedge

calculator

Keywords and Pronunciation
rise: the change in the *y*-coordinates (the vertical change) when moving from one point on a line to another point on the line

run: the change in the *x*-coordinates (the horizontal change) when moving from one point on a line to another point on the line

slope: a number that describes the steepness of a line, computed as the ratio of the change in the *y*-coordinates to the change in the *x*-coordinates (the ratio of rise to run) when moving from one point on the line to another point on the line

Groundwork: Preparing for the Lesson [online]

This activity reviews skills related to subtracting negative numbers. As you work through it, answer the question below and record any notes in the space provided.

Notes
Suppose you know that $a - b = -2$. What is $b - a$?

Learn: Calculating Slope [online]

As you work through this activity, answer the question below and record any notes in the space provided.

Notes

The vertical change between two points is called the _____.

The horizontal change between two points is called the _____.

What is the formula for the slope of a line containing the points (x_1, y_1) and (x_2, y_2)?

Learn: Slopes of Horizontal and Vertical Lines [online]

As you work through this activity, answer the questions below and record any notes in the space provided.

Notes

What is the slope of a vertical line?

What is the slope of a horizontal line?

Worked Examples: Slope, Part 1 [online]

As you work through this activity, record any notes in the space provided.

Notes

Summary: Slope, Part 1 [online]

The slope of a line describes its steepness and the direction in which the line slants.

The slope of a line is defined as the ratio of the rise to the run.

The slope formula is $m = (y_2 - y_1)/(x_2 - x_1)$.

The slope of a horizontal line is zero.

The slope of a vertical line is undefined.

Offline Learning: Slope, Part 1 [offline]

In the Book
Read pages 319–321 in the Reference Guide.

Do the Math
Here is a real-world example using slope.

According to the Americans with Disabilities Act (ADA) Accessibility Guidelines for Buildings and Facilities, Section 4.8.2, the ratio of the vertical distance to the horizontal distance of a disability ramp may be no greater than $\frac{1}{12}$. If a school has a doorway that is 4 feet above the ground, what is the minimum allowable horizontal distance of the ramp?

Since the maximum slope specified by federal guidelines is $\frac{1}{12}$, set the slope of the ramp $\left(\frac{\text{rise}}{\text{run}}\right)$ equal to this value to find the maximum height: $\frac{\text{rise}}{\text{run}} = \frac{1}{12}$

$\frac{4}{x} = \frac{1}{12}$ Substitute the values from the ramp.

$x = 48$ Cross multiply.

The minimum allowable horizontal distance of the ramp is 48 feet.

Problem Sets
Complete Problems 1–3 and 7–10 on page 324 of the Reference Guide.

Extra Practice (optional)
Complete Problems 4–6 and 11–13 on page 324 of the Reference Guide.

Lesson Assessment: Slope, Part 1 Quiz [online]
Now go back online to complete the lesson quiz.

Student Guide

Slope, Part 2

How important is the slope of a line? Consider, for example, a large truck driving down a hill. The amount of stress on the truck's brakes depends greatly on the steepness of the hill. Knowing how steep the hill is can help a driver determine whether the truck will be able to travel safely on that hill. In this lesson, you will use the equation of a line in standard form to find its slope.

Goals for the Lesson
- Find the slope of a line when given an equation.

Graded Activities in This Lesson
Mid-Unit Test (computer-scored)

Materials
Pre-Algebra: A Reference Guide and Problem Sets, pages 319–325
graph paper
straightedge

Optional
Slope Solutions
graphing calculator

Keywords and Pronunciation
rise: the change in the *y*-coordinates (the vertical change) when moving from one point on a line to another point on the line

run: the change in the *x*-coordinates (the horizontal change) when moving from one point on a line to another point on the line

slope: a number that describes the steepness of a line, computed as the ratio of the change in the *y*-coordinates to the change in the *x*-coordinates (the ratio of rise to run) when moving from one point on the line to another point on the line

***x*-intercept:** the *x*-coordinate of the point where a graph intersects the *x*-axis

***y*-intercept:** the *y*-coordinate of the point where a graph intersects the *y*-axis

Groundwork: Preparing for the Lesson [online]

This activity reviews vocabulary associated with the coordinate plane. As you work through the activity, answer the questions below and record any notes in the space provided.

Notes

What is the intersection of the *x*- and *y*-axes called? What ordered pair represents that point?

Learn: Finding Slope Using an Equation [online]

As you work through this activity, answer the questions below and record any notes in the space provided.

Notes

When is the rise a negative value?

When is the run a negative value?

Worked Examples: Slope, Part 2 [online]

As you work through this activity, record any notes in the space provided.

Notes

MathCast: Slope [online]

View the video to see how to solve a typical problem.

Summary: Slope, Part 2 [online]

When you know the equation of a line in standard form, you can find the slope of the line by graphing the line using its intercepts and finding the rise and run.

You can also find the slope by using the values of *A* and *B*.

Offline Learning: Slope, Part 2 [offline]

In the Book
Read page 323 in the Reference Guide.

Do the Math
The equation of a line in standard form is $Ax + By = C$, where *A*, *B*, and *C* are integers and *A* and *B* are not both zero.

The equation of a line such as $4x - 15y = 8$ is not in standard form because $15y$ is *subtracted* from $4x$. In standard form, the terms are added. You can write the equation in standard form by changing the subtraction to addition.

$4x - 15y = 8$ becomes $4x + (-15y) = 8$.

The equation of a horizontal line, such as $y = 3$, *is* in standard form. The equation could be written as $0x + y = 3$, but equations like these are traditionally simplified to the form $y = b$.

The equation of a vertical line, such as $x = 3$, is also in standard form. The equation could be written as $x + 0y = 3$, but, again, equations like these are traditionally simplified to the form $x = a$.

Notice that the definition of standard form states that *A* and *B* cannot both be zero. Why? What would happen if both were equal to zero?

Problem Sets
Complete Problems 15–29 odd on page 325 of the Reference Guide.

Mid-Unit Assessment: Analytic Geometry Test [online]

Now go back online to complete the Mid-Unit Assessment.

Student Guide

Problem Solving

The path of a hurricane is often difficult to predict. Meteorologists use models to determine which course a hurricane will take and when it will make landfall. In this lesson, you will look at several applications that are modeled using linear equations, and you will use graphs to make predictions.

Goals for the Lesson
- Use interpolation to make inferences about linear data.
- Use extrapolation to make inferences about linear data.

Graded Activities in This Lesson
Lesson Quiz (computer-scored)

Materials
Pre-Algebra: A Reference Guide and Problem Sets, pages 326–330

Optional

Problem Solving Solutions

graph paper

straightedge

graphing calculator

Keywords and Pronunciation
interpolation: the process of inferring, or estimating, an unknown value that is between known values

extrapolation: the process of inferring, estimating, or predicting an unknown value that is outside of known values

Groundwork: Preparing for the Lesson [online]
This activity reviews essential skills. As you work through it, answer the question below and record any notes in the space provided.

Notes
How do you use the coordinates of two points on a line to find the slope of the line?

Learn: Using Interpolation [online]

As you work through this activity, answer the question below and record any notes in the space provided.

Notes

How can you determine whether an estimate you make using interpolation is reasonable?

Learn: Using Extrapolation [online]

As you work through this activity, answer the question below and record any notes in the space provided.

Notes

Explain the difference between interpolation and extrapolation.

MathCast: Problem Solving [online]

View the video to see how to solve a typical problem.

Summary: Problem Solving [online]

Many real-world problems are represented and solved using linear models. When data form a linear pattern, you can use interpolation and extrapolation to make inferences.

- Interpolation is a process of inferring, or estimating, an unknown value that is between known values.

- Extrapolation is a process of inferring, estimating, or predicting a value that is outside of known values.

Offline Learning: Problem Solving [offline]

In the Book

Read pages 326–328 in the Reference Guide.

Problem Sets

Complete Problems 6–10 and 16–20 on pages 329–330 of the Reference Guide.

Lesson Assessment: Problem Solving Quiz [online]

Now go back online to complete the lesson quiz.

Student Guide

Relations and Functions, Part 1

The steam engine is a remarkable machine. Putting in the right mixture of coal and water creates steam, which makes the engine run. The inputs and outputs of a function act in a similar way. You can think of the coal and water as the inputs, and the outputs are steam and movement of the engine. In this lesson, you will learn about inputs and outputs of a relation, and how to determine if a relation is a function.

Goals for the Lesson
- Determine the domain and range for a function presented as a table or a set of ordered pairs.

- Determine whether a relation is a function when given a graph or set of ordered pairs.

Graded Activities in This Lesson
Lesson Quiz (computer-scored)

Materials
Pre-Algebra: A Reference Guide and Problem Sets, pages 331–336

Optional

Relations and Functions Solutions

graph paper

straightedge

graphing calculator

Keywords and Pronunciation
domain: in a relation, the set of allowable inputs (the set of first elements of the ordered pair in the relation)

function: a relation that assigns each member of the domain exactly one member of the range

inputs: the first elements of the ordered pair in a relation

outputs: second elements of the ordered pairs in a relation

range: the set of possible outputs (the set of second elements of the ordered pairs in the relation)

relation: a set of ordered pairs

Groundwork: Preparing for the Lesson [online]
This activity reviews essential skills. As you work through this it, answer the question below and record any notes in the space provided.

Notes
How many solutions does a two-variable equation have?

Learn: Domain and Range [online]

As you work through this activity, answer the question below and record any notes in the space provided.

Notes

Will there always be the same number of elements in the domain as in the range? Explain.

Learn: When Is a Relation a Function? [online]

As you work through this activity, answer the question below and record any notes in the space provided.

Notes

Explain why some relations are **not** functions.

Worked Examples: Relations and Functions, Part 1 [online]

As you work through this activity, record any notes in the space provided.

Notes

Summary: Relations and Functions, Part 1 [online]

A relation describes how two sets of data are related to each other. You can show a relation using a table, sets of ordered pairs, or a graph.

The domain of a relation is the set of all first elements of the ordered pairs.

The range of a relation is the set of all second elements in the ordered pairs.

A function is a relation that assigns exactly one output to every input.

Offline Learning: Relations and Functions, Part 1 [offline]

In the Book
Read pages 331–333 in the Reference Guide.

Problem Sets
Complete Problems 1–15 odd on pages 334–335 of the Reference Guide.

Extra Practice (optional)
Complete Problems 2–16 even on pages 334–335 of the Reference Guide.

Lesson Assessment: Relations and Functions, Part 1 Quiz [online]
Now go back online to complete the lesson quiz.

Student Guide

Relations and Functions, Part 2

After you place whole coffee beans into a coffee grinder and turn it on, in a few moments you have ground coffee. Your input is whole coffee beans; your output is ground coffee. Functions act in a similar way. If you input a value into a function and perform its operations correctly, the result is an answer called the output.

Goals for the Lesson
- Evaluate a function for a given value.

Graded Activities in This Lesson
Lesson Quiz (computer-scored)

Materials
Pre-Algebra: A Reference Guide and Problem Sets, pages 331–336

Optional

Relations and Functions Solutions

graph paper

straightedge

graphing calculator

Keywords and Pronunciation
function: a relation that assigns each member of the domain exactly one member of the range

function notation: a notation used in defining a function; for example, $P(n) = 5n - 500$ indicates that P is a function of n

input: the first elements of the ordered pair in a relation

output: second elements of the ordered pairs in a relation

Groundwork: Preparing for the Lesson [online]
This activity reviews essential skills. As you work through it, answer the question below and record any notes in the space provided.

Notes
When is a relation also a function?

Learn: Evaluating Functions [online]

As you work through this activity, answer the question below and record any notes in the space provided.

Notes

What is function notation? Rewrite the equation $y = x + 4$ using function notation.

Worked Examples: Relations and Functions, Part 2 [online]

As you work through this activity, answer the question below and record any notes in the space provided.

Notes

Explain how to find $f(4)$ using the function $f(x) = 3x - 8$.

MathCast: Evaluate Functions [online]

View the video to see how to solve a typical problem.

Summary: Relations and Functions, Part 2 [online]

Some functions can be represented by equations.

When you evaluate a function, you are finding an output value for a given input value.

Often function notation is used to write an equation. In function notation, $f(x)$ is used in place of the variable y.

Offline Learning: Relations and Functions, Part 2 [offline]

In the Book
Read pages 333–334 in the Reference Guide.

Problem Sets
Complete Problems 17–27 on page 336 of the Reference Guide.

Lesson Assessment: Relations and Functions, Part 2 Quiz [online]

Now go back online to complete the lesson quiz.

Student Guide

Systems of Linear Equations

Think about any two streets in the town or city where you live. Some streets are parallel, and some meet at intersections. Now think about lines. If you graph two lines on a coordinate plane, will they always intersect? Could they be parallel? In this lesson, you will learn the answers to these questions and more!

Goals for the Lesson
- Use a graph to solve a system of linear equations.
- Determine the number of solutions for a system of linear equations when given its graph.

Graded Activities in This Lesson
Lesson Quiz (computer-scored)

Materials
Pre-Algebra: A Reference Guide and Problem Sets, pages 337–343

Optional
Systems of Linear Equations Solutions
calculator

Keywords and Pronunciation
system of linear equations: two or more linear equations with the same variables

Groundwork: Preparing for the Lesson [online]
This activity reviews skills that are essential for this lesson. As you work through it, answer the question below and record any notes in the space provided.

Notes
Explain how to solve an equation in two variables for one of the variables if you know the value of the other variable.

Learn: Systems of Linear Equations, Part 1 [online]

As you work through this activity, answer the question below and record any notes in the space provided.

Notes

When you graph a system of linear equations, how can you identify the solution?

How can you check the solution to a system of linear equations?

Learn: Systems of Linear Equations, Part 2 [online]

As you work through this activity, answer the question below and record any notes in the space provided.

Notes

How can you tell if a system of linear equations has *no solution*?

How can you tell if a system of linear equations has *infinitely many solutions*?

Summary: Systems of Linear Equations [online]

You can determine the solution(s) of a system of linear equations in two variables by graphing the equations in the coordinate plane to see where the lines intersect.

A system of linear equations can have no solution, one solution, or an infinite number of solutions.

Offline Learning: Systems of Linear Equations [offline]

In the Book
Read pages 337–339 in the Reference Guide.

Do the Math

Graphing a Linear Equation in Two Variables

One way to graph a linear equation in two variables is by using its intercepts. You can also graph a linear equation by making a table of values. Choose a number for x, substitute the value into the equation, and solve for y. This process gives you one point on the line. Repeat until you have at least three points on the line.

Graph the line $y = -5x + 3$.

Step 1: Make a table. Choose three values for x. Substitute each value into the equation and solve for y.

x	$y = -5x + 3$	Ordered Pair
-1	$y = -5 \cdot (-1) + 3 = 8$	$(-1, 8)$
0	$y = -5 \cdot 0 + 3 = 3$	$(0, 3)$
1	$y = -5 \cdot 1 + 3 = -2$	$(1, -2)$

Step 2: Plot each ordered pair and draw the line.

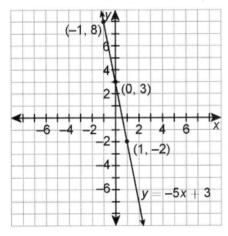

Problem Sets
Complete Problems 1–13 odd on pages 341–342 of the Reference Guide.

Extra Practice (optional)
Complete Problems 2–12 even on pages 341–342 of the Reference Guide.

Lesson Assessment: Systems of Linear Equations Quiz [online]
Now go back online to complete the lesson quiz.

Student Guide

Analytic Geometry Review

You have finished studying the Analytic Geometry unit, which includes points on the plane, two-variable equations, linear equations and intercepts, slope, problem solving, relations and functions, and systems of linear equations. Now it's time to pull together what you have learned. Throughout the review, see how the skills you have learned relate to the Pre-Algebra big ideas.

Goals for the Lesson
* Review the concepts and skills learned in the unit.

Materials
"Analytic Geometry" in *Pre-Algebra: A Reference Guide and Problem Sets*
Preparing for the Unit Test
Analytic Geometry Practice Problems

Unit Review: Analytic Geometry [online]

This is your chance to review the big ideas of Pre-Algebra you have learned in this unit. Under Review These Activities, you will find activities from previous lessons that will review each big idea. Choose the topics you feel you need to review. Under Try These, you will find interactive problems that will test your understanding of each big idea. As you work through this lesson, take notes in the spaces provided.

Big Idea
Analytic geometry models problems in geometry with algebraic proof and reasoning methods. Many real-world applications provide data that are best fit to a description by using the techniques of analytic geometry.

Big Idea
The laws of arithmetic can be used to simplify algebraic expressions and equations. Solving an equation means finding values for the variable or variables that make the equation a true statement.

Big Idea
A function is a correspondence between two sets, the domain and the range, that assigns to each member of the domain exactly one member of the range. Many events in the physical world can be modeled as functions. Many functions can be described by algebraic expressions.

Big Idea
If you can create a mathematical model for a situation, you can use the model to solve other problems that you might not be able to solve otherwise. Algebraic equations can capture key relationships among quantities in the world.

Summary: Analytic Geometry Review [online]

In this unit, you have covered the following topics:

- points on the plane

- two-variable equations

- linear equations and intercepts

- slope

- problem solving

- relations and functions

- systems of linear equations

Offline Learning: Analytic Geometry Review [offline]

How well have you mastered the goals of this unit? Complete the Analytic Geometry Practice Problems. These problems are similar to the problems you will have on the Unit Test.

You can also

- Review the Analytic Geometry unit in *Pre-Algebra: A Reference Guide and Problem Sets*

- Review the notes in your Student Guide

- Read and follow the instructions in Preparing for the Unit Test

Practice Problems

Unit Review

Use the figure to answer Questions 1–15.

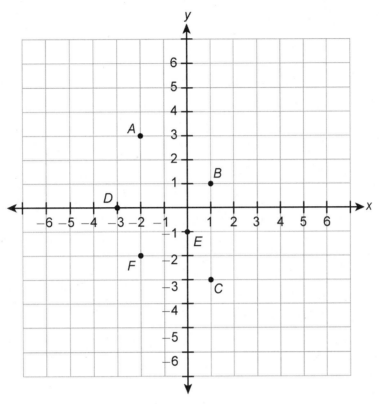

1. What point names the ordered pair (1, −3)?

2. What is the ordered pair for each of the following points?
    A. A

    B. D

    C. F

3. Graph the equation $4x - 2y = -6$.

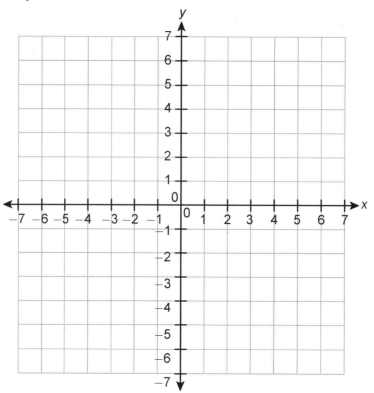

4. Write the equation for the graph.

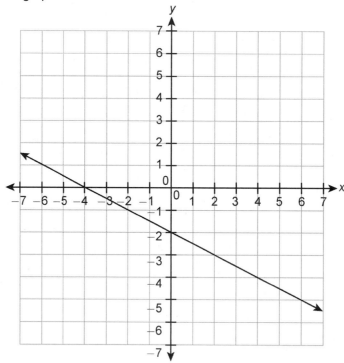

5. Find the following if $f(x) = -2x - 5$.
    A. $f(-4)$
    B. $f(-1)$
    C. $f(0)$
    D. $f(4)$

6. Determine whether the ordered pairs are solutions to the equation $3x - 4y = 12$.
    A. $(-4, -6)$

    B. $(8, -3)$

7. Find the slope of the line whose equation is $-6x + 3y = -9$.

8. Find the slope of the line that passes through points $(-2, 5)$ and $(7, -4)$.

9. State the domain and range of the relation $\{(-2, -3), (0, 4), (2, 5), (3, -6)\}$.

10. State the intercepts of the line.

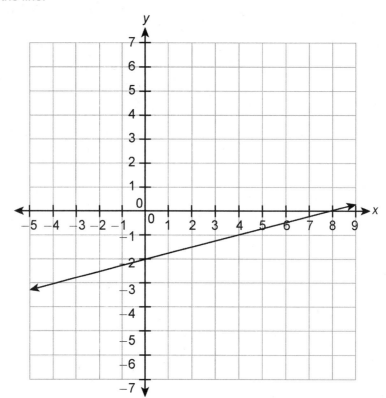

11. State whether each of the following relations is a function.

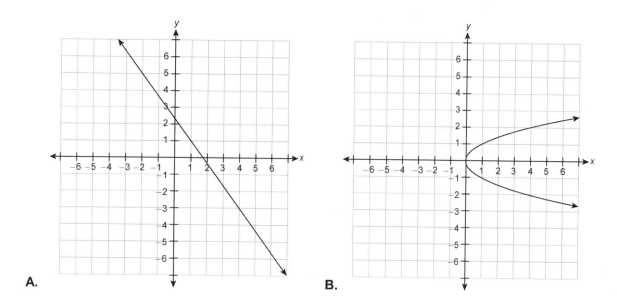

A.

B.

12. To register at a school, Julia must pay a one-time registration fee of $200 and then pay $450 per month as tuition. If m is the number of months and t is the total amount paid, the variables are related by the equation $t = 450m + 200$. Which variable is the independent variable, and which variable is the dependent variable?

For Questions 13–15, state the solution of the linear system of equations.

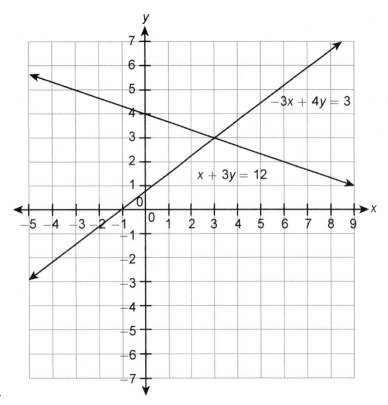

13.

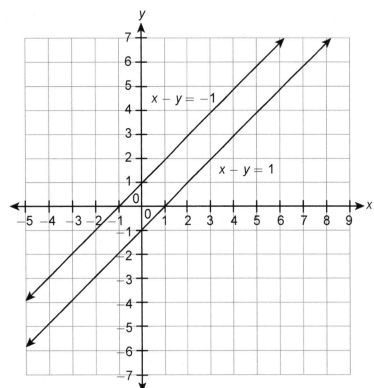

14.

15.

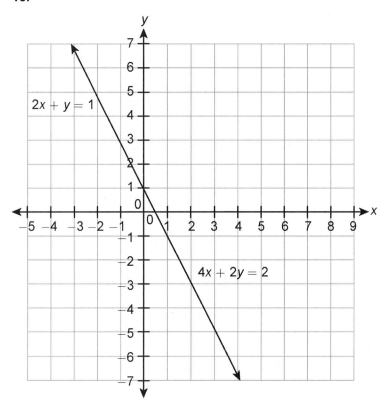

16. Write the equation of the line.

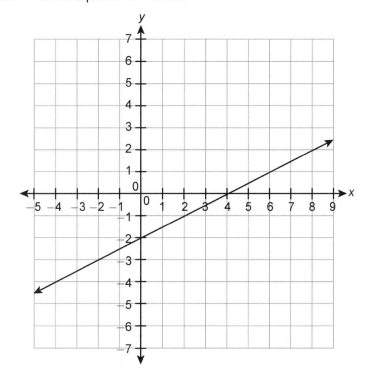

17. The graph shows Andew's progress as he studies for his Social Studies exam. What is a reasonable estimate for the number of units he studied after 8 hours?

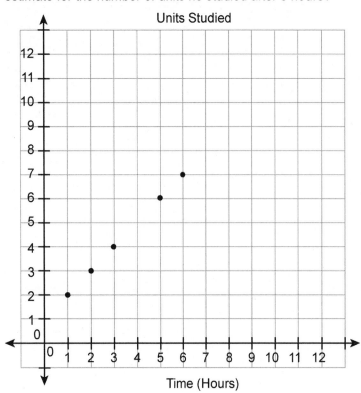

Answers

1. C

2. **A.** (−2, 3)
   B. (−3, 0)
   C. (−2, −2)

3.

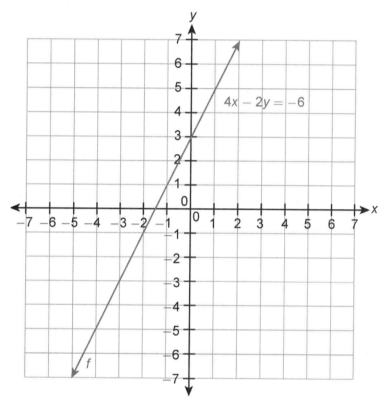

$4x - 2y = -6$

4. $x + 2y = -4$

5. **A.** 3
   B. −3
   C. −5
   D. −13

6. **A.** solution

   B. not a solution

7. 2

8. −1

9. Domain: {−2, 0, 2, 3}

   Range: {−6, −3, 4, 5}

10. x-intercept: 8

    y-intercept: −2

11. **A.** function

    B. not a function

12. m is the independent variable.

    t is the dependent variable.

13. (3, 3)

14. no solution

15. infinite solutions

16. $-x + 2y = -4$ or $x - 2y = 4$

17. 9 units

Unit Assessment

Analytic Geometry Unit Test, Offline

(10 points)

1. Use the graph of the line to answer each question.

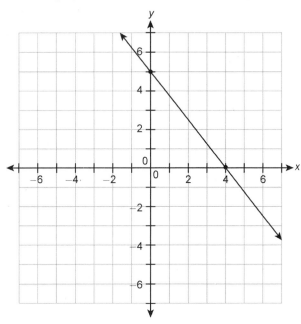

A. What are the intercepts of the line?

B. What is the slope of the line?

C. Write a linear equation for the line.

Score	___ of 10

Student Guide

Types of Polygons

Identify some objects that have at least three straight sides that intersect only at their ends. Examples are the top of a rectangular table and a stop sign. These figures are called *polygons*. Think about the differences among the objects you identified. Some of them may have sides that are of equal length or angles that are of equal measure. How would you describe the polygons you found?

Goals for the Lesson
- Classify a polygon as equilateral, equiangular, both, or neither.
- Plot and connect points on a coordinate plane and classify the resulting polygon.

Graded Activities in This Lesson
Lesson Quiz (computer-scored)

Materials
Pre-Algebra: A Reference Guide and Problem Sets, pages 347–351
graph paper
straightedge

Optional
Types of Polygons Solutions

Keywords and Pronunciation
equiangular polygon: a polygon with all angles congruent

equilateral polygon: a polygon with all sides congruent

polygon: a closed plane figure made up of line segments

regular polygon: a polygon with all its sides congruent and all its angles congruent

side of a polygon: one of the line segments that are the boundaries of a polygon

vertex: a point common to two sides of an angle or polygon; the plural of vertex is *vertices*

Groundwork: Preparing for the Lesson [online]

This activity reviews essential skills. As you work through it, answer the questions below and record any notes in the space provided.

Notes

What is a five-sided polygon called?

Why is a circle not a polygon?

Learn: Describing Polygons [online]

As you work through this activity, do the exercises below and record any notes in the space provided.

Notes

Draw a polygon that is equilateral but not equiangular.

Draw a polygon that is equiangular but not equilateral.

Worked Examples: Types of Polygons [online]

As you work through this activity, record any notes in the space provided.

Notes

Summary: Types of Polygons [online]

In this lesson, you learned how to describe polygons.

You can describe a polygon as equiangular, equilateral, or regular.

Offline Learning: Types of Polygons [offline]

In the Book

Read pages 347–349 in the Reference Guide.

Problem Sets

Complete Problems 9–20 on pages 350–351 of the Reference Guide.

Lesson Assessment: Types of Polygons Quiz [online]

Now go back online to complete the quiz.

Student Guide

Perimeter

A polygon is a closed figure made up of segments joined at their endpoints. The prefix *poly* has Greek origins and means "many." That same prefix is seen in other words, such as *poly*anthus (a primrose with many flowers), *poly*glot (a person who speaks many languages), and *poly*nomial (a math expression with many terms). A polygon has three or more sides, and the distance around a polygon is called the *perimeter*. In this lesson, you will learn how to find the perimeter of polygons.

Goals for the Lesson
- Write a formula to find the perimeter of a polygon.
- Find the perimeter of a polygon.
- Find the perimeter of a figure made up of rectangles or triangles or both.

Graded Activities in This Lesson
Lesson Quiz (computer-scored)

Materials
Pre-Algebra: A Reference Guide and Problem Sets, pages 352–357

Optional
Perimeter Solutions
High-Flying Challenge sheet
High-Flying Challenge answer sheet
graphing calculator

Keywords and Pronunciation
perimeter: distance around a figure; the perimeter of a polygon is the sum of the lengths of all the sides

polygon: a closed plane figure made up of line segments

regular polygon: a polygon with all its sides congruent and all its angles congruent

Groundwork: Peparing for the Lesson [online]
This activity reviews essential skills. As you work through it, answer the question below and record any notes in the space provided.

Notes
What is a quadrilateral?

Learn: Perimeters of Polygons [online]

As you work through this activity, do the exercise below and record any notes in the space provided.

Notes

Describe two methods for finding the perimeter of a regular polygon.

Learn: Perimeters of Complex Figures [online]

As you work through this activity, answer the question below and record any notes in the space provided.

Notes

An equilateral triangle has a perimeter of 21 centimeters, and a square has a perimeter of 28 centimeters. How can you place the figures together to make a pentagon with a perimeter of 35 centimeters? Draw a picture below.

Worked Examples: Perimeter [online]

As you work through this activity, record any notes in the space provided.

Notes

MathCast: Perimeter of a Complex Figure [online]

View the video to see how to solve a typical problem.

Summary: Perimeter [online]

In this lesson, you have learned about polygons and their perimeters.

- To find the perimeter of a polygon, find the sum of the measures of all sides of the polygon.

- You can find the perimeter of a rectangle with length *l* and width *w* by using the formula $P = 2l + 2w$.

- Find the perimeter of a regular polygon by multiplying the length of one side by the total number of sides.

Offline Learning: Perimeter [offline]

In the Book
Read pages 352–353 in the Reference Guide.

Problem Sets
Complete Exercises 1–13 odd and 21–24 on pages 355–357 of the Reference Guide.

Extra Practice (optional)
Complete Exercises 2–14 even and 25–28 on pages 355–357 of the Reference Guide for extra practice.

Extension (optional)
A windy day is the perfect day to fly a kite. Today is the perfect day to find out how designers use geometry to make kites. If you have not already done so, print the High-Flying Challenge sheet and complete the activities.

Lesson Assessment: Perimeter Quiz [online]

Now go back online to complete the quiz.

Name _____   Date _____

Extension
High-Flying Geometry

Earle Newton works for a company that designs kites. At the right is one of his newest designs.

1. Name a line segment parallel to $\overline{DF}$.

   _____

2. Name a right triangle that has $\overline{DF}$ as one of its sides.

   _____

3. What kind of figure is *XLKP*?

   _____

4. If $\overline{BA}$ is congruent to $\overline{AY}$, what kind of triangle is *BAY*?

   _____

5. $\overline{UZ} \parallel \overline{PF}$. What is $\overline{LP}$ called?

   _____

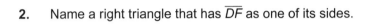

6. $\overline{AE} \parallel \overline{YF}$. ∠*UKP* is congruent to ∠*KPY* because _____

7. What is the most specific name you can give figure *LQPU*? _____

8. Name the trapezoid with one right angle. _____

9. Can you find a trapezoid with no right angles on the kite? _____

10. Can you find a parallelogram that is not a rectangle on the kite? _____

11. In △*IVJ*, $m\angle I = m\angle V = 60°$. What is $m\angle J$? _____

12. What kind of triangle is △*IVJ*? _____

13. Name an obtuse isosceles triangle. _____

14. Name a regular octagon in the kite. _____

15. Figure *XRLMWNZD* is an octagon. Name another octagon. _____

16. Name any pentagon. _____

Student Guide

Areas of Rectangles and Triangles

Rectangles and triangles are just two of many geometric shapes that we see in our everyday lives. Knowing about the relationships that exist between them is useful in determining their areas. In fact, knowing how to find the area of a rectangle can be helpful in finding the area of a triangle.

Goals for the Lesson
- Find the area of a rectangle.

- Find the area of a triangle.

- Use area to find a missing length.

- Find the area of a figure made up of rectangles or triangles or both.

Graded Activities in This Lesson
Lesson Quiz (computer-scored)

Materials
Pre-Algebra: A Reference Guide and Problem Sets, pages 358–363

Optional
Areas of Rectangles and Triangles Solutions
calculator
graph paper
straightedge

Keywords and Pronunciation
area: the number of square units in the interior of a figure

base: the bottom side or face of a geometric figure

height: in a geometric figure, an altitude that is perpendicular to a base

Groundwork: Preparing for the Lesson [online]
This activity reviews skills and knowledge that are essential to this lesson. As you work through it, answer the question below and record any notes in the space provided.

Notes
How many vertices does a triangle have?

Learn: Area of Rectangles [online]

As you work through this activity, answer the question below and record any notes in the space provided.

Sometimes the formula for the area of a rectangle is written $A = lw$, and sometimes it is written $A = bh$. You can use either formula. To find the area of a rectangle, you multiply the lengths of two corresponding sides. It doesn't matter whether you call the sides l and w or b and h.

Notes
What is the area of a figure?

Learn: Area of Triangles [online]

As you work through this activity, answer the question below and record any notes in the space provided.

Notes
How are the area formulas for rectangles and triangles related?

Learn: Finding Missing Lengths [online]

As you work through this activity, record any notes in the space provided.

Notes

Learn: Areas of Complex Figures [online]

As you work through this activity, answer the questions below and record any notes in the space provided.

Notes

Divide the figure into a rectangle and a triangle. What is the area of the rectangle, and what is the area of the triangle? What is the area of the figure?

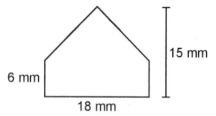

MathCast: Area of a Complex Figure [online]

View the video to see how to solve a typical problem.

Summary: Areas of Rectangles and Triangles [online]

The formula for the area of a rectangle is $A = lw$ (or $A = bh$).

The area of a triangle is one-half the area of a rectangle with the same base and height.

Area is always measured in square units—for example, square inches or square centimeters.

Skills Update: Practice Your Math Skills [online]
Complete the Skills Update online.

Offline Learning: Areas of Rectangles and Triangles [offline]

In the Book
Read pages 358–360 in the Reference Guide.

Do the Math

Finding Missing Lengths

If you know the area of a rectangle and either the base or height of the rectangle, you can find the missing length by using the formula for the area of rectangle.

Problem: The area of a rectangle is 51.6 square feet. The base of the rectangle is 6 feet. What is the height?

Solution: Use the formula. Substitute 51.6 for the area and 6 for the base. Then solve for the height.

$$A = bh$$
$$51.6 = 6 \cdot h$$
$$\frac{51.6}{6} = \frac{6 \cdot h}{6}$$
$$8.6 = h$$

The height of the rectangle is 8.6 feet.

If you know the area of a triangle and either the base or height of the triangle, you can find the missing length by using the formula for the area of triangle.

Problem: The area of a triangle is 49 square inches. The height of the triangle is 14 inches. What is the base?

Solution: Use the formula. Substitute 49 for the area and 14 for the height. Then solve for the base.

$$A = \frac{1}{2}bh$$
$$49 = \frac{1}{2} \cdot b \cdot 14$$
$$49 = 7b$$
$$\frac{49}{7} = \frac{7b}{7}$$
$$7 = b$$

The base of the triangle is 7 inches.

Problem Sets
Complete Problems 1–10 and 18–23 on pages 361–362 of the Reference Guide.

Another Look (optional)

You know that the formula for the area of a triangle is $A = \frac{1}{2}bh$. But which side is the base and where is the height?

If the triangle is a right triangle like triangle *ABC* below, it is easiest to pick one of the perpendicular sides as the base and the other perpendicular side as the height.

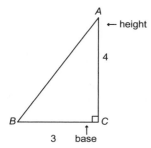 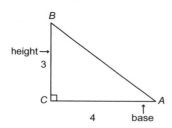

If the triangle is acute, you can pick any side as the base. Once you have a base, draw a perpendicular segment from the opposite vertex down to the base.

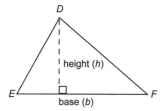

If the triangle is obtuse, things get more interesting. Depending on the side you select as the base, the height might not be inside the triangle. That's okay; just extend the base with a dotted line and then draw a dotted perpendicular line down to the dotted base.

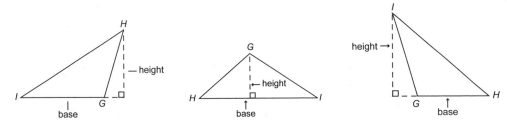

Whichever side you pick for the base, the area will be the same.

Lesson Assessment: Areas of Rectangles and Triangles Quiz

[online]
Now go back online to complete the quiz.

Student Guide

Special Quadrilaterals

If someone asked you to draw a quadrilateral, what kind of shape would you draw? Think of the meaning of the word *quadrilateral*—*quad* means "four," and *lateral* means "sides." Therefore, if your drawing is a four-sided polygon, then you would be correct. In this lesson, you will learn how to identify and classify types of quadrilaterals.

Goals for the Lesson
- Identify properties of a quadrilateral.
- Classify a figure as a special type of quadrilateral.
- Plot given vertices and identify the type of quadrilateral they form.

Graded Activities in This Lesson
Lesson Quiz (computer-scored)

Materials
Pre-Algebra: A Reference Guide and Problem Sets, pages 364–369
graph paper
straightedge

Optional
Special Quadrilaterals Solutions
calculator

Keywords and Pronunciation
parallelogram: a quadrilateral with two pairs of parallel sides

polygon: a closed plane figure made up of line segments

quadrilateral: a polygon with four sides

rectangle: a quadrilateral with four right angles

rhombus: a parallelogram with four congruent sides; the plural is *rhombi* (RAHM-biy)

square: a quadrilateral with four congruent sides and four right angles

trapezoid: a quadrilateral with exactly one pair of parallel sides

Groundwork: Preparing for the Lesson [online]

This activity shows you different figures and asks you to determine which are polygons.

Notes

How can you tell if a figure is **not** a polygon?

Learn: Quadrilateral Characteristics [online]

As you work through this activity, answer the questions below and record any notes in the space provided.

Notes

Look at the Venn diagram. Is it true that every square is a rhombus? Is every rectangle a rhombus?

The coordinates of three vertices of a square are (–1, 0), (0, 2), and (2, 1). What are the coordinates of the missing vertex?

Learn: Try It [online]

As you work through this activity, answer the questions below and record any notes in the space provided.

Notes

Look at this statement: **A parallelogram is a square.** Is that statement *always true*, *sometimes true*, or *never true*? Why?

Summary: Special Quadrilaterals [online]

In this lesson, you have learned how to identify special quadrilaterals such as parallelograms, rectangles, rhombi, squares, and trapezoids.

Skills Update: Practice Your Math Skills [online]

Complete the Skills Update online.

Offline Learning: Special Quadrilaterals [offline]

In the Book
Read pages 364–367 in the Reference Guide.

Problem Sets
Complete Problems 1, 2, 4–5, 9–12, and 21–23 on page 368 of the Reference Guide.

Extra Practice (optional)
Complete Problems 13–15, and 24–25 on page 368 of the Reference Guide.

Extension (optional)
A diagonal is a segment that joins two nonconsecutive vertices of a polygon.

Diagonals of a quadrilateral have some special properties. They may—

- form two congruent triangles

- bisect each other

- be congruent

- be perpendicular

- bisect the opposite angles

In different quadrilaterals, diagonals have different properties. Which of the above properties belong to each of these special quadrilaterals: parallelograms, rectangles, rhombi, squares, and isosceles trapezoids? More than one property may belong to any given quadrilateral.

Lesson Assessment: Special Quadrilaterals Quiz [online]

Now go back online to complete the lesson quiz.

Student Guide

Areas of Special Quadrilaterals

You can find the area of a rectangle or square by multiplying the length of the base by the height. You can find areas of other special quadrilaterals, such as parallelograms and trapezoids, by using the same general formulas. In this lesson, you will find and use formulas for finding the areas of parallelograms and trapezoids.

Goals for the Lesson

- Find the area of a trapezoid.

- Find the area of a parallelogram.

- Use area to find a missing side length of a quadrilateral.

Graded Activities in This Lesson
Mid-Unit Test (computer-scored)

Materials
Pre-Algebra: A Reference Guide and Problem Sets, pages 370-375
graph paper
straightedge

Optional
Areas of Special Quadrilaterals Solutions
calculator

Keywords and Pronunciation
base of a parallelogram: a selected side or face

height: the perpendicular distance between the bases of a geometric figure; in triangles, cones, and pyramids, the perpendicular distance from the base to the opposite vertex

Groundwork: Preparing for the Lesson [online]
This activity reviews rectangles and squares. As you work through it, answer the question below and record any notes in the space provided.

Notes
How do you find the width of a rectangle when you know its length and area?

Learn: Area of Parallelograms [online]

As you work through this activity, answer the question below and record any notes in the space provided.

Notes

How is the height of a parallelogram related to the base?

Learn: Area of Trapezoids [online]

As you work through this activity, answer the question below and record any notes in the space provided.

Notes

How do you know which sides of a trapezoid are the bases?

MathCast: Find the Missing Side of a Parallelogram [online]

View the video to see how to solve a typical problem.

Summary: Areas of Special Quadrilaterals [online]

In this lesson, you learned to find the areas of parallelograms and trapezoids.

- The formula for the area of a parallelogram with base b and height h is $A = bh$.

- The formula for the area of a trapezoid with bases b_1 and b_2 and height h is $A = \frac{1}{2}h(b_1 + b_2)$.

Offline Learning: Areas of Special Quadrilaterals [offline]

In the Book
Read pages 370–372 in the Reference Guide.

Do the Math

Finding Missing Lengths

If you know the area of a parallelogram and either its base or its height, you can find the missing length by using the formula for the area of parallelogram.

Problem: The area of a parallelogram is 308 square feet. The base of the rectangle is 11 feet. What is the height?

Solution: Use the formula. Substitute 308 for the area and 11 for the base. Then solve for the height.

$$A = bh$$

$$308 = 11 \cdot h$$

$$\frac{308}{11} = \frac{11 \cdot h}{11}$$

$$28 = h$$

The height of the parallelogram is 28 feet.

If you know the area of a trapezoid and either both of its bases or one of its bases and its height, you can find the missing length by using the formula for the area of a trapezoid.

Problem: The area of a trapezoid is 140 square inches. The bases of the trapezoid are 12 inches and 16 inches. What is the height?

Solution: Use the formula. Substitute 140 for the area and 12 and 16 for the bases. Then solve for the height.

$$A = \frac{1}{2} h (b_1 + b_2)$$

$$140 = \frac{1}{2} \cdot h \cdot (12 + 16)$$

$$140 = \frac{1}{2} \cdot h \cdot (28)$$

$$140 = 14h$$

$$\frac{140}{14} = \frac{14h}{14}$$

$$10 = h$$

The height of the trapezoid is 10 inches.

Problem Sets
Complete Problems 1–19 odd on pages 373–374 of the Reference Guide.

Another Look (optional)

You have seen that you can find the formula for the area of a trapezoid by combining the areas of two triangles. You can also find the formula by dividing a trapezoid into two triangles.

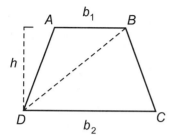

In the diagram above, trapezoid $ABCD$ has been divided into two triangles. Triangle ABD has height h and base b_1. Triangle BCD, meanwhile, has height h and base b_2. So the areas of these two triangles are as follows:

Area of triangle ABD: $A = \frac{1}{2}b_1h$

Area of triangle BCD: $A = \frac{1}{2}b_2h$

The area of trapezoid $ABCD$ is the sum of the areas of the two triangles:

$$A = \frac{1}{2}b_1h + \frac{1}{2}b_2h$$

Using the commutative and distributive properties, you can simplify this formula to

$$A = \frac{1}{2}h(b_1 + b_2)$$
$$A = \frac{1}{2}(b_1 + b_2)h$$

Either way you get there, the formula is the same.

Mid-Unit Assessment: Perimeter and Area Test [online]

Now go back online to complete the mid-unit test.

Student Guide

Circumference, Part 1

When you order a pizza, you might ask for one that is 16 inches. But what part of the pizza is 16 inches? The answer is its diameter. A "16-inch pizza" refers to a circular pizza with a diameter of 16 inches; it does not mean that 16 inches is the distance around the outside of the pizza. That measurement is called the *circumference*. In this lesson, you will learn about the relationship between the diameter and the circumference of a circle.

Goals for the Lesson

- Find the exact circumference of a circle when given a radius or diameter.

- Use an approximation for π (pi) to estimate the circumference of a circle.

Graded Activities in This Lesson

Lesson Quiz (computer-scored)

Materials

Pre-Algebra: A Reference Guide and Problem Sets, pages 376–381

Optional

Circumference Solutions
calculator

Keywords and Pronunciation

circle: the set of all points in a plane that are equidistant from a given point in the plane, called the *center*

circumference: distance around a circle

diameter: a chord that contains the center of a circle or a sphere; the length of this chord is also called the diameter

radius (RAY-dee-us): a line segment that connects the center of the circle to a point on the circle; the plural of radius is radii (RAY-dee-iy)

Groundwork: Preparing for the Lesson [online]

This activity illustrates how regular polygons look as the number of sides increases. As you work through this activity, record any notes in the space provided.

Notes

Learn: Finding Circumference [online]

As you work through this activity, answer the questions below and record any notes in the space provided.

Notes

What is the ratio of the circumference of a circle to its diameter?

What approximation is commonly used for π?

What two formulas can be used to find the circumference of a circle?

MathCast: Circumference [online]

View the video to see how to solve a typical problem.

Summary: Circumference, Part 1 [online]

In this lesson, you have learned how to find the circumference of a circle, given its radius or diameter.

An exact circumference contains the constant π in its representation. An approximate circumference is one in which an approximation for π is used. An approximation should use the "is approximately equal to" symbol instead of an equals symbol.

Offline Learning: Circumference, Part 1 [offline]

In the Book
Read pages 376–377 in the Reference Guide.

Problem Sets
Complete Problems 1–5 and 11 on page 380.

Extra Practice (optional)
Complete Problems 6–8 and 12 on page 380 for extra practice.

Lesson Assessment: Circumference, Part 1 Quiz [online]
Now go back online to complete the quiz.

Student Guide

Circumference, Part 2

Have you ever ridden on a Ferris wheel? Did you wonder how far you traveled as you went around and around? If you know the diameter of the Ferris wheel and the number of revolutions it made during your ride, you can figure out how far you traveled. In this lesson, you will learn how to solve word problems involving circumference.

Goals for the Lesson
- Find the perimeter of a figure that has part of a circle or parts of both circles and polygons.

- Solve a word problem involving the circumference of a circle.

Graded Activities in This Lesson
Lesson Quiz (computer-scored)

Materials
Pre-Algebra: A Reference Guide and Problem Sets, pages 376–381

Optional
Circumference Solutions
calculator
straightedge

Keywords and Pronunciation
circumference: distance around a circle
semicircle: half of a circle

Groundwork: Preparing for the Lesson [online]
This activity reviews perimeters of rectangles. As you work through it, do the exercise and record any notes in the space provided.

Notes
Explain how to find the perimeter of a rectangle.

Learn: Partial and Composite Figures [online]

As you work through this activity, answer the question below and record any notes in the space provided.

Notes

Bror said the perimeter of the figure below was about 15.7 feet.

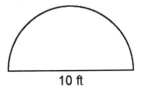

10 ft

Bror's Solution:

$$C = \frac{\pi d}{2}$$

$$= \frac{\pi \cdot 10}{2}$$

$$= 5\pi$$

$$\approx 15.7$$

Is Bror's solution correct or incorrect? Explain.

Worked Examples: Circumference, Part 2 [online]

As you work through this activity, record any notes in the space provided.

Notes

MathCast: Perimeter and Circumference [online]

View the video to see how to solve a typical problem.

Summary: Circumference, Part 2 [online]

In this lesson, you learned how to find the perimeters of partial and combination figures by using the formulas for the circumference of semicircles and quarter circles.

You also learned how to solve word problems involving circumference.

Offline Learning: Circumference, Part 2 [offline]

In the Book

Read pages 377–379 in the Reference Guide.

Do the Math

What Are the Parts of a Circle?

The wheel is one of the oldest and most important inventions. You can think of the parts of a wheel as parts of a circle.

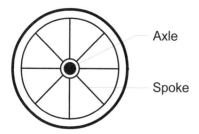

Axle

Spoke

Think of the axle of the wheel as the *center* of the circle.

Think of a spoke on the wheel as a *radius* of the circle.

Think of two spokes that join at the axle and form a straight line as the *diameter* of the circle.

Problem Sets

Complete Problems 13–16, 19 and 22, 25, 27 on page 381 of the Reference Guide.

Extra Practice (optional)

Complete Problems 17–18 and 24 on page 381 for extra practice.

Lesson Assessment: Circumference, Part 2 Quiz [online]

Now go back online to complete the quiz.

Student Guide

Areas of Circles, Part 1

Can a circle be square? No, but a circle's area can be measured in square units. That might not seem logical, but it's true. To find the area of a circle, you need to use π—the same π you use to find a circle's circumference. In this lesson, you will use a formula that includes π to find the area of a circle.

Goals for the Lesson

- Find the exact area of a circle with a given radius or diameter.

- Use an approximation for pi to estimate the area of a circle.

Graded Activities in This Lesson
Lesson Quiz (computer-scored)

Materials
Pre-Algebra: A Reference Guide and Problem Sets
calculator

Optional
Areas of Circles Solutions
Circle Area with Wedges sheet
graph paper

Groundwork: Preparing for the Lesson [online]
This activity reviews areas and circles. As you work through it, answer the question and record any notes in the space provided.

Notes
How do you find the circumference of a circle?

Learn: Area of a Circle [online]

As you work through this activity, answer the question and record any notes in the space provided.

Notes

How is finding the approximate area of a circle different from finding the exact area of a circle?

Worked Examples: Areas of Circles, Part 1 [online]

As you work through this activity, record any notes in the space provided.

Notes

Summary: Areas of Circles, Part 1 [online]

In this lesson, you learned how to find the area of a circle when you know the circle's radius or diameter.

The formula for the area of a circle is $A = \pi \cdot r^2$.

Skills Update: Practice Your Math Skills [online]

Complete the Skills Update online.

Offline Learning: Areas of Circles, Part 1 [offline]

In the Book
Read pages 382–383 through Example 1 in the Reference Guide.

Problem Sets
Complete Problems 1–6 on page 386 of the Reference Guide.

Extra Practice (optional)
Complete Problems 7–10 on page 386 of the Reference Guide.

Another Look (optional)
If you have not already done so, print the Circle Area with Wedges sheet. Cut out the circle wedges divided into eighths and then cut out the circle wedges divided into sixteenths. Arrange the wedges in a zigzag fashion to create a figure that is almost a parallelogram. The height of this figure is about r. The base is approximately one-half the circumference of the circle, or πr. Therefore, the area is πr^2. Notice that the approximation gets better as the circle is divided into smaller and smaller wedges.

Lesson Assessment: Areas of Circles, Part 1 Quiz [online]
Now go back online to complete the quiz.

Name _____   Date _____

Circle Area with Wedges

Areas of Circles

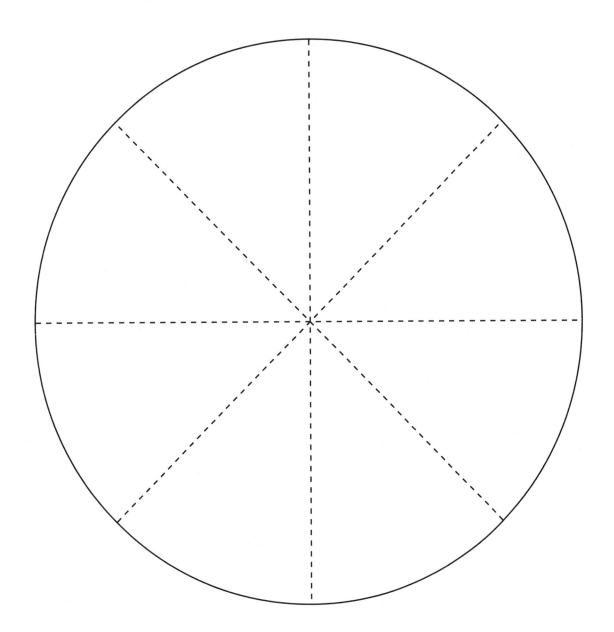

Circle Area with Wedges

Areas of Circles

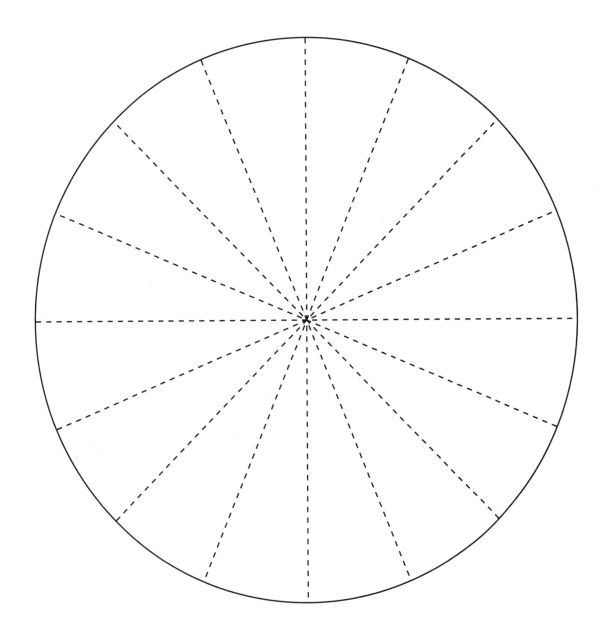

Student Guide

Areas of Circles, Part 2

You can take the skills needed to find the area of a circle and apply them so that you can solve problems. In this lesson, you will find solutions to problems that involve areas of circles.

Goals for the Lesson

- Find the area of a figure that has part of a circle or parts of both circles and polygons.

- Find the area defined as the difference of two figures involving circles or both circles and polygons.

- Solve a word problem involving the area of a circle.

Graded Activities in This Lesson
Lesson Quiz (computer-scored)

Materials
Pre-Algebra: A Reference Guide and Problem Sets, pages 382-387

Optional
Areas of Circles Solutions
calculator

Groundwork: Preparing for the Lesson [online]
This activity reviews perimeters and areas. As you work through it, answer the question and record any notes in the space provided.

Notes
How do you find the area of a triangle?

Learn: Problem Solving [online]

As you work through this activity, answer the question below and record any notes in the space provided.

Notes

Bror ate one-fourth of a 24-inch pizza. He said that he ate about 113 square inches of pizza.

Bror's Solution:

$$A = \frac{\pi(12)^2}{4}$$

$$= \frac{\pi \cdot 144}{4}$$

$$= 36\pi$$

$$\approx 113$$

Is Bror correct about the amount of pizza he ate? Explain.

Worked Examples: Areas of Circles, Part 2 [online]

As you work through this activity, record any notes in the space provided.

Notes

MathCast: Find the Area of a Shaded Region [online]

View the video to see how to solve a typical problem.

Summary: Areas of Circles, Part 2 [online]

You can use the formula for the area of a circle to find the formulas for the area of a semicircle and the area of a quarter circle.

You can also use these formulas to solve real-world problems.

Offline Learning: Areas of Circles, Part 2 [offline]

In the Book
Read pages 383–385 in the Reference Guide.

Problem Sets
Complete Problems 15–29 odd on page 387 of the Reference Guide.

Extra Practice (optional)
Complete Problems 16–30 even on page 387 of the Reference Guide.

Lesson Assessment: Areas of Circles, Part 2 Quiz [online]

Now go back online to complete the quiz.

Student Guide

Perimeter and Area Review

You have finished studying the Perimeter and Area unit, which includes types of polygons, perimeter, areas of rectangles and triangles, special quadrilaterals, areas of special quadrilaterals, circumference, and areas of circles. Now it's time to pull together what you have learned. Throughout the review, see how the skills you have learned relate to the Pre-Algebra big ideas.

Goals for the Lesson
*   Review the concepts and skills learned in the unit.

Materials
"Perimeter and Area" in *Pre-Algebra: A Reference Guide and Problem Sets*
Perimeter and Area Practice Problems
Preparing for the Unit Test

Unit Review: Perimeter and Area [online]

This is your chance to review the big ideas of Pre-Algebra you have learned in this unit. Under Review These Activities, you will find activities from previous lessons that will review each big idea. Choose the topics you feel you need to review. Under Try These Activities, you will find interactive problems that will test your understanding of each big idea. As you work through this lesson, take notes in the spaces provided.

Big Idea
There are several useful aspects of every geometric figure that can be measured, calculated, or approximated. A segment has a finite length that can be measured.

Big Idea
Area is a measure of how much material is needed to cover a plane figure. Volume is a measure of the amount of space a figure occupies.

Big Idea

If you can create a mathematical model for a situation, you can use the model to solve other problems that you might not be able to solve otherwise. Algebraic equations can capture key relationships among quantities in the world.

Summary: Perimeter and Area Review [online]

In this unit, you have covered the following topics:

- types of polygons
- perimeter
- areas of rectangles and triangles
- special quadrilaterals
- areas of special quadrilaterals
- circumference
- areas of circles

Offline Learning: Perimeter and Area Review [offline]

How well have you mastered the goals of this unit? Complete the Perimeter and Area Practice Problems. These problems are similar to the problems you will have on the Unit Test.

You can also—

- Review the Perimeter and Area unit in *Pre-Algebra: A Reference Guide and Problem Sets*
- Review the notes in your Student Guide
- Read and follow the instructions in Preparing for the Unit Test

Practice Problems

Perimeter and Area

1. Identify each of the polygons as equilateral, equiangular, or regular.

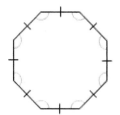

A.

B.

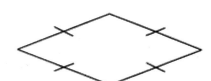

C.

2. Find the perimeter and area of the figure.

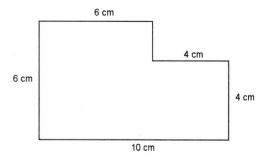

3. Find the area and perimeter of each figure.

A.

12 in

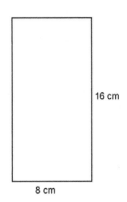

B.

16 cm

8 cm

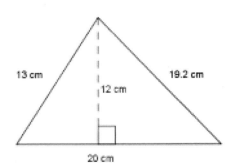

13 cm   12 cm   19.2 cm

20 cm

C.

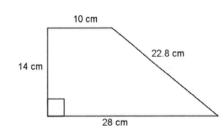

10 cm

14 cm   22.8 cm

28 cm

D.

4. Find the approximate circumference and area of a circle whose radius is 9 inches. Use $\pi = 3.14$.

5. Find the exact circumference and area of the circle.

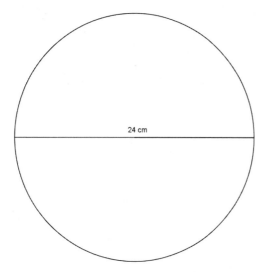

24 cm

6. Write all of the classifications that apply to each of the following quadrilaterals.

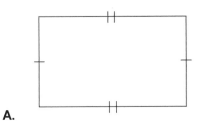

A.

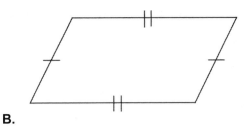

B.

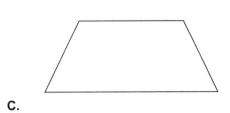

C.

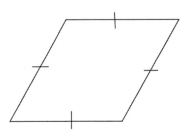

D.

7. State whether the polygon whose vertices are (−1, 5), (3, 5), (3, 1), and (-1, 1) is equilateral, equilangular, or regular.

8. Find the approximate area of the figure. Use $\pi = 3.14$.

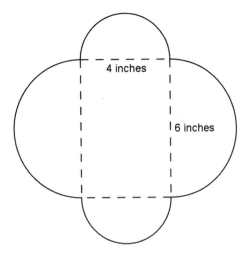

4 inches

6 inches

Answers

1. A. regular
    B. equiangular
    C. equilateral

2. P = 32 cm; A = 52 cm^2

3. A. 144 in^2
    B. 128 cm^2
    C. 120 cm^2
    D. 266 cm^2

4. C ≈ 56.5 cm; A ≈ 254.3 cm^2

5. C = 24π cm; A = 144π cm^2

6. A. parallelogram, rectangle
    B. parallelogram
    C. trapezoid
    D. parallelogram, rhombus

7. regular

8. 64.8 in^2

☼

Unit Assessment Answer Key

Perimeter and Area Unit Test, Offline

(10 points)

1. The sign outside Mrs. Washington's catering company is in the shape of a trapezoid, as shown below.

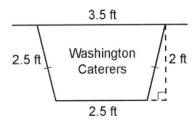

Score

    a. What is the perimeter of the sign?

    b. What is the area of the sign?

(10 points)

2. A flagpole stands on a concrete region, as shown below.

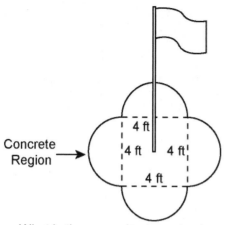

Concrete
Region →

4 ft

4 ft   4 ft

4 ft

a. What is the approximate perimeter of the concrete region?

b. What is the approximate area of the concrete region?

Student Guide

Rational Square Roots

Civilization credits Pythagoras (puh-THAG-uh-ruhs), a Greek mathematician who lived in the sixth century B.C., with discovering the formula for finding the lengths of the sides of a right triangle. Surveyors, carpenters, cabinetmakers, and architects are just a few of the people who use right triangles to solve problems. To work with right triangles, you must understand the concept of *square root*. In this lesson, you will study square roots and solve equations that involve square roots.

Goals for the Lesson
- Find square roots of a perfect square.
- Solve a simple equation with squares.

Graded Activities in This Lesson
Lesson Quiz (computer-scored)

Materials
Pre-Algebra: A Reference Guide and Problem Sets, pages 391–394

Optional
Rational Square Roots Solutions
calculator
graph paper

Keywords and Pronunciation
perfect square: a rational number whose square root is also a rational number

principal square root: the nonnegative square root, indicated by the square root sign

rational square root: a square root that is a rational number

square root: a factor of a number that when multiplied by itself results in the number; the nonnegative square root is called the principal square root and is indicated by the square root sign

Groundwork: Preparing for the Lesson [online]
This activity reviews essential skills. As you work through it, answer the question and record any notes in the space provided.

Notes
How can the square of a negative number be positive?

Learn: What is a Square Root? [online]

As you work through this activity, answer the questions below and record any notes in the space provided.

Notes

Is 225 a perfect square? Explain.

What are the square roots of 225?

What is the principal square root of 225?

Worked Examples: Rational Square Roots [online]

As you work through this activity, record any notes in the space provided.

Notes

MathCast: Solve an Equation [online]

View the video to see how to solve a typical problem.

Summary: Rational Square Roots [online]

- A square root is a factor of a number that when multiplied by itself results in the number.

- If a square root of a number is a rational number, it is called a rational square root.

- The principal square root is the nonnegative square root of a number.

- You can solve equations with square roots by using the square root property.

Skills Update: Practice Your Math Skills [online]
Complete the Skills Update online.

Offline Learning: Rational Square Roots [offline]

In the Book
Read pages 391–393 in the Reference Guide.

Do the Math
Do you think the following statements are true?

$$\sqrt{a+b} = \sqrt{a} + \sqrt{b} \quad \text{and} \quad \sqrt{a-b} = \sqrt{a} - \sqrt{b}$$

Try substituting specific positive real numbers for a and b to test the statements.

For example, let $a = 10$ and $b = 6$. (In the following examples, $\sqrt{10}$ and $\sqrt{6}$ are rounded to the hundredths place.)

Does $\sqrt{10+6} = \sqrt{10} + \sqrt{6}$?   Does $\sqrt{10-6} = \sqrt{10} - \sqrt{6}$?

Does $\quad\sqrt{16} = 3.16 + 2.45$?   Does $\quad\sqrt{4} = 3.16 - 2.45$?

$\qquad\qquad 4 \neq 5.61$ $\qquad\qquad 2 \neq 0.71$

$\qquad\sqrt{a+b} \neq \sqrt{a} + \sqrt{b}$ $\qquad\sqrt{a-b} \neq \sqrt{a} - \sqrt{b}$

One counterexample is all you need to show that a statement is not true. Therefore, neither of these statements is always true.

Problem Sets
Complete Problems 1–29 odd and 39–40 on pages 393–394 of the Reference Guide.

Extra Practice (optional)
Complete Problems 7–8, 16–18, and 26–30 on pages 393–394 for extra practice.

Another Look (optional)

The word *root* comes from an Indo-European word meaning "the source from which something grows." In nature, a tree grows up from its roots. In math, a square is built up from the length of its sides. In a sense, the side is the source from which a square grows—it is the square's root.

On the provided grid, draw a square with an area of 25. Then try to draw another square with an area of 32. Remember, all four sides of a square are the same length.

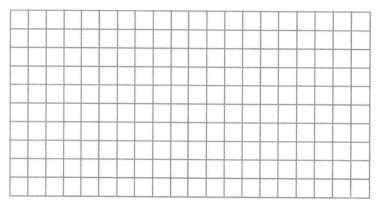

You probably didn't have any trouble drawing a square with an area of 25. That's because 25 is a perfect square. Each side is exactly 5 units, so the square root of 25 is 5. It is impossible, however, to use whole-number units for the sides of a square with an area of 32. You have to estimate the length of the sides. You should have estimated that the length of each side was somewhere between 5 and 6. The square root of 32, rounded to hundredths, is 5.66. The answer key shows two ways you can draw a square with an area of 32 units.

Lesson Assessment: Rational Square Roots Quiz [online]
Now go back online to complete the quiz.

Answers

Another Look

There are two ways to draw a square with an area of 32.

- You can approximate the length of the sides if you realize that the sides are between 5 and 6 units, as shown below (square on the left). In this case, the area of 32 is also an approximation.

- You can draw a more accurate square by drawing it diagonally, as shown below (square on the right). Count all of the squares and half-squares in this figure. They add up to 32. (The dashed lines group a 4-by-4 square to help you count the total number of squares.)

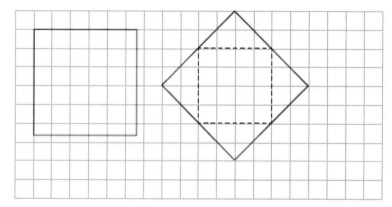

Student Guide

Irrational Square Roots, Part 1

Throughout history, people have used a variety of methods and tools to find square roots of numbers. These methods and tools include paper-and-pencil algorithms, the "binary chop" method, slide rules, published tables of values, and calculators. Sometimes a mental estimation also works well. In this lesson, you will learn about irrational square roots and two methods for approximating them.

Goals for the Lesson
- Determine whether a square root is rational or irrational.

- Find consecutive integers between which a square root lies.

- Approximate a square root to the nearest tenth.

Graded Activities in This Lesson
Lesson Quiz (computer-scored)

Materials
Pre-Algebra: A Reference Guide and Problem Sets, pages 395–399

Optional
Irrational Square Roots Solutions
calculator

Keywords and Pronunciation
irrational number: any real number that is not rational; in decimal form, all irrational numbers are nonterminating and nonrepeating

perfect square: a rational number whose square root is also a rational number

rational number: any number that can be expressed as a ratio (*a/b*) where *a* and *b* are integers and *b* is nonzero

Groundwork: Preparing for the Lesson [online]
This activity reviews square roots. As you work through it, answer the question below and record any notes in the space provided.

Notes
What is the principal square root of a number?

Learn: Identifying Irrational Square Roots [online]

As you work through this activity, answer the question below and record any notes in the space provided.

Notes

How can you tell if a whole number has rational square roots or irrational square roots?

Learn: Approximating Irrational Square Roots [online]

As you work through this activity, answer the question below and record any notes in the space provided.

Notes

What inequality would you write to find two consecutive integers between which $\sqrt{5}$ lies?

Worked Examples: Irrational Square Roots, Part 1 [online]

As you work through this activity, record any notes in the space provided.

Notes

Summary: Irrational Square Roots, Part 1 [online]

Whole numbers that are not perfect squares have irrational square roots.

You can approximate irrational square roots by using inequalities and by using a number line.

Offline Learning: Irrational Square Roots, Part 1 [offline]

In the Book
Read pages 395–396 in the Reference Guide.

Problem Sets
Complete Problems 1–5, 11–15, and 21–25 on page 398 of the Reference Guide.

Extra Practice (optional)
Complete Problems 6–8, 16–18, and 26–28 on page 398 of the Reference Guide.

Lesson Assessment: Irrational Square Roots, Part 1 Quiz [online]

Now go back online to complete the quiz.

Student Guide

Irrational Square Roots, Part 2

Suppose you have a square yard with an area of 2400 square feet, and you want to put fencing around the yard. How much fencing will you need? Knowing how to calculate a square root is essential for solving this problem.

Goals for the Lesson

- Write the square root of a positive whole number in simplified radical form.

- Solve a word problem involving square roots.

Graded Activities in This Lesson
Lesson Quiz (computer-scored)

Materials
Pre-Algebra: A Reference Guide and Problem Sets, pages 395–399

Optional
Irrational Square Roots Solutions
calculator

Groundwork: Preparing for the Lesson [online]

This activity reviews skills needed to find square roots. As you work through it, do the exercise below and record any notes in the space provided.

Notes

Describe how to find the approximate value of $\sqrt{140}$ by using a number line.

Learn: Simplifying Radicals [online]

As you work through this activity, answer the questions below and record any notes in the space provided.

Notes

What are the different ways you can factor $\sqrt{20}$? Which factorization allows you to write it in simplified radical form?

Learn: Problem Solving [online]

As you work through this activity, answer the question below and record any notes in the space provided.

Notes

Why do you disregard the negative square roots when you solve the equations in these real-world problems?

MathCast: Solve a Problem [online]

View the video to see how to solve a typical problem.

Summary: Irrational Square Roots, Part 2 [online]

In this lesson, you learned how to simplify radicals by using the product property of radicals.

You also learned how to solve real-world problems involving square roots.

Offline Learning: Irrational Square Roots, Part 2 [offline]

In the Book
Read page 397 in the Reference Guide.

Do the Math
Decide whether the statement is *always true*, *sometimes true*, or *never true*.

1. The square root of a number is a whole number.

2. The principal square root of a number can be negative.

3. Irrational numbers can be approximated by using a repeating decimal.

4. The product of two perfect squares is also a perfect square.

5. The square root of a prime number is an irrational number.

Problem Sets
Complete Problems 31-39 odd and 41-46 on pages 398–399 of the Reference Guide.

Lesson Assessment: Irrational Square Roots, Part 2 Quiz [online]
Now go back online to complete the lesson quiz.

Answers

Do the Math

1. sometimes true

2. never true

3. never true

4. always true

5. always true

Student Guide

The Pythagorean Theorem, Part 1

The Pythagorean theorem is one of the most famous and useful theorems in all of mathematics. It is named after Pythagoras, a Greek mathematician and philosopher who was born more than 2500 years ago. The Pythagorean theorem was discovered and proven in ancient times, and it continues to be widely used today.

Goals for the Lesson

- Identify the hypotenuse and legs of a right triangle.

- Use the Pythagorean theorem to find the length of the hypotenuse of a right triangle.

- Use the Pythagorean theorem to find the length of a leg of a right triangle.

Graded Activities in This Lesson

Mid-Unit Test (computer-scored)

Materials

Pre-Algebra: A Reference Guide and Problem Sets, pages 400-405

Optional

The Pythagorean Theorem Solutions
calculator

Keywords and Pronunciation

hypotenuse (hiy-PAH-tuh-noos): the side opposite the right angle in a right triangle

leg of a right triangle: the two sides of a right triangle that form the right angle

Groundwork: Preparing for the Lesson [online]

This activity reviews essential skills. As you work through it, do the exercise below and record any notes in the space provided.

Notes

Explain how to round a decimal to the nearest tenth.

Learn: Right Triangles [online]

As you work through this activity, do the exercise and answer the question below. Record any notes in the space provided.

Notes

Draw a right triangle. Label the legs and the hypotenuse. How did you know which side was the hypotenuse?

Learn: The Pythagorean Theorem [online]

As you work through this activity, answer the question below and record any notes in the space provided.

Notes

Why do you disregard the negative square root when using the Pythagorean Theorem?

MathCast: The Pythagorean Theorem [online]

View the video to see how to solve a typical problem.

Summary: The Pythagorean Theorem, Part 1 [online]

- The Pythagorean theorem states that the square of the hypotenuse of a right triangle is the sum of the squares of the other two sides.

- You can use the Pythagorean theorem to find a missing length in a right triangle.

Offline Learning: The Pythagorean Theorem, Part 1 [offline]

In the Book
Read pages 400–402 in the Reference Guide.

Do the Math (optional)
Pythagoras believed numbers have a mystical quality. During his lifetime, he traveled to different parts of the world in his quest for knowledge.

One place, Egypt, greatly affected Pythagoras in his discovery of the Pythagorean theorem. In Egypt, Pythagoras met people called "rope-stretchers." Rope-stretchers used a special technique to lay out the foundations of their buildings.

Use the Internet to research rope-stretching. What is rope-stretching, and why do you think it had an impact on Pythagoras's discovery of the Pythagorean theorem? Also, why do you think the side opposite the right angle in a right triangle was given the name "hypotenuse"? *(Hint: Find the Greek words from which the word* hypotenuse *is derived.)*

Problem Sets
Complete Problems 1–11 odd on page 404 of the Reference Guide.

Extra Practice (optional)
Complete Problems 2–10 even on page 404 of the Reference Guide.

Mid-Unit Assessment: Square Roots and Right Triangles Test

[online]
Now go back online to complete the mid-unit test.

Student Guide

The Pythagorean Theorem, Part 2

Pythagoras was not the first to know of the relationship among the lengths of the legs of a right triangle. Approximately 1000 years before he was born, the Babylonians, the Chinese, and the Indians all knew of the connection. Why do you think people from ancient civilizations had such a deep interest in this relationship?

Goals for the Lesson

- Solve a word problem involving right triangles.

- Identify Pythagorean triples.

Graded Activities in This Lesson

Lesson Quiz (computer-scored)

Materials

Pre-Algebra: A Reference Guide and Problem Sets, pages 400–405

Optional

The Pythagorean Theorem Solutions
calculator

Keywords and Pronunciation

Pythagorean triple: a set of three positive integers *a*, *b*, and *c* such that the sum of the squares of *a* and *b* is equal to the square of *c*

Groundwork: Preparing for the Lesson [online]

This activity reviews essential skills. As you work through it, record any notes in the space provided.

Notes

Learn: Pythagorean Triples [online]

As you work through this activity, answer the question below and record any notes in the space provided.

Notes

How do you determine whether a set of three integers is a Pythagorean triple?

Learn: Putting Pythagoras to Work [online]

As you work through this activity, answer the question below and record any notes in the space provided.

Notes

What types of word problems can be solved by using the Pythagorean theorem?

MathCast: Using the Pythagorean Theorem [online]

View the video to see how to solve a typical problem.

Summary: The Pythagorean Theorem, Part 2 [online]

The Pythagorean theorem is useful for solving many real-world problems that involve the missing lengths of right triangles.

Offline Learning: The Pythagorean Theorem, Part 2 [offline]

In the Book
Read pages 402–403 in the Reference Guide.

Do the Math (optional)
In a primitive Pythagorean triple, a, b, and c are relatively prime. Here are some examples of primitive Pythagorean triples:

3, 4, 5	5, 12, 13	7, 24, 25
8, 15, 17	9, 40, 41	11, 60, 61
12, 35, 37	13, 84, 85	16, 63, 65

1. What do you notice about the greatest integer of each set?

2. How many of the integers in each set are even numbers?

3. How many of the integers in each set are divisible by five?

4. Do you notice anything else the sets have in common?

Problem Sets
Complete Problems 13–22 on page 405 of the Reference Guide.

Lesson Assessment: The Pythagorean Theorem, Part 2 Quiz [online]

Now go back online to complete the lesson quiz.

Answers

Do the Math

1. They are all odd numbers.

2. Exactly one

3. Exactly one

4. Possible answers:
   One of the two lesser integers in the set is odd and one is even.
   Exactly one of the two lesser integers is divisible by three.
   Exactly one of the two lesser integers is divisible by four.

Student Guide

The Distance Formula

It's common knowledge that the shortest distance between two points is a straight line. Suppose those two points lie on a coordinate plane. How can you determine the distance between them? One way, of course, is to measure the distance by using a ruler. However, you do not need a ruler. In this lesson, you will learn about the distance formula and will use it to find the distance between two points on a coordinate plane.

Goals for the Lesson
• Find the distance between two points on a coordinate grid.

• Find the perimeter of a figure on a coordinate plane.

Graded Activities in This Lesson
Lesson Quiz (computer-scored)

Materials
Pre-Algebra: A Reference Guide and Problem Sets, pages 406–409

Optional
The Distance Formula Solutions
calculator

Groundwork: Preparing for the Lesson [online]
This activity reviews essential skills. As you work through it, answer the questions below and record any notes in the space provided.

Notes
What do *a* and *b* represent in the Pythagorean theorem? What does *c* represent?

Learn: The Distance Formula [online]

As you work through this activity, do the exercise below and record any notes in the space provided.

Notes

Explain how the Pythagorean theorem can be used to find the distance between two points on a coordinate plane.

Learn: Using the Distance Formula [online]

As you work through this activity, record any notes in the space provided.

Notes

Worked Examples: The Distance Formula [online]

As you work through this activity, record any notes in the space provided.

Notes

MathCast: Using the Distance Formula [online]

View the video to see how to solve a typical problem.

Summary: The Distance Formula [online]

The distance formula is used to find the distance between two points on the coordinate plane.

You can use the distance formula to find perimeters of geometric figures on the coordinate plane.

Offline Learning: The Distance Formula [offline]

In the Book
Read pages 406–407 in the Reference Guide.

Do the Math (optional)
The distance formula can also be used to find the distance between actual locations. A coordinate system can be superimposed on a map of the United States. In this example, each interval on the grid represents 100 miles.

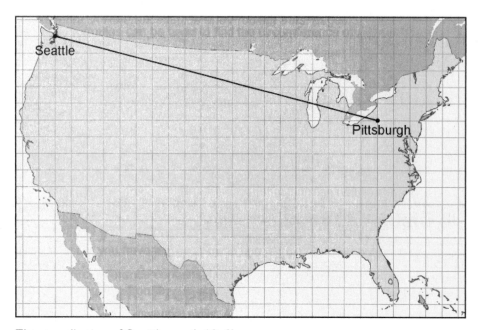

The coordinates of Seattle are (−16, 6).

The coordinates of Pittsburgh are (6, 1).

Use the distance formula to find the distance between Seattle and Pittsburgh.

Problem Sets
Complete Problems 1–9 odd and 16–17 on page 408 of the Reference Guide.

Extra Practice (optional)
Complete Problems 11–15 odd and 18–19 on page 408 of the Reference Guide.

Lesson Assessment: The Distance Formula Quiz [online]
Now go back online to complete the quiz.

Answer

Do the Math

$$d = \sqrt{[6 - (-16)]^2 + (1 - 6)^2}$$
$$= \sqrt{(22)^2 + (-5)^2}$$
$$= \sqrt{484 + 25}$$
$$= \sqrt{509}$$
$$\approx 22.56$$

The distance between Seattle and Pittsburgh is about $22.56 \cdot 100 \approx 2256$ miles.

Student Guide

Special Types of Triangles, Part 1

Special triangles have special properties. Some triangles have two or three sides that are congruent, and some triangles have sides in a particular ratio. Special *right* triangles have unique properties that allow you to use shortcuts to solve right-triangle problems with relatively few computations.

Goals for the Lesson

- Use properties of isosceles and equilateral triangles to find missing measures.

- Use properties of 45°-45°-90° triangles to find missing values.

- Use properties of 30°-60°-90° triangles to find missing values.

Graded Activities in This Lesson
Lesson Quiz (computer-scored)

Materials
Pre-Algebra: A Reference Guide and Problem Sets, pages 410–416

Optional
Special Types of Triangles Solutions
calculator

Keywords and Pronunciation
equilateral triangle: a triangle in which all three sides have equal length

isosceles triangle: a triangle in which at least two side lengths are equal

45°-45°-90° right triangle: a special right triangle with acute angles of 45°

30°-60°-90° right triangle: a special right triangle with acute angles of 30° and 60°

Groundwork: Preparing for the Lesson [online]
This activity reviews skills essential for this lesson. As you work through it, answer the questions below and record any notes in the space provided.

Notes
What is the sum of the measures of the angles of a triangle?

If a triangle is equiangular, what is the measure of each angle?

Learn: Isosceles and Equilateral Triangles [online]

As you work through this activity, answer the questions below and record any notes in the space provided.

Notes

Is every isosceles triangle also equilateral? Explain.

Is every equilateral triangle also isosceles? Explain.

Learn: What Makes Some Triangles Special? [online]

As you work through this activity, do the exercises below and record any notes in the space provided.

Notes

Draw a 45°-45°-90° triangle. Label one of the legs *x*. Now label the remaining sides in terms of *x*.

Draw a 30°-60°-90° triangle. Label the shorter leg *x*. Now label the remaining sides in terms of *x*.

Summary: Special Types of Triangles, Part 1 [online]

Triangles are named based on the length of their sides.

You can use algebra and the properties of isosceles triangles to find missing side lengths.

Some special right triangles are particularly useful.

An isosceles right triangle is also known as a 45°-45°-90° triangle. Any triangle with those degree measures has the same relationship between its side lengths.

If you divide an equilateral triangle in half, you get a 30°-60°-90° triangle. Any triangle with those degree measures has the same relationship between its side lengths.

Offline Learning: Special Types of Triangles, Part 1 [offline]

In the Book

Read pages 410–413 in the Reference Guide.

Problem Sets

Complete Problems 1–12 on page 415 of the Reference Guide.

Lesson Assessment: Special Types of Triangles, Part 1 Quiz [online]

Now go back online to complete the quiz.

Student Guide

Special Types of Triangles, Part 2

How far is a throw from first base to third base in baseball? How can you find the area of a regular hexagon? Believe it or not, you can answer these and similar questions by using your knowledge of special right triangles.

Goals for the Lesson
- Solve a word problem involving a special right triangle.

Graded Activities in This Lesson
Lesson Quiz (computer-scored)

Materials
Pre-Algebra: A Reference Guide and Problem Sets, pages 410-416

Optional
Special Types of Triangles Solutions
calculator

Groundwork: Preparing for the Lesson [online]

This activity reviews the relationships among the sides of special right triangles. As you work through this activity, answer the questions below and record any notes in the space provided.

Notes
What are the relationships among the sides of a 45°-45°-90° right triangle?

What are the relationships among the sides of a 30°-60°-90° right triangle?

Learn: Using Special Right Triangles for Problem Solving [online]

As you work through this activity, answer the question below and record any notes in the space provided.

Notes

How can you use the Pythagorean theorem to check your answers to a problem involving a special right triangle?

MathCast: Using Special Right Triangles [online]

View the video to see how to solve a typical problem.

Summary: Special Types of Triangles, Part 2 [online]

Knowing the relationships of special right triangles can be very helpful when you need to solve real-world or geometric problems.

Skills Update: Practice Your Math Skills [online]

Complete the Skills Update online.

Offline Learning: Special Types of Triangles, Part 2 [offline]

In the Book

Read pages 413–414 in the Reference Guide.

Do the Math

Here are shortcut formulas you can use when solving problems involving special right triangles.

Shortcut formulas used **only** with 45°-45°-90° right triangles:

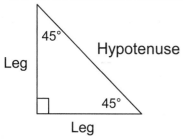

H = Hypotenuse Length
L = Leg Length

$$H = L \cdot \sqrt{2}$$

$$L = \frac{1}{2} \cdot H \cdot \sqrt{2}$$

Shortcut formulas used **only** with 30°-60°-90° right triangles:

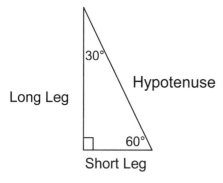

H = Hypotenuse Length

LL = Long Leg Length (across from 60°)

SL = Short Leg Length (across from 30°)

$$SL = \frac{1}{2} \cdot H$$

$$LL = \frac{1}{2} \cdot H \cdot \sqrt{3}$$

$$LL = SL \cdot \sqrt{3}$$

Problem Sets

Complete Problems 13–21 odd on page 416 of the Reference Guide.

Extra Practice (optional)

Complete Problems 22–23 on page 416 of the Reference Guide.

More Practice: Optional Assignment [offline, optional]

For extra practice, print the Optional Assignment and complete one or more of the problems. Submit the assignment to your teacher on or before the due date to receive feedback on your work.

Lesson Assessment: Special Types of Triangles, Part 2 Quiz [online]

Now go back online to complete the lesson quiz.

Name: _____   Date: _____

Optional Assignment

Special Types of Triangles

1. A person needs to package a 15-inch vase to give as a gift. The only box available is just 14 inches tall and has a square-shaped base that is 11 inches by 11 inches. The person wrapping the gift realizes that the only possible way to use the box might be to lay the vase diagonally across the bottom. Will the vase fit in the box? Show the formulas you use to solve this problem. Indicate the exact length of the diagonal *and* approximate it to the nearest hundredth.

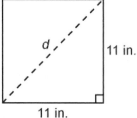

Answer:

2. A small tent has an entrance shaped like an equilateral triangle. The height of the tent is 28 inches. The entrance is covered by two flaps shaped like right triangles, as shown.

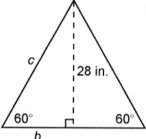

A. How long is the shorter side of one of the flaps, *b*? Round to the nearest tenth of an inch.

B. How long is one side of the tent, *c*? Round to the nearest tenth of an inch.

Answer:

Student Guide

Trigonometric Ratios

Skills related to working with ratios, square roots, and similar triangles provide a solid foundation for the study of trigonometry. Trigonometry is the branch of mathematics that examines the relationships between the angles and sides of right triangles. In this lesson, you will learn about three trigonometric ratios and how they can help you solve problems involving triangles.

Goals for the Lesson
- Find the sine, cosine, and tangent of an angle when given the side lengths.

- Use trigonometric ratios to find the side lengths of a right triangle.

Graded Activities in This Lesson
Quiz (computer-scored)

Materials
Pre-Algebra: A Reference Guide and Problem Sets, pages 417–421

Optional
Trigonometric Ratios Solutions
calculator

Keywords and Pronunciation
cosine (KOH-siyn): for an acute angle in a right triangle, the ratio of the length of the adjacent side to the length of the hypotenuse; the abbreviation for cosine is *cos*

sine (siyn): for an acute angle in a right triangle, the ratio of the length of the opposite side to the length of the hypotenuse; the abbreviation for sine is *sin*

tangent (TAN-juhnt): for an acute angle in a right triangle, the ratio of the length of the opposite side to the length of the adjacent side; the abbreviation for tangent is *tan*

trigonometric ratios: any of the sine, cosine, and tangent ratios

Groundwork: Preparing for the Lesson [online]

This activity reviews essential skills. As you work through it, answer the question below and record any notes in the space provided.

Notes

How can you identify the hypotenuse of a right triangle?

Learn: What Is a Trigonometric Ratio? [online]

As you work through this activity, solve the problem below and record any notes in the space provided.

Notes

Why do similar triangles have the same trigonometric ratios?

Learn: Finding Side Lengths of a Right Triangle [online]

As you work through this activity, answer the questions below and record any notes in the space provided.

Notes

When can you use a trigonometric ratio to find a missing side length of a right triangle?

Summary: Trigonometric Ratios [online]

For any acute angle *A* in a right triangle the following are true:

- The sine of *A* is the ratio of the opposite side to the hypotenuse.

- The cosine of *A* is the ratio of the adjacent to the hypotenuse.

- The tangent of *A* is the ratio of the opposite side to the adjacent side.

Offline Learning: Trigonometric Ratios [offline]

In the Book
Read pages 417–418 in the Reference Guide.

Do the Math
Here is a simple way to remember the trigonometric ratios sine, cosine, and tangent.

Many people remember the definitions of the trigonometric ratios by looking to the name of the legendary Native American princess Sohcahtoa. If you spell her name correctly using syllables, you'll see a code to the definitions.

SOH refers to the **S**ine as the ratio of **O**pposite to **H**ypotenuse.

CAH refers to the **C**osine as the ratio of **A**djacent to **H**ypotenuse.

TOA refers to the **T**angent as the ratio of the **O**pposite to **A**djacent.

Problem Sets
Complete Problems 1–24 and 25–29 odd on pages 420–421 of the Reference Guide.

Lesson Assessment: Trigonometric Ratios Quiz [online]
Now go back online to complete the quiz.

Student Guide

Square Roots and Right Triangles Review

You have finished studying the Square Roots and Right Triangles unit, which includes rational square roots, irrational square roots, the Pythagorean theorem, the distance formula, special types of triangles, and trigonometric ratios. Now it's time to pull together what you have learned. Throughout the review, see how the skills you have learned relate to the Pre-Algebra big ideas.

Goals for the Lesson
* Review the concepts and skills learned in the unit.

Materials
"Square Roots and Right Triangles" in *Pre-Algebra: A Reference Guide and Problem Sets*
Square Roots and Right Triangles Practice Problems
Preparing for the Unit Test

Unit Review: Square Roots and Right Triangles [online]

This is your chance to review the big ideas of Pre-Algebra you have learned in this unit. Under Review These Activities, you will find activities from previous lessons that will review each big idea. Choose the topics you feel you need to review. Under Try These, you will find interactive problems that will test your understanding of each big idea. As you work through this lesson, take notes in the spaces provided.

Big Idea
A number is any entity that obeys the laws of arithmetic; all numbers obey the laws of arithmetic. The laws of arithmetic can be used to simplify algebraic expressions and equations.

Big Idea
Euclidean geometry uses five basic axioms to model real-world geometry and derives an amazing array of true results that apply extremely well to real-world geometry.

Big Idea
Analytic geometry models problems in geometry with algebraic proof and reasoning methods. Many real-world applications provide data that are best fit to a description by using the techniques of analytic geometry.

Big Idea
Many problems can be solved by using the properties of angles, triangles, and circles. Each trigonometric ratio can be described as the ratio of the lengths of two sides of a right triangle.

Big Idea
If you can create a mathematical model for a situation, you can use the model to solve other problems that you might not be able to solve otherwise. Algebraic equations can capture key relationships among quantities in the world.

Summary: Square Roots and Right Triangles Review [online]

In this unit, you have covered the following topics:

- rational square roots

- irrational square roots

- the Pythagorean theorem

- the distance formula

- special types of triangles

- trigonometric ratios

Offline Learning: Square Roots and Right Triangles Review [offline]

How well have you mastered the goals of this unit? Complete the Square Roots and Right Triangles Practice Problems. These problems are similar to the problems you will have on the Unit Test.

You can also

- Review the Square Roots and Right Triangles unit in *Pre-Algebra: A Reference Guide and Problem Sets*

- Review the notes in your Student Guide

- Read and follow the instructions in Preparing for the Unit Test

Practice Problems

Square Roots and Right Triangles

For Questions 1–3 , simplify the square roots.

1. $\sqrt{49}$

2. $\sqrt{\dfrac{25}{121}}$

3. $\sqrt{48}$

4. Between what two consecutive integers does $\sqrt{114}$ lie?

5. Identify the following numbers as rational or irrational.

    A. $\sqrt{35}$

    B. $\sqrt{100}$

    C. $\sqrt{81}$

    D. $\sqrt{90}$

For Questions 6–7, solve the equations.

6. $x^2 = 64$

7. $x^2 - 4 = 21$

8. A square has an area of 45 square centimeters. To the nearest tenth of a centimeter, what is the length of one side of the square?

For questions 9–10, find the values of x and y.

9.

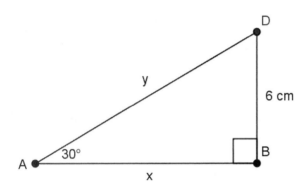

10.

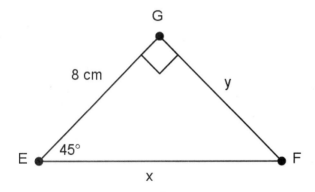

11. What is the length *c* of the hypotenuse of the right triangle?

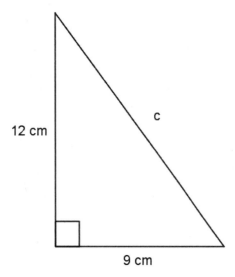

12 cm

c

9 cm

12. The numbers 10, 24, and *c* are a Pythagorean triple, and *c* is the length of the hypotenuse. What is the value of *c*?

13. Use the figure to answer each of the following questions.
- **A.** Find the distance from point *A* to point *B*.
- **B.** Find the distance from point *B* to point *C*.
- **C.** Find the distance from point *A* to point *C* to the nearest tenth.
- **D.** Find the perimeter of triangle *ABC*.

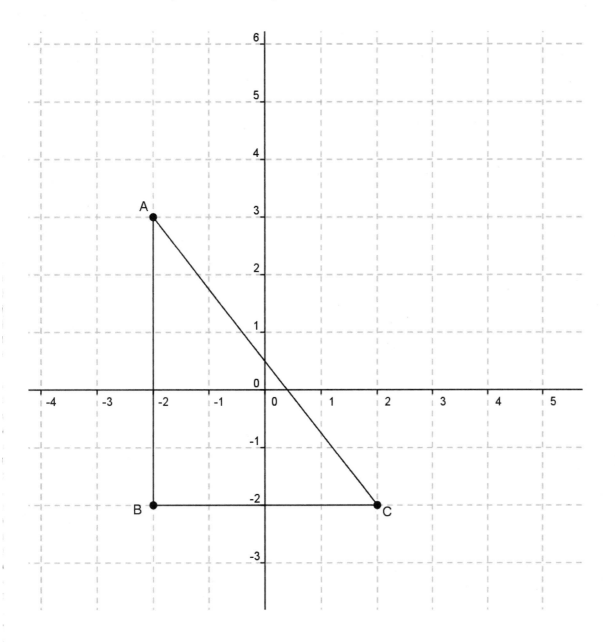

Answers

1. 7

2. $\dfrac{5}{11}$

3. $4\sqrt{3}$

4. 10 and 11

5. **A.** irrational

   B. rational

   C. rational

   D. irrational

6. $x = -8$ or 8

7. $x = -5$ or 5

8. 6.7 cm

9. $x = 6\sqrt{3}$ cm ; $y = 12$ cm

10. $x = 8\sqrt{2}$ cm ; $y = 8$ cm

11. 15 cm

12. 26

13. **A.** point A to point B: 5 units
    B. point B to point C: 4 units
    C. point A to point C: 6.4 units
    D. perimeter = 15.4 units

Unit Assessment

Square Roots and Right Triangles Unit Test, Offline

(10 points)

1. The Parks Department wants to put a sidewalk diagonally across a rectangular park. The length of the park is $2\sqrt{3}$ miles.

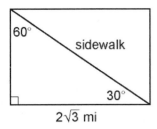

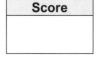

Score

A. What is the width of the park?

B. What will the length of the sidewalk be?

(10 points)

2. The length of the shadow of a building is 50 feet. tan P = 0.8.

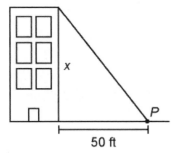

50 ft

A. Write an equation involving a trigonometric ratio that can be used to find the height x of the building. Explain why your equation is correct.

B. Find the height x of the building by using your equation. Show all your work.

Score	___ of 20

Student Guide

Volume and Capacity, Part 1

Some containers are in the shape of a cube. When you are packing or storing items, you might need to know how much room the container you are using contains. To determine how much space is inside a container, you need to be able to find its volume. In this lesson, you will learn about the volume of certain three-dimensional figures and how to find the volume of a cube.

Goals for the Lesson
- Find the volume of a cube.

Graded Activities in This Lesson
Lesson Quiz (computer-scored)

Materials
Pre-Algebra: A Reference Guide and Problem Sets, pages 425–429

Optional
Volume and Capacity Solutions
calculator

Keywords and Pronunciation
cube: a sold figure made up of six square faces that meet at right angles

cubic unit: a cube whose edges are each one unit long; a cubic unit is used to measure volume

volume: the measure of the space inside (or the space occupied by) a three-dimensional figure

---

Groundwork: Preparing for the Lesson [online]

This activity reviews areas of rectangles. As you work through it, answer the question and record any notes in the space provided.

Notes
How do you calculate the area of a square?

Learn: Finding the Volume of a Cube [online]

As you work through this activity, do the excise and answer the question below and record any notes in the space provided.

Notes

Draw a cube whose volume is 8 cubic units.

What is the formula for the volume of a cube?

Worked Examples: Volume and Capacity, Part 1 [online]

As you work through this activity, record any notes in the space provided.

Notes

Summary: Volume and Capacity, Part 1 [online]

The volume of a three-dimensional figure is a measure of the space inside the figure. Volume is measured in cubic units.

You can use the formula $V = s^3$ to find the volume of a cube.

Offline Learning: Volume and Capacity, Part 1 [offline]

In the Book
Read pages 425–426 in the Reference Guide.

Do the Math (optional)
A cube is a special type of three-dimensional figure called a prism.

The volume of any prism can be found by multiplying the area of the base times the height.

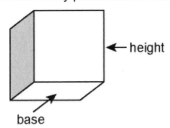

← height

base

Show that the formula $V = Area_{base} \times Height$ is equivalent to the formula $V = s^3$ for any cube with side lengths of s.

Problem Sets
Complete Problems 1–7 odd on page 428 of the Reference Guide.

Extra Practice (optional)
Complete Problems 2–6 even on page 428 of the Reference Guide for extra practice.

Lesson Assessment: Volume and Capacity, Part 1 Quiz [online]
Now go back online to complete the lesson quiz.

Answers

Do the Math

$V = Area_{base} \times Height$

$Area_{base} = s \times s = s^2$

$Height = s$

Therefore, $V = s^2 \times s = s^3$.

Student Guide

Volume and Capacity, Part 2

You decide to buy a new aquarium tank in the shape of a cube for your fish. You want a tank that has a side length of 30 centimeters and therefore know that the volume of the tank must be 27,000 cubic centimeters. When you go online to do research, you notice that aquariums are measured by their capacity, not their volume. In this lesson, you will discover the difference between volume and capacity and learn how to find the capacity of a cube.

Goals for the Lesson
- Find the capacity of a cube in mL or L.
- Convert measures of volume in cubic centimeters to measures of capacity in mL or L.

Graded Activities in This Lesson
Lesson Quiz (computer-scored)

Materials
Pre-Algebra: A Reference Guide and Problem Sets, pages 425–429

Optional
calculator
Volume and Capacity, Part 2 Solutions

Keywords and Pronunciation
capacity: a measure indicating an amount a container can hold

volume: the measure of the space inside (or the space occupied by) a three-dimensional figure

Groundwork: Preparing for the Lesson [online]
This activity reviews skills needed to find volume. As you work through it, record any notes in the space provided.

Notes

Learn: Finding the Capacity of a Cube [online]

As you work through this activity, answer the questions below and record any notes in the space provided.

Notes

What does capacity measure?

How do you convert milliliters to liters?

Worked Examples: Volume and Capacity, Part 2 [online]

As you work through this activity, answer the questions below and record any notes in the space provided.

Notes

How do you convert millimeters to centimeters?

In Example 3, why did you need to convert millimeters to centimeters before you found the volume of the cube?

MathCast: Volume and Capacity [online]

View the video to see how to solve a typical problem.

Summary: Volume and Capacity, Part 2 [online]

Capacity is a measure of the amount a container can hold. Liters and milliliters are common metric units of capacity.

You can find the capacity of a cube by first finding its volume and then converting the volume measurement to a capacity measurement.

Offline Learning: Volume and Capacity, Part 2 [offline]

In the Book
Read pages 426–427 in the Reference Guide.

Problem Sets
Complete Problems 11–29 odd on page 429 of the Reference Guide.

Extra Practice (optional)
Complete Problems 16–22 even on page 429 of the Reference Guide.

Lesson Assessment: Volume and Capacity, Part 2 Quiz [online]

Now go back online to complete the quiz.

Student Guide

Volumes of Prisms and Cylinders, Part 1

Cheese is often sold in the shape of a rectangular prism. This means that when you cut a slice of cheese, it would probably be in the shape of a rectangle. Not all prisms, however, are rectangular. In this lesson, you will learn about different types of prisms and how to find their volumes.

Goals for the Lesson
* Find the volume of a right prism.

Graded Activities in This Lesson
Lesson Quiz (computer-scored)

Materials
Pre-Algebra: A Reference Guide and Problem Sets, pages 430–435

Optional
Volumes of Prisms and Cylinders, Part 1 Solutions
calculator

Keywords and Pronunciation
base of a prism: one of the parallel, congruent faces of the prism; a base of a prism is a polygon

lateral face of a prism: a face that is not a base; in a *right prism*, the lateral faces are rectangles

prism: a three-dimensional figure whose surfaces, called *faces*, are polygons; at least two faces are parallel and congruent and are called *bases*, and all other faces are parallelograms (in a right prism, all other faces are rectangles)

volume: the measure of the space inside (or the space occupied by) a three-dimensional figure

---

Groundwork: Preparing for the Lesson [online]
This activity reviews skills needed to find the areas of different figures. As you work through it, record any notes in the space provided.

Notes

Learn: What Is a Prism? [online]

As you work through this activity, answer the questions below and record any notes in the space provided.

Notes

What is the name of a prism whose bases are hexagons?

How many lateral faces does a rectangular prism have? How many does a pentagonal prism have? An octagonal prism?

Learn: Finding the Volume of a Prism [online]

As you work through this activity, do the exercise below and record any notes in the space provided.

Notes

Explain how to find the volume of a triangular prism.

Worked Examples: Volumes of Prisms and Cylinders, Part 1 [online]

As you work through this activity, record any notes in the space provided.

Notes

MathCast: Volume of a Trapezoidal Right Prism [online]
View the video to see how to solve a typical problem.

Summary: Volumes of Prisms and Cylinders, Part 1 [online]
- A prism is a solid figure with two parallel, congruent bases that are polygons. The sides are called lateral faces. A prism is named by the shape of its bases.

- A general formula for finding the volume of a prism is $V = Bh$; that is, the volume is equal to the base area times the height.

Skills Update: Practice Your Math Skills [online]
Complete the Skills Update online.

Offline Learning: Volumes of Prisms and Cylinders, Part 1 [offline]

In the Book
Read pages 430–432 in the Reference Guide.

Problem Sets
Complete Problems 1–9 all on page 434 of the Reference Guide.

Lesson Assessment: Volumes of Prisms and Cylinders, Part 1
Quiz [online]
Now go back online to complete the quiz.

Student Guide

Volumes of Prisms and Cylinders, Part 2

Cylinders are like prisms because both have two bases that are parallel. The main difference between a prism and a cylinder is that the bases of a prism are always polygons, and the bases of a cylinder are circles. In this lesson, you will learn more about cylinders and how to find the volume of a cylinder.

Goals for the Lesson

- Find the exact volume of a cylinder.

- Use an approximation for pi to estimate the volume of a cylinder.

Graded Activities in This Lesson

Lesson Quiz (computer-scored)

Materials

Pre-Algebra: A Reference Guide and Problem Sets, pages 430–435

Optional
Volumes of Prisms and Cylinders, Part 2 Solutions
calculator

Keywords and Pronunciation

base of a cylinder: one of the parallel, congruent faces of the cylinder; a base of a cylinder is a circle

cylinder: a three-dimensional figure with two congruent, parallel bases that are circles and a curved lateral surface that joins them

lateral face: a face that is not a base

lateral surface: the curved surface of a cylinder or cone; in a prism, any surface that connects the two bases; in a pyramid, any surface that rises from the base to the vertex

volume: the measure of the space inside (or the space occupied by) a three-dimensional figure

Groundwork: Preparing for the Lesson [online]

This activity reviews volumes of prisms and areas of circles. As you work through it, answer the questions below and record any notes in the space provided.

Notes

How do you find the exact area of a circle?

How do you find the approximate area of a circle?

Learn: Defining Cylinders [online]

As you work through this activity, answer the questions below and record any notes in the space provided.

Notes

How is a cylinder different from a prism?

How is a cylinder similar to a prism?

Learn: Finding the Volume of a Cylinder [online]

As you work through this activity, do the exercise below and record any notes in the space provided.

Notes

Explain how to find the volume of a cylinder.

MathCast: Volume of a Cylinder [online]

View the video to see how to solve a typical problem.

Summary: Volumes of Prisms and Cylinders, Part 2 [online]

A general formula for the volume of a cylinder is V = base area • height. Since the bases of a cylinder are circles, the base area is found by using the formula for the area of a circle.

Remember, volume is always expressed in cubic units such as cm^3 or ft^3.

Skills Update: Practice Your Math Skills [online]
Complete the Skills Update online.

Offline Learning: Volumes of Prisms and Cylinders, Part 2 [offline]

In the Book
Read pages 432–433 in the Reference Guide.

Do the Math
A cylinder has a height of 5 inches and a radius of 4 inches. If you double the height and the radius, does the volume also double? Explain.

Problem Sets
Complete Problems 13–29 on page 435 of the Reference Guide.

Lesson Assessment: Volumes of Prisms and Cylinders, Part 2
Quiz [online]
Now go back online to complete the lesson quiz.

Name: _____   Date: _____

Optional Assignment

Volumes of Prisms and Cylinders

1. Find the volume of the triangular prism. Use $\pi = 3.14$.

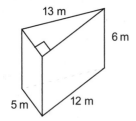

Answer:

2. Find the volume of the cylinder. Find both the exact volume in terms of π and the approximate volume using $\pi \approx 3.14$.

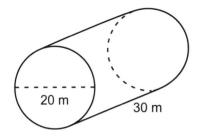

20 m

30 m

Answer:

Student Guide

Volumes of Pyramids and Cones, Part 1

Perhaps you have seen photos of the Egyptian pyramids or of the glass pyramid at the Louvre Museum in Paris, France. Pyramids are striking figures, but what makes a figure a pyramid? In this lesson, you will learn to identify and find the volume of pyramids.

Goals for the Lesson
• Find the volume of a right pyramid.

Graded Activities in This Lesson
Lesson Quiz (computer-scored)

Materials
Pre-Algebra: A Reference Guide and Problem Sets, pages 436–441

Optional
Volumes of Pyramids and Cones, Part 1 Solutions
calculator
Make a Polyhedron sheet

Keywords and Pronunciation
pyramid: a three-dimensional figure with one base that is a polygon and all other faces (called lateral faces) are triangles that meet at a single vertex

vertex: a point common to two sides of an angle or polygon; the plural of vertex is vertices

Groundwork: Preparing for the Lesson [online]
This activity reviews volumes of prisms and cylinders. As you work through it, do the exercise below and record any notes in the space provided.

Notes
In your own words, describe how to find the volume of a prism.

Learn: Defining Pyramids [online]

As you work through this activity, answer the question below and record any notes in the space provided.

Notes

How is a pyramid different from a prism?

Learn: Finding the Volume of a Pyramid [online]

As you work through this activity, answer the question below and record any notes in the space provided.

Notes

Will the volume of a pyramid always be less than the volume of a prism with the same base area and height? Explain why or why not.

Worked Examples: Volumes of Pyramids and Cones, Part 1 [online]

As you work through this activity, record any notes in the space provided.

Notes

Summary: Volumes of Pyramids and Cones, Part 1 [online]

The volume of a pyramid is one-third the volume of a prism with the same base area and height.

Offline Learning: Volumes of Pyramids and Cones, Part 1 [offline]

In the Book
Read pages 436–437 in the Reference Guide.

Problem Sets
Complete Problems 1–9 odd and 17–19 on pages 440–441 of the Reference Guide.

Extra Practice (optional)
Complete Problems 2–16 even on pages 440–441 of the Reference Guide.

Extension (optional)
A polyhedron is a three-dimensional figure whose surfaces are polygons. Prisms and pyramids are polyhedrons.

Print the Make a Polyhedron sheet. Follow the directions to make three mobiles by using the polyhedron patterns for a dodecahedron, octahedron, and tetrahedron.

What is another name for a tetrahedron?

Lesson Assessment: Volumes of Pyramids and Cones, Part 1
Quiz [online]
Now go back online to complete the lesson quiz.

Extension

Make a Polyhedron

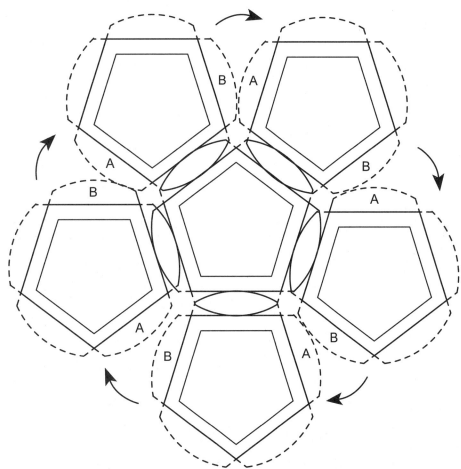

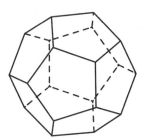

Dodecahedron

Pentagonal Pattern: color and cut out two sets.

1. Color each of the pentagons in both sets of the pentagonal pattern – be creative!

2. Cut out each of the shapes along the dotted outside lines.

3. Cut out the 'corners' of the tabs on the inside pentagon along the dotted lines.

4. Fold the tabs of each outside pentagon inward along their solid edges.

5. Then fold the outside pentagons inward along the line where they meet the inside pentagon.

6. Align each of the six pentagons and staple or glue each tab A to the tab B next to it. The figure should look like a small bucket.

7. Repeat for the other half of the dodecahedron that you cut out.

8. Fit the two halves together and glue the tabs. The tabs should match up with each other.

9. You now have a dodecahedron, like the figure on the left of the paper!

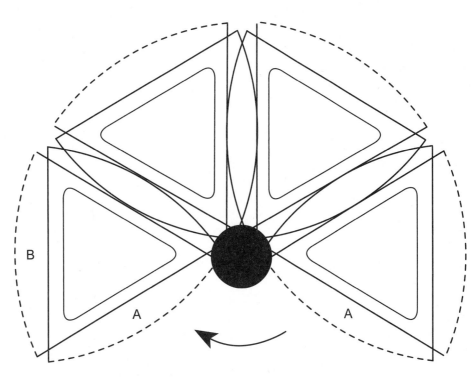

Octahedron Pattern: color and cut out two sets.

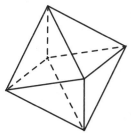

Octahedron

1. Color each of the triangles in both sets of the octahedron pattern – be creative!

2. Cut out each of the triangles in both patterns along their dotted lines.

3. Fold the tabs on the edges of the triangles along the solid line.

4. Glue tab A to tab A on both pieces. Then glue tab B on the first half to tab B on the second half. Glue the rest of the tabs together (they will already be matched up).

5. Repeat with the remaining triangles.

6. Match the two halves and staple or glue them together.

7. You now have an octahedron!

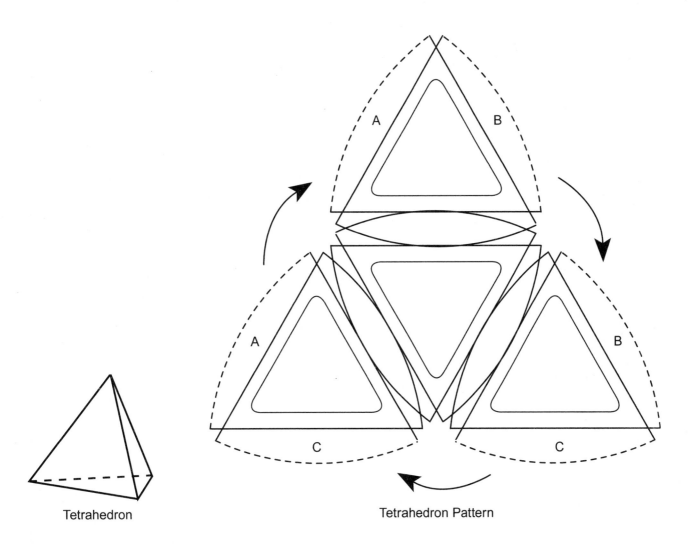

Tetrahedron

Tetrahedron Pattern

1. Color each of the triangles tetrahedron pattern – be creative!

2. Cut out the pattern along the dotted lines.

3. Cut out the 'corners' of the tabs on the inside triangle along the dotted lines.

4. Fold the tabs on the solid edges.

5. Match and glue the A tabs, the B tabs, and the C tabs.

6. You now have a tetrahedron!

Student Guide

Volumes of Pyramids and Cones, Part 2

Have you ever noticed that a substance like dirt or sand forms a cone-shaped pile when you pour it on a flat surface? You can find the volume of the cone-shaped pile of dirt if you know the dimensions of the cone. In this lesson, you will learn how to find the volume of a cone.

Goals for the Lesson
- Find the exact volume of a cone.

- Use an approximation for pi to estimate the volume of a cone.

Graded Activities in This Lesson
Mid-Unit Test (computer-scored)

Materials
Pre-Algebra: A Reference Guide and Problem Sets, pages 436–441

Optional
calculator
Comparing Volumes worksheet
Volumes of Pyramids and Cones, Part 2 Solutions

Keywords and Pronunciation
cone: a three-dimensional figure with one base that is a circle, a curved lateral surface, and a point called a vertex

vertex: a point common to two sides of an angle or polygon; the plural of *vertex* is *vertices*

Groundwork: Preparing for the Lesson [online]
This activity reviews volumes of pyramids. As you work through it, do the exercise below and record any notes in the space provided.

Notes
In your own words, describe how to find the volume of a pyramid.

Learn: Defining Cones [online]

As you work through this activity, answer the questions below and record any notes in the space provided.

Notes

How is a cone like a pyramid? How is it different from a pyramid?

How is a cone like a cylinder? How is it different from a cylinder?

Learn: Finding the Volume of a Cone [online]

As you work through this activity, answer the question below and record any notes in the space provided.

Notes

Will the volume of a cone always be less than the volume of a cylinder with the same base area and height? Explain why or why not.

MathCast: Volume of a Cone [online]

View the video to see how to solve a typical problem.

Summary: Volumes of Pyramids and Cones, Part 2 [online]

A cone is a solid with one circular base and a curved lateral surface that converges at a vertex.

- The height of a cone is the perpendicular distance from the vertex to the base.

- The volume of a cone is one-third the volume of a cylinder with the same base area and height.

Offline Learning: Volumes of Pyramids and Cones, Part 2 [offline]

In the Book
Read pages 438–439 in the Reference Guide.

Problem Sets
Complete Problems 21–23 and 25–26 on pages 440–441.

Extension (optional)
Print and complete the Comparing Volumes sheet.

Mid-Unit Assessment: Solid Figures Test [online]
Now go back online to complete the Mid-Unit Assessment.

Extension

Comparing Volumes

To conduct an experiment to compare volumes of a cone and a cylinder having the same height and radius, you will need some tape, scissors, and sand.

Follow the steps below:

    a.   Use the patterns of a cone and cylinder on the next page.

    b.   Cut along the solid line.

    c.   Fold along the dashed lines and tape together.

    d.   The cone and cylinder should be open at one end.

    e.   The open circular base should be the same size, and the height should be the same.

    f.   Fill the cone with sand, leveling it with the edge of a ruler.

    g.   Pour the sand from the cone into the cylinder.

1.   Estimate how many times steps f and g must be performed before the cylinder is full and level.

Continue to fill the cylinder with the leveled cones until it is full and level. Compare your estimate to the actual result.

2.   Tell how the result of the experiment is related to the formula for the volume of the cone and the formula for the volume of the cylinder.

3.   Design and explain a similar experiment to compare the volume of a square pyramid with the volume of a square prism.

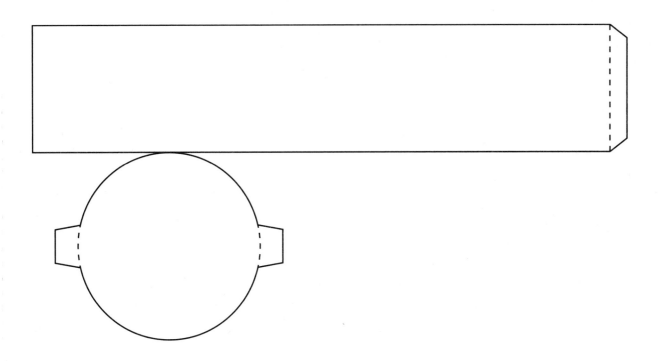

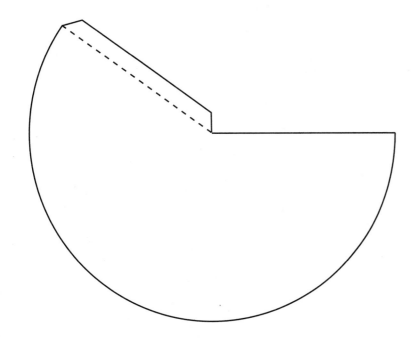

Student Guide

Surface Area

A company that makes cardboard boxes needs to know the total area of cardboard needed to build a box. A painter painting a room needs to know the area of the four walls of a room. These are just two examples that involve finding surface area. In this lesson, you will learn how to find the lateral and surface areas of rectangular prisms.

Goals for the Lesson
- Find the lateral area of a rectangular prism.
- Find the total surface area of a rectangular prism.
- Find the surface area of a cube.
- Find the surface area of figures made up of rectangular prisms.

Graded Activities in This Lesson
Lesson Quiz (computer-scored)

Materials
Pre-Algebra: A Reference Guide and Problem Sets, pages 442–448

Optional
Surface Area Solutions
calculator

Keywords and Pronunciation
lateral surface area: the sum of the areas of all surfaces of a three-dimensional figure except the base(s**)**

surface area: the sum of the areas of all surfaces of a three-dimensional figure

---

Groundwork: Preparing for the Lesson [online]
This activity reviews essential skills. As you work through it, answer the question below and record any notes in the space provided.

Notes
What shape are all the faces of a rectangular prism?

Learn: Finding the Lateral Area of a Prism [online]

As you work through this activity, do the exercises below and record any notes in the space provided.

Notes

Define *lateral area*.

Describe two ways to find the lateral area of a rectangular prism.

Learn: Finding the Surface Area of a Prism [online]

As you work through this activity, answer the question and do the exercise below. Record any notes in the space provided.

Notes

How is surface area different from lateral area?

Describe two ways to find the lateral area of a rectangular prism.

Learn: Finding the Surface Area of a Cube [online]

As you work through this activity, answer the question below and record any notes in the space provided.

Notes

Bror was asked to find the surface area of a cube with a side length of 12 meters. This is his solution.

Bror's Solution:

$$S = 6s^2$$
$$= 6 \cdot 12^2$$
$$= 72^2$$
$$= 5184 \text{ m}^2$$

Is Bror's solution correct or incorrect? Explain.

Summary: Surface Area [online]

The surface area of a rectangular prism can be found by using the formula $SA = 2lw + 2lh + 2wh$.

You can also find the surface area of a rectangular prism by using the general formula $SA = LA + 2B$.

If you replace LA with the product of the height h and the perimeter P of the base, the formula can also be written as $SA = Ph + 2B$.

The surface area of a cube with side length s is $SA = 6s^2$.

Offline Learning: Surface Area [offline]

Do The Math

Finding the Surface Area of Complex Three-Dimensional Figures

You can use what you know about finding areas of complex regions to find a surface area that is made up of more than one rectangular prism. Look at the figure below:

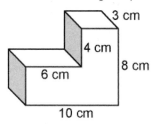

You can break up the surfaces into six regions: Front, Back, Top, Bottom, Left, and Right. Notice that the area of opposing faces is always the same. For example, the area of the top is the same as the area of the bottom, and so on.

Therefore, you can find the surface area of the figure by finding the area of the Front, Left, and Top and then doubling the result:

$$\text{Area of Front} = (10 \text{ cm})(8 \text{ cm}) - (6 \text{ cm})(4 \text{ cm}) = 80 \text{cm}^2 - 24 \text{ cm}^2 = 56 \text{ cm}^2$$

$$\text{Area of Left} = (4 \text{ cm})(3 \text{ cm}) + (4 \text{ cm})(3 \text{ cm}) = 12 \text{ cm}^2 + 12 \text{ cm}^2 = 24 \text{ cm}^2$$

$$\text{Area of Top} = (4 \text{ cm})(3 \text{ cm}) + (6 \text{ cm})(3 \text{ cm}) = 12 \text{ cm}^2 + 18 \text{ cm}^2 = 30 \text{ cm}^2$$

The sum of areas of the Front, Left, and Top is $56 \text{ cm}^2 + 24 \text{ cm}^2 + 30 \text{ cm}^2 = 110 \text{ cm}^2$.

The surface area of the figure is $2(110 \text{ cm}^2) = \textbf{220 cm}^2$.

In the Book

Read pages 442–444 in the Reference Guide.

Problem Sets

Complete Problems 1–29 odd on pages 446–448 of Reference Guide.

Extra Practice (optional)

Complete Problems 27, 28, and 30 on page 448 for extra practice.

Lesson Assessment: Surface Area Quiz [online]

Now go back online to complete the lesson quiz.

Student Guide

Surface Areas of Prisms and Cylinders

Companies that manufacture products in aluminum cans need to know how much aluminum each can uses. This knowledge helps the company determine how much the aluminum costs as well as how much to charge the consumer for the product. To find how much aluminum is used in making a can, you need to find the surface area of the can. In this lesson, you will learn how to find the surface areas of prisms and cylinders.

Goals for the Lesson
- Find the surface area of a prism.
- Find the exact surface area of a cylinder.
- Use an approximation for pi to estimate the surface area of a cylinder.
- Compute the surface area to volume ratio of a figure.

Graded Activities in This Lesson
Lesson Quiz (computer-scored)

Materials
Pre-Algebra: A Reference Guide and Problem Sets, pages 449–453

Optional
calculator

Groundwork: Preparing for the Lesson [online]
This activity reviews finding circumferences. As you work through it, answer the question below and record any notes in the space provided.

Notes
What is the relationship between a radius and a diameter of a circle?

Learn: Finding the Surface Area of a Prism [online]

As you work through this activity, answer the question below and record any notes in the space provided.

Notes

Are the height of the base of a triangular prism and the height of the prism the same value? Explain.

Learn: Finding the Surface Area of a Cylinder [online]

As you work through this activity, answer the question below and record any notes in the space provided.

Notes

Why does P equal $2\pi r$ in the formula for finding the surface area of a cylinder?

MathCast: Surface Area to Volume Ratio [online]

View the video to see how to solve a typical problem.

Summary: Surface Areas of Prisms and Cylinders [online]

To find the surface area (SA) of any prism or cylinder, you can use the formulas SA = 2B + LA or SA = 2B + Ph, where LA is the lateral area, B is the base area, P is the perimeter of the base, and h is the height.

You can also use the formula SA = $2\pi r^2 + 2\pi rh$ to find the volume of a cylinder.

Offline Learning: Surface Areas of Prisms and Cylinders [offline]

In the Book
Read pages 449–450 in the Reference Guide.

Do the Math

Finding Surface Area to Volume Ratios

Manufacturers of containers benefit from knowing the surface area to volume of a container. The smaller the ratio, the more cost-effective it is to manufacture the container.

Look at the cylindrical container below.

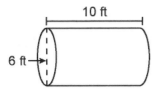

The surface area is

$SA = 2B + LA$

$\quad = 2\pi r^2 + 2\pi rh$

$\quad = 2(\pi \cdot 3^2) + 2\pi \cdot 3 \cdot 10$

$\quad = 18\pi + 60\pi$

$\quad = 78\pi$

The volume is

$V = \pi r^2 h$

$\quad = \pi \cdot 3^2 \cdot 10$

$\quad = 90\pi$

The surface area is 78π square feet, and the volume is 90π cubic feet.

The surface area to volume ratio is $\dfrac{78\pi}{90\pi} \approx 0.87$.

Can you draw a cylinder that has a smaller surface area to volume ratio, while keeping at least the same volume?

Problem Sets
Complete Problems 1–19 odd and 23–28 all on pages 452–453.

Challenge (optional)
Complete Problems 29–30 on page 453.

Lesson Assessment: Surface Areas of Prisms and Cylinders Quiz

[online]
Now go back online to complete the lesson quiz.

Student Guide

Solid Figures Review

You have finished studying the Solid Figures unit, which includes volume and capacity, volumes of prisms and cylinders, volumes of pyramids and cones, surface area, and surface areas of prisms and cylinders. Now it's time to pull together what you have learned. Throughout the review, see how the skills you have learned relate to the Pre-Algebra big ideas.

Goals for the Lesson
* Review the concepts and skills learned in the unit.

Materials
"Solid Figures" in *Pre-Algebra: A Reference Guide and Problem Sets*
Preparing for the Unit Test

Unit Review: Solid Figures [online]

This is your chance to review the big ideas of Pre-Algebra you have learned in this unit. Under Review These Activities, you will find activities from previous lessons that will review each big idea. Choose the topics you feel you need to review. Under Try These, you will find interactive problems that will test your understanding of each big idea. As you work through this lesson, take notes in the spaces provided.

Big Idea
There are several useful aspects of every geometric figure that can be measured, calculated, or approximated. A segment has a finite length that can be measured. Area is a measure of how much material is needed to cover a plane figure. Volume is a measure of the amount of space a figure occupies.

Summary: Solid Figures Review [online]

In this unit, you have covered the following topics:

- volume and capacity
- volumes of prisms and cylinders
- volumes of pyramids and cones
- surface area
- surface areas of prisms and cylinders

Offline Learning: Solid Figures Review [offline]

To prepare for the Unit Test, you can also review the following:

- "Solid Figures" in *Pre-Algebra: A Reference Guide and Problem Sets*
- Problem Sets sections of your Student Guides for this unit
- Preparing for the Unit Test

Practice Problems

Solid Figures

1. Find the exact volume of the cone.

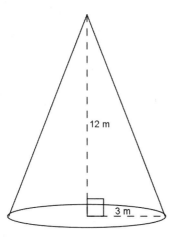

2. Find the volume of the pyramid.

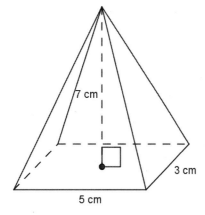

3. Find the volume of the prism.

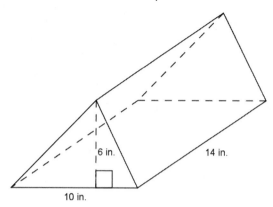

6 in.

14 in.

10 in.

4. Find the volume and the surface area of the cube.

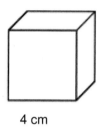

4 cm

5. Find the volume and the surface area of the prism.

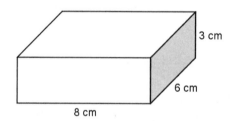

3 cm

6 cm

8 cm

6. Find the approximate volume and surface area of the cylinder. Use 3.14 for pi.

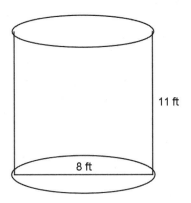

11 ft

8 ft

7. How many milliliters equal 4363 cubic centimeters?

8. What is the capacity in liters of the cube in Problem 4?

9. What is the surface area of the figure?

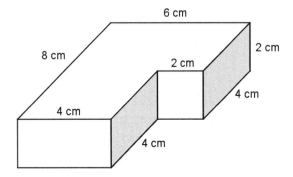

6 cm

8 cm

2 cm

2 cm

4 cm

4 cm

4 cm

10. Find the lateral area of the prism.

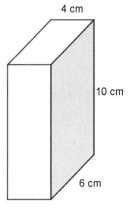

4 cm

10 cm

6 cm

Answers

1. 36π m^3

2. 35 cm^3

3. 420 in^3

4. V = 64 cm^3

   SA = 96 cm^2

5. V = 144 cm^3
   SA = 180 cm^2

6. V ≈ 552.6 ft^3
   SA ≈ 376.8 ft^2

7. 4363 mL

8. 0.064 L

9. 136 cm^2

10. 200 cm^2

Unit Assessment Answer Key

Solid Figures Unit Test, Offline

(10 points)

1. A container company wants to design a cardboard container in the shape of a triangular prism, as shown below.

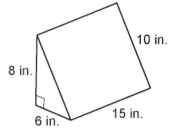

Score

   A. Find the surface area of the container. Show your work.

   B. Find the volume of the container. Show your work.

   C. The company will manufacture the container if the surface-area-to-volume ratio is less than 1. Determine whether the company should manufacture the container. Show and explain your work.

(8 points)

2. Three identical cubes are put together to form a square prism. The volume of each cube is 64 cubic centimeters. .

Score

    A. Find the volume of the prism.

    B. Find the surface area of the prism.

Score	____ of 18

Student Guide

Counting Principles

When you were younger, one of the first things you learned in math was how to count. You may not have thought about it, but counting has continued to play an important role in your study of math. In this lesson, you will learn about two counting principles and how they are used to find the number of ways you can do more than one thing. Later in this unit, you will use counting principles to find probabilities.

Goals for the Lesson
- Use the sum rule to find the number of ways a task can be done.
- Use the product rule to find the number of ways a task can be done.
- Determine whether a situation is best modeled with the sum or product rule.
- Solve a word problem involving the sum or product rule.

Graded Activities in This Lesson
Lesson Quiz (computer-scored)

Materials
Pre-Algebra: A Reference Guide and Problem Sets, pages 457–461

Optional
Counting Principles Solutions
calculator

Keywords and Pronunciation
none

Groundwork: Preparing for the Lesson [online]
This activity reviews sums and products. As you work through it, record any notes in the space provided.
Notes

Learn: The Sum Counting Principle [online]

As you work through this activity, answer the question below and record any notes in the space provided.

Notes

When can you use the sum counting principle to find the number of ways of doing more than one thing?

Learn: The Product Counting Principle [online]

As you work through this activity, answer the question below and record any notes in the space provided.

Notes

When can you use the product counting principle to find the number of ways of doing more than one thing?

Worked Examples: Counting Principles [online]

As you work through this activity, record any notes in the space provided.

Notes

MathCast: Using the Counting Principles [online]

View the video to see how to solve a typical problem.

Summary: Counting Principles [online]

Counting principles can help you find the number of choices you have or the number of ways something can be done.

- If a task can be done two or more ways, but the task cannot be broken down into separate stages, then you can use the sum counting principle to find the number of ways the task can be done.

- When a task can be broken into stages, you can figure out the number of ways of doing the task by using the product counting principle.

Offline Learning: Counting Principles [offline]

In the Book

Read pages 449–450 in the Reference Guide.

Do the Math

Bror packed 3 pairs of pants, 4 shirts, and 2 jackets for his business trip. He wants to know how many outfits he will be able to create.

Bror's solution:

> The number of different outfits is $3 \cdot 4 \cdot 2 = 24$.

Is Bror correct or incorrect? Explain.

Problem Sets

Complete Problems 1–19 odd on pages 460–461 of the Reference Guide.

Extra Practice (optional)

Complete Problems 2–10 even on pages 460–461 of the Reference Guide.

Lesson Assessment: Counting Principles Quiz [online]

Now go back online to complete the lesson quiz.

Answer

Do the Math

Bror is choosing outfits with one shirt, one pair of pants, *and* one jacket, so he can use the product counting principle. Therefore, his answer (24 outfits) is correct.

Student Guide

Permutations

In an Olympic swimming competition many outcomes are possible, but only three swimmers can win the gold, silver, and bronze medals. In general, there are many possible arrangements of a given set of people, objects, or outcomes. In this lesson, you will learn how to use mathematical operations to find the exact number of possible arrangements for such a set.

Goals for the Lesson
- Evaluate a factorial expression.
- Evaluate a permutation expression.
- Solve a word problem involving permutations.

Graded Activities in This Lesson
Lesson Quiz (computer-scored)

Materials
Pre-Algebra: A Reference Guide and Problem Sets, pages 462–467

Optional
calculator
Permutations Solutions

Keywords and Pronunciation
factorial: the product of the whole numbers from 1 through the given number; the symbol for factorial is !; for example, 4! = 4 x 3 x 2 x 1

permutation: an arrangement of items in which the order of the items is important

Groundwork: Preparing for the Lesson [online]
This activity reviews essential skills. As you work through it, record any notes in the space provided.

Notes

Learn: Factorials [online]

As you work through this activity, do the exercise below and record any notes in the space provided.

Notes

In your own words, describe how to find the factorial of an integer.

Learn: What Is a Permutation? [online]

As you work through this activity, do the exercise and answer the question below. Record any notes in the space provided.

Notes

List all the permutations of the letters W, X, Y, and Z. How many permutations are there?

MathCast: Permutations [online]

View the video to see how to solve a typical problem.

Summary: Permutations [online]

The factorial of a positive integer is the product of all the positive integers less than or equal to the integer.

A permutation is an arrangement of items in which the order of the items is important.

If you have *n* items to be arranged in *n* places, then there are *n*! ways to arrange the items.

If you have *n* items to be arranged in *r* places, then there are $n \cdot (n-1) \cdot (n-2) \cdot \ldots$ (carry out *r* factors) ways to arrange the items.

You can also use formulas to calculate numbers of permutations.

Offline Learning: Permutations [offline]

In the Book
Read pages 462–465 in the Reference Guide.

Challenge (optional)
Calculating Factorials

Check to see if your calculator has a factorial key (*x*!) or option. If so, you can save time when doing calculations.

Just for fun, guess how high the value of *n* can be before your calculator can no longer display the answer for *n*!. Then test your prediction.

Problem Sets
Complete Problems 1–24 on page 466 of the Reference Guide.

Extra Practice (optional)
Complete Problems 25–29 on page 466 of the Reference Guide.

Lesson Assessment: Permutations Quiz [online]
Now go back online to complete the lesson quiz.

Student Guide

Combinations

Colossal Ball is a lottery that consists of selecting 6 numbers from a collection of 60 numbers. To win, the order in which you pick the numbers does not matter—you need only pick the correct group of 6. What are your chances of winning the lottery? Your chances are 1 out of 50,063,860; that is, there are 50,063,860 different combinations of numbers that you could pick. In this lesson you will examine combinations, which are collections of things in which order does not matter.

Goals for the Lesson

- Evaluate a combination expression.

- Solve word problems involving combinations.

- Determine whether a situation is best modeled with a permutation or a combination.

Graded Activities in This Lesson
Mid-Unit Test (computer-scored)

Materials
Pre-Algebra: A Reference Guide and Problem Sets, pages 468–472

Optional
calculator
Combinations Solutions

Keywords and Pronunciation
combination: a collection of items in which the order of the items is not important

permutation: an arrangement of items in which the order of the items is important

Groundwork: Preparing for the Lesson [online]
This activity reviews essential skills. As you work through it, record any notes in the space provided.

Notes

Learn: Solving Problems Using Combinations [online]

As you work through this activity, do the exercise below and record any notes in the space provided.

Notes

In your own words, explain how a combination is different from a permutation.

Summary: Combinations [online]

The formula for calculating the number of combinations can be used to find the number of ways in which a given number of objects can be chosen from a larger group, without regard to order.

The difference between a combination and a permutation is that in a combination the order of the objects does not matter.

Skills Update: Practice Your Math Skills [online]

Complete the Skills Update online.

Offline Learning: Combinations [offline]

In the Book

Read pages 468–471 in the Reference Guide.

Do the Math

It's important for you to know how to tell the difference between a permutation and a combination.

Can you tell which is a permutation and which is a combination? The answers to the first three questions are given.

1. In how many different ways can 5 people go through a gate?

   Order is important because after one person goes through the gate, he or she won't go through it again. This is a permutation.

2. How many groups of 4 pieces of fruit can you choose from 3 apples, 2 bananas, and 3 oranges?

   Order does not matter because you can choose a specific piece of fruit for several different combinations. This is a combination.

3. In how many ways can you award first-, second-, and third-place ribbons in a contest between 8 runners?

   Order does matter, so this is a permutation.

State whether each problem is a permutation or a combination, and write the appropriate formula to find the answer.

4. Suppose you are a car salesperson. For a display in your showroom you have 10 cars to choose from, but your showroom floor holds only 4 cars. In how many different ways can you arrange 4 of the 10 cars in a row on the showroom floor?

5. In how many different ways can you and your 7 teammates line up?

6. In how many ways can you select 3 horses from a group of 8 horses?

Challenge (optional)
How many angles are shown?

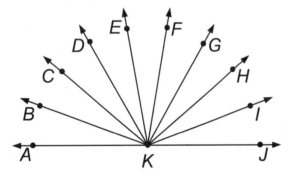

Problem Sets
Complete Problems 1–25 odd on pages 471–472 of the Reference Guide.

Mid-Unit Assessment: Counting and Probability Test [online]
Now go back online to complete the Mid-Unit Assessment.

Answers

Do the Math

4. Order is important, so this is a permutation.

$$_{10}P_4 = 10 \bullet 9 \bullet 8 \bullet 7 = 5040$$

5. Order is important, so this is a permutation.

$$_8P_8 = 8 \bullet 7 \bullet 6 \bullet 5 \bullet 4 \bullet 3 \bullet 2 \bullet 1 = 40{,}320$$

6. Order is not important, so this is a combination.

$$_8C_3 = \frac{8 \bullet 7 \bullet 6}{3 \bullet 2 \bullet 1} = \frac{336}{6} = 56$$

Challenge

$$_{10}C_2 = \frac{10!}{(10-2)!2!} = \frac{10!}{8!2!} = 45 \text{ angles}$$

Student Guide

Probability

The language of probability can be heard in everyday events such as the weather forecast and predictions of the outcomes of sporting events. Probability is one of the most useful areas of mathematics. The ability to calculate probability can help you make better decisions. In this lesson, you will determine the probability of a variety of events. As you learn more about probability, you will be able to see its countless applications.

Goals for the Lesson
- List the sample space for an experiment.
- Find the probability of an event when the outcomes are equally likely.
- Calculate the experimental probability of an event.

Graded Activities in This Lesson
Lesson Quiz (computer-scored)

Materials
Pre-Algebra: A Reference Guide and Problem Sets, pages 473–477

Optional
calculator
Probability Solutions

Keywords and Pronunciation
event: a set of one or more outcomes; an event is a subset of the sample space

experiment: any process or action that has a result

outcome: the result of an experiment

probability: a number from 0 to 1 that describes how likely an event is to occur

sample space: the set of all possible outcomes of an experiment

Groundwork: Preparing for the Lesson [online]
This activity reviews essential skills. As you work through it, record any notes in the space provided.

Notes

Learn: Calculating the Probability of an Event [online]

As you work through this activity, answer the questions below and record any notes in the space provided.

Notes

What does it mean when the probability of an event is 0?

What does it mean when the probability of an event is 1?

Can the probability of an event ever be greater than 1 or less than 0? Explain.

Learn: Experimental Probability [online]

As you work through this activity, answer the question below and record any notes in the space provided.

Notes

What is the difference between *theoretical probability* and *experimental probability*?

MathCast: Theoretical and Experimental Probability [online]

View the video to see how to solve a typical problem.

Summary: Probability [online]

The probability of an event $P(E)$ is the ratio (usually written as a fraction, percent, or decimal) of the number of outcomes favoring the event $n(E)$ to the number of possible outcomes $n(S)$.

Skills Update: Practice Your Math Skills [online]
Complete the Skills Update online.

Offline Learning: Probability [offline]

In the Book
Read pages 473–474 in the Reference Guide.

Do the Math

Exploring Sample Spaces

1. List the sample space when a coin is tossed. How many elements are in the sample space?

2. List the sample space when two coins are tossed. How many elements are in the sample space?

3. List the sample space when three coins are tossed. How many elements are in the sample space?

4. Do you notice a pattern? Describe the pattern.

5. What do you think $n(S)$ will be when four coins are tossed?

6. What do you think $n(S)$ will be when 10 coins are tossed?

Problem Sets
Complete Problems 1–11 odd on page 477 of the Reference Guide.

Extra Practice (optional)
Complete Problems 2–10 even on page 477 of the Reference Guide.

Lesson Assessment: Probability Quiz [online]
Now go back online to complete the quiz.

Answers

Do the Math

1. {H, T}; 2

2. {HH, HT, TH, TT}; 4

3. {HHH, HHT, HTH, HTT, TTT, TTH, THT, THH}; 8

4. Possible Answer: Yes. The number of elements in the sample space is equal to 2 raised to the number of coins that are tossed.

5. $2^4 = 16$

6. $2^{10} = 1024$

Student Guide

Mutually Exclusive Events

Occasionally you might hear someone say, "I cannot be in two places at the same time!" Is this always true? Suppose you are in Philadelphia. You can be in Philadelphia and in Pennsylvania at the same time. Could you be in Hawaii and in Pennsylvania at the same time? That would be impossible. Being in Hawaii and being in Pennsylvania are *mutually exclusive events*. In this lesson, you will learn how to determine whether two events are mutually exclusive and how to find the probability of a set of mutually exclusive events.

Goals for the Lesson

- Identify a set of mutually exclusive events.

- Find the probability of a set of mutually exclusive events.

Graded Activities in This Lesson

Lesson Quiz (computer-scored)

Materials

Pre-Algebra: A Reference Guide and Problem Sets, 479–482

Optional

Calculator
Mutually Exclusive Events Solutions

Keywords and Pronunciation

mutually exclusive events: events that cannot happen at the same time

probability: a number from 0 to 1 that describes how likely an event is to occur

Groundwork: Preparing for the Lesson [online]

This activity reviews essential skills. As you work through it, record any notes in the space provided.

Notes

Learn: Mutually Exclusive Events [online]

As you work through this activity, do the exercises below and record any notes in the space provided.

Notes

One card is drawn from a standard deck of cards. Explain why drawing a face card (a king, queen, or jack) and drawing a spade are not mutually exclusive events.

One card is drawn from a standard deck of cards. Explain why drawing a face card and drawing the 2 of clubs are mutually exclusive events.

Worked Examples: Mutually Exclusive Events [online]

As you work through this activity, record any notes in the space provided.

Notes

MathCast: Mutually Exclusive Events [online]

View the video to see how to solve a typical problem.

Summary: Mutually Exclusive Events [online]

Two events are mutually exclusive if they cannot happen at the same time.

If *A* and *B* are mutually exclusive events, then *P(A or B) = P(A) + P(B)*.

Skills Update: Practice Your Math Skills [online]

Complete the Skills Update online.

Offline Learning: Mutually Exclusive Events [offline]

In the Book

Read pages 479–481 in the Reference Guide.

Do the Math

The spinner below is spun one time.

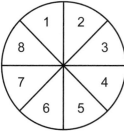

Bror said that the probability of landing on 8 or landing on an even number is $\frac{5}{8}$.

> Bror's solution:
>
> $P(8 \text{ or even}) = P(8) \text{ or } P(\text{even})$
>
> $= \frac{1}{8} + \frac{4}{8}$
>
> $= \frac{5}{8}$

Is Bror correct or incorrect? Explain.

Problem Sets
Complete Problems 1–6 odd on page 482.

Lesson Assessment: Mutually Exclusive Events Quiz [online]
Now go back online to complete the quiz.

Answers
Do the Math

The answer is incorrect. The probability of landing on 8 and landing on an even number are not mutually exclusive, because 8 is an even number.

Student Guide

Samples and Prediction

Probabilities are used to predict the likelihood that an event will occur. Statistics are used to draw conclusions based on events that have already occurred. When you combine the two, you are able to use the past to predict the likelihood of future events. For example, you can predict how an athlete might perform in the future, based on data from past performances. In this lesson, you will learn methods of sampling and working with statistics to predict the probability that similar future events will occur.

Goals for the Lesson
- Identify samples as biased or unbiased.
- Determine sources of bias in a sample procedure.
- Use random samples and repeated observations to estimate probability.

Graded Activities in This Lesson
Lesson Quiz (computer-scored)

Materials
Pre-Algebra: A Reference Guide and Problem Sets, pages 484–487

Optional
calculator
Samples and Prediction Solutions

Keywords and Pronunciation
biased sample: a sample that is not representative of the population

population: a group of individuals or objects about which information is wanted

sampling: a method used to estimate probability by selecting a part of a larger group

unbiased sample: a sample that is representative of the population

Groundwork: Preparing for the Lesson [online]
This activity reviews essential skills. As you work through it, record any notes in the space provided.

Notes

Learn: Exploring Probabilities [online]

As you work through this activity, answer the question below and record any notes in the space provided.

Notes
What does the "percent of total" column represent?

Learn: Samples and Prediction [online]
As you work through this activity, answer the questions below and record any notes in the space provided.

Notes
Why are samples used for surveys?

Why should a sample be unbiased?

Worked Examples: Samples and Prediction [online]
As you work through this activity, record any notes in the space provided.

Notes

MathCast: Making Predictions [online]
View the video to see how to solve a typical problem.

Summary: Samples and Prediction [online]

- By surveying an entire population or a sample of the population, you can make predictions about the whole group.

- An unbiased sample accurately represents the population, but a biased sample does not.

- Calculating probabilities from past performance or from samples of the population can help you predict future results.

Offline Learning: Samples and Prediction [offline]

In the Book
Read pages 484–485 in the Reference Guide.

Problem Sets
Complete Problems 1–15 on pages 486–487 of the Reference Guide.

Lesson Assessment: Samples and Prediction Quiz [online]
Now go back online to complete the lesson quiz.

More Practice: Optional Assignment [offline, optional]
For extra practice, print the Optional Assignment and complete one or more of the problems. Submit the assignment to your teacher or learning coach on or before the due date to receive feedback on your work.

Exploring Probabilities

Using Experiments to Estimate Probabilities

When you are rolling a number cube or flipping a coin, you can tell exactly what the probability is for each outcome. Sometimes it's not that simple. You might need to run some experiments so you can make good estimates of each probability.

What if someone gives you a spinner but doesn't tell you how big each section is? You could try looking at the sections to estimate their percentage of the whole, but a more accurate way of estimating the probability would be to spin the spinner numerous times. Each time you spin the spinner, you are running an experiment. The more times you run the experiment, the better the estimate of the true probability.

If you spin a spinner 10 or more times and record the result of each spin, you can use the results to estimate the true probability of landing on each section.

Using the Spinner

The Estimating Probabilities online activity provides you with an opportunity to perform experiments with a spinner quickly and easily. For each exercise, the number of sections in the spinner varies. In addition, the sizes of each of the sections vary, so the probabilities for the outcomes are not necessarily equal.

For each exercise, press the appropriate button to select the number of spins, and watch the outcomes for each color. Record the count for each color, then calculate the percentages for each color in the table provided.

Once you've completed your experiments, answer the Estimating Probabilities Follow-Up Questions on the last page of this worksheet.

Estimating Probabilities Exercise Instructions

Click Learn: Exploring Probabilities to start the Estimating Probabilities online activity. Press the appropriate button to select the number of spins, record the count for each color, and then calculate the percentages for each color, rounded to the nearest tenth of a percent. Be sure to spin the spinner 10 or more times before recording the count for each color.

Exercise 1: Three Possible Outcomes

Probability Spinner 1		
Total Spins:		
	Count	% of Total
Red		
Green		
Blue		

Exercise 2: Four Possible Outcomes

Probability Spinner 2		
Total Spins:		
	Count	% of Total
Red		
Green		
Blue		
Orange		

Exercise 3: Six Possible Outcomes

Probability Spinner 3		
Total Spins:		
	Count	% of Total
Red		
Green		
Blue		
Orange		
Pink		
Purple		

Estimating Probabilities Follow-Up Questions

1. What do the probabilities tell you about the area of each section?

2. If you run one of the experiments again with the exact same number of total spins, do you think you will get the exact same results?

3. If you ran one experiment for five total spins and another for 1000 total spins, which results do you expect would provide better predictions of future results? Why?

Name: _____ Date: _____

Optional Assignment

The Probability of an Event

1. The numbers 1 through 6 are painted on a game cube, with one number on each face. Find the following probabilities for one roll of the cube. Explain each answer.

    a. an odd number

    b. 2

    c. a fraction

    d. a number greater than 2

Answer:

2. Find the probability that the pointer stops on a wedge of the type described.

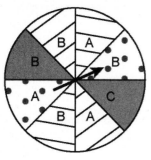

a. striped

b. B

c. solid gray

d. C

e. solid gray or B

f. striped and A

Answer:

Student Guide

Counting and Probability Review

You have finished studying the Counting and Probability unit, which includes counting principles, permutations, combinations, probability, mutually exclusive events, and samples and prediction. Now it's time to pull together what you have learned. Throughout the review, see how the skills you have learned relate to the Pre-Algebra big ideas.

Goals for the Lesson
* Review the concepts and skills learned in the unit.

Materials
"Counting and Probability" in *Pre-Algebra: A Reference Guide and Problem Sets*
Preparing for the Unit Test
Counting and Probability Practice Problems

Unit Review: Counting and Probability [online]

This is your chance to review the big ideas of Pre-Algebra you have learned in this unit. Under Review These Activities, you will find activities from previous lessons that will review each big idea. Choose the topics you feel you need to review. Under Try These Activities, you will find interactive problems that will test your understanding of each big idea. As you work through this lesson, take notes in the spaces provided.

Big Idea
Probability is a measure of how likely it is that some event will occur.

Summary: Counting and Probability Review [online]

In this unit, you have covered the following topics:

- counting principles

- permutations

- combinations

- probability

- mutually exclusive events

- samples and prediction

Offline Learning: Counting and Probability Review [offline]

How well have you mastered the goals of this unit? Complete the Counting and Probability Practice Problems. These problems are similar to the problems you will have on the Unit Test.

You can also—

- Review the Counting and Probability unit in *Pre-Algebra: A Reference Guide and Problem Sets*.

- Review the notes in your Student Guide.

- Read and follow the instructions in Preparing for the Unit Test.

Practice Problems

Counting and Probability

1. Simplify the following expressions.

    A. 5!

    B. 3! g4!

    C. $\dfrac{6!}{4!}$

    D. $\dfrac{8!3!}{5!}$

2. What is the sample space if you:
    A. toss one coin?

    B. toss one coin and then toss another coin?

3. Louis is choosing a shirt to wear. He has 2 blue shirts, 5 red shirts, and 3 green shirts. How many shirt choices does he have?

4. Cassandra is ordering dinner at a restaurant. She has 5 choices for her appetizer, 8 choices for her entrée, and 4 choices for her dessert. How many different meals could she order?

5. Find each of the following:
    A. $_9C_3$

    B. $_8P_4$

6. A class has 10 students. How many ways can students be chosen for class president, vice president, and treasurer?

7. Out of 12 ice-cream flavors, 3 may be chosen to make a sundae. How many ways can the flavors be chosen for the sundae?

8. Without looking, a child reaches into a bag that contains 6 cherry, 10 grape, and 5 orange lollipops. What is the probability that the child pull out a cherry lollipop?

9. A card is randomly selected from a standard deck. What is the probability that an ace or a king will be pulled?

10. In a group of 20 cats, 3 are calicos. Based on this observation, how many cats in a group of 160 are likely to be calico?

11. Two dice are rolled. For each of the following pairs of events, state whether or not they are mutually exclusive.

    A. The same number is rolled on both dice. The sum of the numbers rolled is odd.

    B. The sum of the numbers rolled is 3. One of the numbers rolled is 2.

    C. The sum of the numbers rolled is 11. One of the numbers rolled is 3.

12. Events *A* and *B* are mutually exclusive. $P(A) = 0.4$ and $P(B) = 0.55$. What is $P(A$ or $B)$?

13. A jar contains 22 red gumballs and 18 blue gumballs. Without looking, Jose reaches into the jar and pulls out a gumball, records the color, and then returns it to the jar. He does this 10 times. The table shows Jose's results.

Outcome	Red	Blue
Frequency	6	4

    A. If Jose pulls another gumball from the jar, what is the theoretical probability it will be blue?

    B. If Jose pulls another gumball from the jar, what is the experimental probability it will be blue?

Answers

1. A. 120

   B. 144

   C. 30

   D. 2016

2. A. {H, T}
   B. {HH, HT, TH, TT}

3. 10 choices

4. 160 meals

5. A. 84
   B. 1680

6. 720 ways

7. 220 ways

8. $P(\text{cherry}) = \dfrac{6}{21} = \dfrac{2}{7}$

9. $P(\text{ace or king}) = \dfrac{8}{52} = \dfrac{2}{13}$

10. 24 cats

11. A. mutually exclusive
    B. not mutually exclusive
    C. mutually exclusive

12. $P(A \text{ or } B) = 0.95$

13. A. $P(\text{blue}) = \dfrac{18}{40} = \dfrac{9}{20}$

    B. $P(\text{blue}) = \dfrac{4}{10} = \dfrac{2}{5}$

Unit Assessment Answer Key

Counting and Probability Unit Test, Offline

(10 points)

1. A bag contains red, blue, green, and yellow marbles. Seth takes a marble from the bag without looking, records the color of the marble, and then puts the marble back in the bag. He repeats the process until he has recorded the colors of the marbles 35 times. The chart below shows the results of his experiment.

Score

Outcome	Red	Blue	Green	Yellow
Frequency	10	5	13	7

Use the results of this experiment to find each probability. Write each answer as a fraction in lowest terms.

A. Find the experimental probability that the next marble he chooses is yellow.

B. Find the experimental probability that the next marble he chooses is either blue or red.

Score	___ of 10

Student Guide

Graphs

Data given in numerical form may not be easy to understand; data presented in a picture can be easier to interpret. Bar graphs, circle graphs, broken-line graphs, and scatter plots are useful ways to present data in a picture. There are some differences between these types of graphs. In this lesson, you will learn how to construct and interpret bar graphs, circle graphs, broken-line graphs, and scatter plots.

Goals for the Lesson
- Interpret a bar graph.
- Interpret a circle graph.
- Construct a bar or circle graph for given data.
- Interpret a broken-line graph.
- Interpret a scatter plot.
- Construct a broken-line graph or scatter plot.

Graded Activities in This Lesson
Lesson Quiz (computer-scored)

Materials
Pre-Algebra: A Reference Guide and Problem Sets, pages 491–497

Optional
calculator
Graphs Solutions

Keywords and Pronunciation
bar graph: a graph that uses bars to display and compare data

broken-line graph: a graph in which points representing data are connected with line segments; a broken-line graph is also called a line graph

circle graph: a graph that uses sectors of a circle to display and compare data

scatter plot: a graph that displays two sets of data as points; scatter plot points represent ordered pairs

Groundwork: Preparing for the Lesson [online]

This activity reviews converting fractions to percents. As you work through it, record any notes in the space provided.

Notes

Learn: Reading and Constructing Bar Graphs [online]

As you work through this activity, do the exercise below and record any notes in the space provided.

Notes

Explain how to choose a scale for a bar graph.

Learn: Reading and Constructing Circle Graphs [online]

As you work through this activity, do the exercise and answer the question below. Record any notes in the space provided.

Notes

Explain how to calculate the angle measure for each section or category when you are creating a circle graph.

What is the sum of the percents in a circle graph?

Learn: Reading and Constructing Broken-Line Graphs [online]

As you work through this activity, do the exercise below and record any notes in the space provided.

Notes
Explain how to create a broken-line graph.

Learn: Reading and Constructing Scatter Plots [online]

As you work through this activity, do the exercise below and record any notes in the space provided.

Notes
Describe the relationships shown by a scatter plot.

Summary: Graphs [online]

- A bar graph compares two or more measurements of the same data.
- A circle graph shows the relationship of each part to the whole.
- A broken-line graph displays data using points plotted on a set of coordinate axes. These points are then connected by line segments.
- A broken-line graph is used to display data that vary over time.
- A scatter plot is used to show the relationship between two quantities.

- A scatter plot can show a positive correlation, a negative correlation, or no correlation.

Offline Learning: Graphs [offline]

In the Book
Read pages 491–493 in the Reference Guide.

Do the Math
Bror looked at the circle graph below. Fifty people were surveyed about their favorite pizza topping.

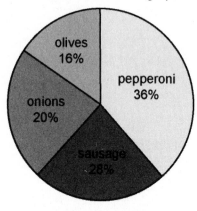

> Bror said that 36 of the people surveyed chose pepperoni as their favorite pizza topping.

Is Bror correct or incorrect? Explain.

Problem Sets
Complete Problems 1–21 on pages 495–497.

Lesson Assessment: Graphs Quiz [online]
Now go back online to complete the lesson quiz.

Answers

Do the Math

Bror is incorrect. The graph shows that 36 percent of the 50 people surveyed chose pepperoni as their favorite topping.

The correct answer should have been 50 • 0.36 = 18.

Therefore, 18 people chose pepperoni as their favorite pizza topping.

Student Guide

Measures of Center

How much does a family usually spend on groceries each week? What is the typical cost of a home in a certain neighborhood? What women's shoe size is ordered most frequently by shoe stores? Answers to these questions can be found by calculating measures of center for data sets. In this lesson, you will learn how to calculate the mean, median, and mode for a data set and use them to solve problems.

Goals for the Lesson

- Compute the mean of a set of data.

- Compute the median of a set of data.

- Compute the mode of a set of data.

- Solve problems using measures of central tendency.

Graded Activities in This Lesson

Mid-Unit Test (computer-scored)

Materials

Pre-Algebra: A Reference Guide and Problem Sets, pages 498-502

Optional
calculator
Measures of Center Solutions

Keywords and Pronunciation

mean: the sum of the values in a data set divided by the number of values; also called *average*

median: for a data set with an odd number of values, the middle value after the values have been ordered from least to greatest; for a data set with an even number of values, the mean of the two middle values after the values have been ordered from least to greatest

mode: the data value(s) occurring most often in a data set

Groundwork: Preparing for the Lesson [online]

This activity reviews essential skills. As you work through it, record any notes in the space provided.

Notes

Learn: The Center of Data Sets [online]

As you work through this activity, do the exercise and answer the question below. Record any notes in the space provided.

Notes

Give an example of a data set that has no mode.

What is the first step you must take when you want to find the median of a data set?

MathCast: Mean, Median, and Mode [online]

View the video to see how to solve a typical problem.

Summary: Measures of Center [online]

Measures of center are used to describe a typical value in a data set.

The mean, mode, and median are three types of measures of center.

Skills Update: Practice Your Math Skills [online]

Complete the Skills Update online.

Offline Learning: Measures of Center [offline]

In the Book
Read pages 498–501 in the Reference Guide.

Another Look (optional)
Of the three statistical measures of center (mean, median, and mode), the best one to use varies depending on the situation. Which measure of center would be the best for each of the following situations?

What sizes of clothing are most popular?

The statistic needed here is the size that the most people buy. The *mode* is the measure of center best suited to this question.

What is the cost of a midrange home in a particular neighborhood?

In this case, the middle price is needed, so the *median* is the best measure of center.

What was your average grade for all the tests in a course?

The average is determined by totaling all the grades and dividing by the number of tests. The *mean* is the best measure of center to use.

Name the best measure of center for these situations.

1. Joey scored between 5 and 10 points in each of the last 8 soccer games. He wants to figure out his average points per game.

2. Allison's parents plan to rent a medium-priced car for their vacation. The choices range from super-economy to luxury class.

3. The manager of the skating rink is ordering rental skates for a new rink. She needs to figure out what sizes are the most common for boys and girls.

Extension (optional)
Develop a deeper understanding of the statistical measures of mean, median, and mode by answering these questions.

1. Which statistical measure or measures might not be one of the data values in a set?

2. If you had four data values (6, 10, 10, and 15), which of the three statistical measures would change if you included 50 as an additional piece of data?

3. A shoe retailer knows that the shoe size requested most often by women is $7\frac{1}{2}$. Which statistical measure would represent this size?

4. Is it possible for a set of data to have the same mean, median, and mode? If so, what might the values of such a data set be?

Problem Sets
Complete Problems 1–15 odd and 29–35 on pages 501–502.

Extra Practice (optional)

Complete Problems 2–8 even on page 501 for extra practice.

Mid-Unit Assessment: Statistics Test [online]

Now go back online to complete the mid-unit test.

Answers

Another Look

1. mean

2. median

3. mode

Extension

1. The mean and median; all could be actual data values but would not have to be. The mode *must* be an actual value.

2. The mean would change. In this example, the median and mode would still be 10.

3. The mode. This shoe size is the one that occurs most often even though it may not represent the average shoe size for women.

4. Yes. Answers will vary but may include, for example, the following two sets of data:
1, 1, 1, 1, 1 or 0, 1, 2, 2, 3, 4.

Student Guide

Stem-and-Leaf Plots

There is more than one way to represent a set of data values. Bar graphs, circle graphs, broken-line graphs, and scatter plots are just a few of the ways that a particular set of data values can be represented. Stem-and-leaf plots can be useful for representing and organizing large amounts of data. In this lesson, you will learn how to construct and interpret a stem-and-leaf plot.

Goals for the Lesson
- Construct a stem-and-leaf plot from a set of data.

- Interpret a stem-and-leaf plot.

- Compute the range, median, and quartiles for a given data set.

Graded Activities in This Lesson
Lesson Quiz (computer-scored)

Materials
Pre-Algebra: A Reference Guide and Problem Sets, pages 503–508

Optional
calculator
Stem-and-Leaf Plots Solutions

Keywords and Pronunciation
quartile: one of the three values that separate an ordered data set into four equal parts; the second quartile Q_2 is the median of the data set; the first quartile Q_1 is the median of the lower half of the data set; the third quartile Q_3 is the median of the upper half of the data set

range of a data set: the difference of the maximum and minimum values in the data set

stem-and-leaf plot: a data display that lists the last digits (leaves) of the data values to the right of the earlier digits (stems)

Groundwork: Preparing for the Lesson [online]
This activity reviews finding means, medians, and modes. As you work through it, do the exercise below and record any notes in the space provided.

Notes
Explain how to find the median of a data set.

Learn: Reading and Constructing Stem-and-Leaf Plots [online]

As you work through this activity, answer the questions below and record any notes in the space provided.

Notes

How do you think the stem-and-leaf plot got its name?

What are the benefits of displaying data in a stem-and-leaf plot?

Learn: Analyzing Data with a Stem-and-Leaf Plot [online]

As you work through this activity, answer the questions below and record any notes in the space provided.

Notes

What does the range of a data set tell you about the data?

How do you find the second quartile (Q_2) of a data set?

MathCast: Stem-and-Leaf Plots and Quartiles [online]

View the video to see how to solve a typical problem.

Summary: Stem-and-Leaf Plots [online]

A stem-and-leaf plot is a graphical way to represent data in an organized manner.

The number of leaves should equal the number of values in the data set.

You can use a stem-and-leaf plot to find measures of center and measures of spread.

Offline Learning: Stem-and-Leaf Plots [offline]

In the Book
Read pages 503–506 in the Reference Guide.

Extension (optional)
Write a paragraph in the form of a report to the head of the Pentagon Soccer League informing him of the results of your findings about the heights of the 12-year-olds in the league. Include in your report not only the values of the range, mean, median, and mode but also an interpretation of what those values indicate. (The definitions of the range, mean, median, and mode will help you with your interpretations.)

Challenge (optional)
Conduct research to find the average high temperatures of at least three cities in your state for each month last year. Construct a stem-and-leaf plot that combines all your data. Construct a separate stem-and-leaf plot for each city. Numerically, where do you find most of the temperatures concentrated?

Problem Sets
Complete Problems 1–15 odd on page 507 of the Reference Guide.

Extra Practice (optional)
Complete Problems 1–16 even on page 507 of the reference guide for extra practice.

Lesson Assessment: Stem-and-Leaf Plots Quiz [online]
Now go back online to complete the lesson quiz.

Answers

Extension

Answers will vary greatly, but the report should include the values and interpretations of the range, mean, median, and mode. The sample paragraphs below provide the essential ingredients of the report; the organization and wording may differ significantly.

> The players vary greatly in height. In fact, because the shortest player is 54 inches tall and the tallest player is 71 inches tall, the difference in the players' heights is almost a foot and a half (actually, 17 inches). The average height is a little over 5 feet, at 61.68 inches.

> There is a pretty even spread. It is hard to say that most of the players are a particular height, because as many as three players have a below-average height of 56 inches, another three are almost equal to the average height at 62 inches each, and another three are above the average height at 64 inches each.

The paragraph might also discuss playing positions with respect to the heights and may include substitution patterns in the games, the varying uniform and shoe sizes that will have to be ordered, or any other aspects for which height may be a factor.

Challenge

Answers will vary.

Student Guide

Frequency Tables and Histograms

Frequency tables and histograms can be effective for organizing and displaying large amounts of data. They are especially useful when you need to know how often data with the same or similar values occur in a data set. In this lesson, you will learn to organize data sets into frequency tables and histograms and to interpret the information within them.

Goals for the Lesson

- Construct a frequency table for a set of data.

- Construct a histogram for a set of data.

- Interpret a frequency table.

- Interpret a histogram.

Graded Activities in This Lesson
Lesson Quiz (computer-scored)

Materials
Pre-Algebra: A Reference Guide and Problem Sets, pages 513–519

Optional
calculator
Frequency Tables and Histograms Solutions

Keywords and Pronunciation
frequency: the number of times one item appears in a data set

frequency table: data arranged in a table to show how often each item appears in a set of data

histogram: a bar graph that displays the frequency of data values that occur within certain intervals; the height of each bar gives the frequency in the respective interval

Groundwork: Preparing for the Lesson [online]
This activity reviews essential skills. As you work through it, do the exercise below and record any notes in the space provided.

Notes
Explain how to find the range of a data set.

Learn: Frequency Tables [online]

As you work through this activity, answer the question below and record any notes in the space provided.

Notes

What does a frequency table show?

Learn: Histograms [online]

As you work through this activity, answer the question below and record any notes in the space provided.

Notes

What is the first step you should take when creating a histogram for a data set?

MathCast: Frequency Tables and Histograms [online]

View the video to see how to solve a typical problem.

Summary: Frequency Tables and Histograms [online]

A frequency table organizes data into categories and number of occurrences so that the data can be interpreted more easily.

A histogram is a type of bar graph that displays the data in a frequency table graphically.

Offline Learning: Frequency Tables and Histograms [offline]

In the Book
Read pages 513–517 in the Reference Guide.

Challenge (optional)
Conduct a survey among friends or neighbors (in person, by phone, or by e-mail) to find out how many pets each person has. Survey at least 20 people and organize your data into a frequency distribution. Find the range, mean, median, and mode of your data. Write a short paragraph that summarizes your findings.

Problem Sets
Complete Problems 1–5 odd, 6–13, and 18–19 on pages 517–519 of the Reference Guide.

Extra Practice (optional)
Complete Problems 2–4 even and 15–16 on pages 517–519 of the Reference Guide.

Lesson Assessment: Frequency Tables and Histograms Quiz

[online]
Now go back online to complete the lesson quiz.

More Practice: Optional Assignment [offline, optional]
For extra practice, print the Optional Assignment and complete one or more of the problems. Submit the assignment to your teacher or learning coach on or before the due date to receive feedback on your work.

Name: _____   Date: _____

Optional Assignment

Statistical Measures

1. The table below shows the percentage of the population in seven countries who have completed high school. Make a bar graph to illustrate the data.

Country	Completed High School
Canada	84.9%
France	74.3%
Germany	86.4%
Italy	52.1%
Japan	90.6%
United Kingdom	86.6%
United States	86.9%

Answer:

2. The following data show the number of students enrolled in a community college from 1981 to 1997. Make a broken-line graph to illustrate the data.

Year	Enrollment
1981	750
1983	650
1985	760
1987	805
1989	1310
1991	1815
1993	2120
1995	2000
1997	1400

Answer:

3. Find the range, mean, median, and mode of the following set of data:
180, 207, 191, 180, 195, 191, 202, 203, 191, 200

Answer:

Student Guide

Box-and-Whisker Plots

The box-and-whisker plot can be another useful way to display data. Box-and-whisker plots use "boxes" and a pair of "whiskers" that make it easy to see the three quartiles as well as the range of the data. In this lesson, you will learn to construct and interpret box-and-whisker plots.

Goals for the Lesson
- Construct a box-and-whisker plot from a set of data.
- Interpret a box-and-whisker plot.
- Calculate the interquartile range for a data set.

Graded Activities in This Lesson
Lesson Quiz (computer-scored)

Materials
Pre-Algebra: A Reference Guide and Problem Sets, pages 509–512

Optional
calculator
Box-and-Whisker Plots Solutions

Keywords and Pronunciation
box-and-whisker plot: shows the distribution or spread of data; it uses the minimum, the maximum, and the three quartiles of the data

interquartile range: found by subtracting the first quartile Q_1 from the third quartile Q_3; $IQR = Q_3 - Q_1$; interquartile range represents the middle half of the data

quartile: one of the three values that separate an ordered data set into four equal parts; the second quartile Q_2 is the median of the data set; the first quartile Q_1 is the median of the lower half of the data set; the third quartile Q_3 is the median of the upper half of the data set

Groundwork: Preparing for the Lesson [online]

This activity reviews essential skills. As you work through it, record any notes in the space provided.

Notes

Learn: Reading and Constructing Box-and-Whisker Plots [online]

As you work through this activity, answer the questions below and record any notes in the space provided.

Notes

How do you think the box-and-whisker plot got its name?

What are the benefits of displaying data in a box-and-whisker plot?

MathCast: Box-and-Whisker Plots [online]

View the video to see how to solve a typical problem.

Summary: Box-and-Whisker Plots [online]

A box-and-whisker plot allows you to interpret data through a visual display of the data grouped into four equal groups.

A box-and-whisker plot uses five numbers: the minimum, the maximum, the median, and the quartiles. The quartiles divide the data set into fourths.

The interquartile range (IQR) can be a good way to represent the spread of a data set.

Skills Update: Practice Your Math Skills [online]

Complete the Skills Update online.

Offline Learning: Box-and-Whisker Plots [offline]

In the Book
Read pages 509–511 in the Reference Guide.

Do the Math
To create a box-and-whisker plot, you must follow these steps.

1. Order the data from least to greatest.

2. Find each of the following values:

    *   the median of the data set

    *   the lower extreme (minimum value)

    *   the first quartile (median of the lower half of the data)

    *   the third quartile (median of the upper half of the data)

    *   the upper extreme (maximum value)

3. Plot the data values on a number line.

4. Draw the box and the whiskers for the plot.

Extension (optional)
If each section of a box-and-whisker plot represents one-fourth of the data, why aren't the sections the same size?

Challenge (optional)
Use an almanac or the Internet to find statistics about your favorite sport, such as free-throw percentages in basketball, batting averages in softball or baseball, assists and goals in hockey or soccer, yards per carry in football, or times in swimming. Create a box-and-whisker plot comparing two or more players or teams.

Problem Sets
Complete Problems 1–5 odd and 9–15 on pages 511–512 of the Reference Guide.

Extra Practice (optional)
Complete Problems 2–4 even and 17–19 on pages 511–512 of the Reference Guide.

Lesson Assessment: Box-and-Whisker Plots Quiz [online]
Now go back online to complete the lesson quiz.

Answers

Extension
Some of the data may be closer together than others. For example, several values may be squeezed together at the low end of the set of data, but there may be one or two values at the high end.

Challenge
Answers will vary.

Student Guide

Statistics Review

You have finished studying the Statistics unit, which includes graphs, measures of center, stem-and-leaf plots, box-and-whisker plots, and frequency tables and histograms. Now it's time to pull together what you have learned. Throughout the review, see how the skills you have learned relate to the Pre-Algebra big ideas.

Goals for the Lesson
- Review the concepts and skills learned in the unit.

Materials
"Statistics" in *Pre-Algebra: A Reference Guide and Problem Sets*
Preparing for the Unit Test
Statistics Practice Problems

Unit Review: Statistics [online]

This is your chance to review the big ideas of Pre-Algebra you have learned in this unit. Under Review These Activities, you will find activities from previous lessons that will review each big idea. Choose the topics you feel you need to review. Under Try These Activities, you will find interactive problems that will test your understanding of each big idea. As you work through this lesson, take notes in the spaces provided.

Big Idea
Statistics is a branch of mathematics concerned with collecting, analyzing, and making decisions or interpretations about data. Statistics can be used to summarize characteristics of a group of numbers.

Summary: Statistics Review [online]

In this unit, you have covered the following topics:

- graphs
- measures of center
- stem-and-leaf plots
- frequency tables and histograms
- box-and-whisker plots

Offline Learning: Statistics Review [offline]

How well have you mastered the goals of this unit? Complete the Statistics Practice Problems. These problems are similar to the problems you will have on the Unit Test.

You can also—

- Review the Statistics unit in *Pre-Algebra: A Reference Guide and Problem Sets*.
- Review the notes in your Student Guide.
- Read and follow the instructions in Preparing for the Unit Test.

Practice Problems

Statistics

The graph below shows the approximate number of fat grams per cup of each type of food. Use the graph to answer Questions 1–2.

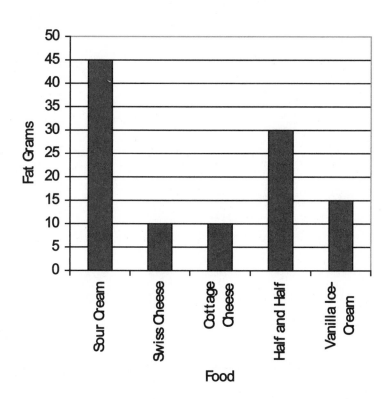

Fat Grams Per Cup

1. How many more fat grams are there in a cup of sour cream than in a cup of vanilla ice cream?

2. Which food has twice the number of fat grams than a cup of vanilla ice cream?

Use this graph to answer Questions 3–4.

Favorite Types of Books

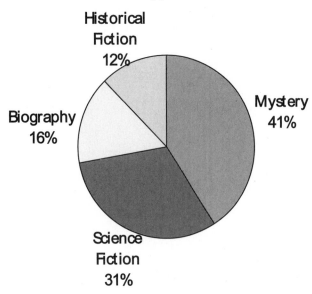

Historical
Fiction
12%

Biography
16%

Mystery
41%

Science
Fiction
31%

3. What percent of people chose science fiction or mystery was their favorite book type?

4. What percent of people chose biography or historical fiction as their favorite book type?

Use this graph to answer Questions 5–6.

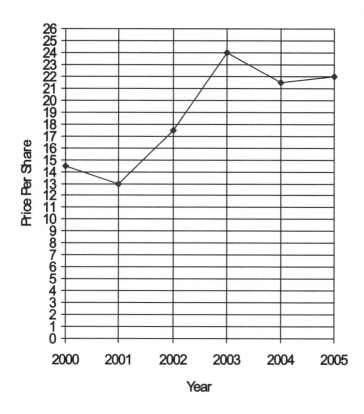

Stock Price for Company A

5. Between what two years did the stock price increase the most?

6. Between what two years did the stock price decrease the most?

7. For the following graphs, state whether each shows a positive correlation, a negative correlation, or no correlation.

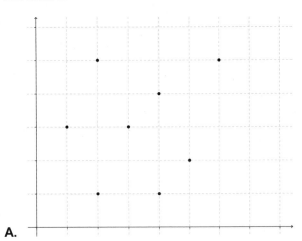

A.

B.

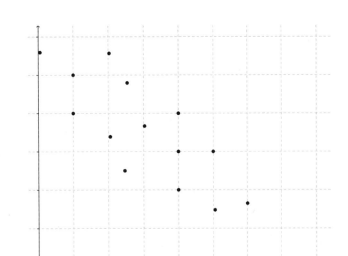

C.

8. A data set is displayed in the stem-and-leaf plot. What is the mean, median, mode and range?

6	2, 5, 8
7	0, 1, 3, 5, 8
8	0, 0, 1, 2, 4, 8, 8, 8
9	3, 6

9. Mrs. Ruiz kept track of the number of students she had in her kindergarten class for eight consecutive years. What is the mean, median, mode, and range of the data?

Year	Students
2002	25
2003	22
2004	17
2005	16
2006	19
2007	22
2008	23
2009	24

Use the histogram to answer Questions 10–12.

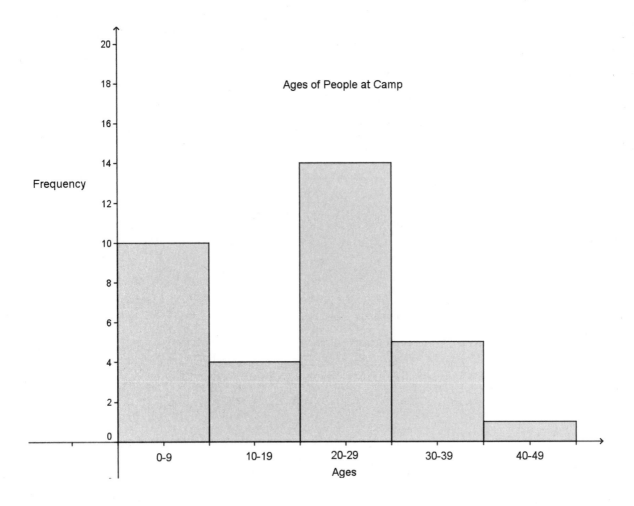

10. How many people at the camp are more than 19 years old?

11. How many people at the camp are less than 10 years old?

12. How many people at the camp are 30 to 49 years old?

Answers

1. 30 grams

2. Half-and-half

3. 72%

4. 28%

5. 2002–2003

6. 2003–2004

7. A. No correlation
    B. Positive correlation
    C. Negative correlation

8. Mean = 79
    Median = 80
    Mode = 80
    Range = 34

9. Mean = 21
    Median = 22
    Mode = 22
    Range = 9

10. 20

11. 10

12. 6

Unit Assessment

Statistics Unit Test, Offline

(10 points)

Score

1. The data show the ages of 13 people attending a dinner party.
   37, 42, 44, 46, 47, 49, 51, 53, 54, 55, 57, 61, 63

   A. Find the minimum, first quartile, median, third quartile, and maximum of the data set.

   B. Construct a box-and-whisker plot. Make sure your box-and-whisker plot clearly shows the values of the minimum, first quartile, median, third quartile, and maximum.

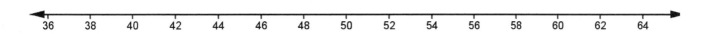

36   38   40   42   44   46   48   50   52   54   56   58   60   62   64

Score	____ of 10

Student Guide

Semester Review

You have finished this semester of Pre-Algebra. You have covered ratio, proportion, and percent; analytic geometry; perimeter and area; square roots and right triangles; solid figures; counting and probability; and statistics. You have covered a lot of material in this semester. This is your opportunity to review before the Semester Test.

Goals for the Lesson

• Review the concepts and skills learned in the semester.

Materials

Pre-Algebra: A Reference Guide and Problem Sets

Semester Review Solutions

Semester Review: Preparing for the Assessment [online]

This is your chance to review the Big Ideas of Pre-Algebra that you have studied in this course. Under Review These Activities, you will find pieces from previous lessons that will help you review each Big Idea. Choose the topics that you feel you need to review. Under Try These, you will find interactive problems that will test your understanding of each Big Idea. As you work through this lesson, take notes in the spaces provided.

Big Idea

A number is any entity that obeys the laws of arithmetic; all numbers obey the laws of arithmetic. The laws of arithmetic can be used to simplify algebraic expressions.

Big Idea

Analytic geometry models problems in geometry with algebraic proof and reasoning methods. Many real-world applications provide data that are best fit to a description by using the techniques of analytic geometry.

Big Idea

A function is a correspondence between two sets, the domain and the range, that assigns to each member of the domain exactly one member of the range. Many events in the physical world can be modeled as functions. Many functions can be described by algebraic expressions.

Big Idea

There are several useful aspects of every geometric figure that can be measured, calculated, or approximated. A segment has a finite length that can be measured. Area is a measure of how much material is needed to cover a plane figure. Volume is a measure of the amount of space a figure occupies.

Big Idea

Euclidean geometry uses five basic axioms to model real-world geometry and derives an amazing array of true results that apply extremely well to real-world geometry.

Big Idea

Many problems can be solved by using the properties of angles, triangles, and circles. Each trigonometric ratio can be described as the ratio of the lengths of two sides of a right triangle.

Big Idea

Probability is a measure of how likely it is that some event will occur.

Big Idea

Statistics is a branch of mathematics concerned with collecting, analyzing, and making decisions or interpretations about data. Statistics can be used to summarize characteristics of a group of numbers.

Summary: Semester Review [online]

In this semester you have covered the following topics:

- Ratio, proportion, and percent: ratio; proportion; percents, fractions, and decimals; similarity and scale; working with percent; percent of increase and decrease; and simple interest

- Analytic geometry: points on the plane, two-variable equations, linear equations and intercepts, slope, problem solving, relations and functions, and systems of linear equations

- Perimeter and area: types of polygons, perimeter, areas of rectangles and triangles, special quadrilaterals, areas of special quadrilaterals, circumference, and areas of circles

- Square roots and right triangles: rational square roots, irrational square roots, the Pythagorean theorem, the distance formula, special types of triangles, and trigonometric ratios

- Solid figures: volume and capacity, volumes of prisms and cylinders, volumes of pyramids and cones, surface area, and surface areas of prisms and cylinders

- Counting and probability: counting principles, permutations, combinations, probability, mutually exclusive events, and samples and prediction

- Statistics: graphs, measures of center, stem-and-leaf plots, frequency tables and histograms, and box-and-whisker plots

Offline Learning: Semester Review [offline]

To prepare for the semester test, you can also review the following:

- Units 1 through 7 of the reference guide

- Previous Unit Tests

- Previous Problem Sets sections of your Student Guides

- The notes in your Student Guide for each lesson in Units 1–7

Practice Problems

Semester 2

1. Nia has 18 coins. Twelve are dimes and the rest are nickels. Find the ratio of nickels to dimes.

2. In a classroom, students complete 10 math problems every 15 minutes.
   A. Write and solve a proportion to find the number of problems students can compete in 90 minutes.

   B. Find the amount of time, in minutes, it would take students to complete 45 problems.

3. The price of Stock A increases from $24 per share to $30 per share. The price of Stock B decreases from $48 per share to $42 per share.

   A. What is the percent of increase in Stock A's price?

   B. What is the percent of decrease in Stock B's price?

4. Find the slope of each of the following lines.

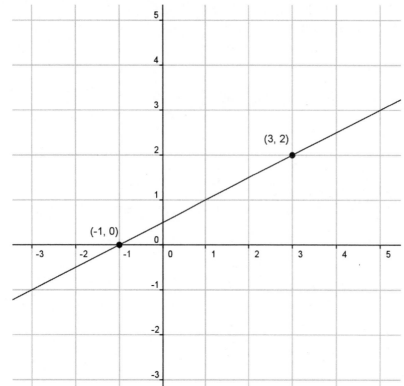

A.

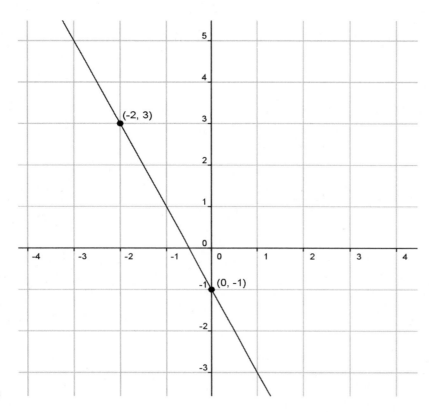

B.

For the following functions, find $f(-2)$.

    A. $f(x) = -4x - 5$

    B. $f(x) = -2(1 - x)$

5. Find sin A, cos A, and tan A for the triangle shown here.

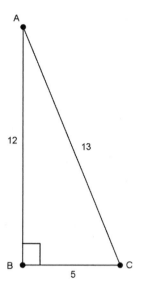

6. The vertices of a quadrilateral are (0, 2), (2, 4), (7, 4), and (5, 2). What type of quadrilateral is it?

7. Find the circumference of each of the circles shown here. Use 3.14 for π. Round your answers to the nearest tenth of a centimeter.

    A.

                                                                                B.

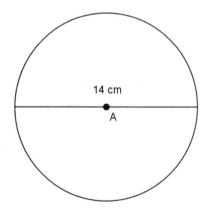

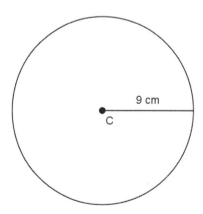

8. Simplify the following radical expressions.

 A. $\sqrt{16}$

 B. $\sqrt{20}$

 C. $\sqrt{45}$

9. A child's slide is 7 feet high, and the bottom of the slide is 9 feet from the base. How long is the slide? Round your answer to the nearest foot.

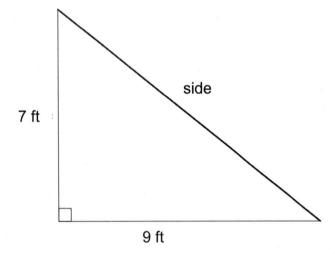

7 ft

side

9 ft

10. A trapezoid is graphed in the coordinate plane. The vertices of the trapezoid have coordinates (2, 4), (5, 4), (7, 1), and (0, 1). Find the perimeter of the trapezoid. Round your answer to the nearest tenth of a unit.

11. Find the volume and surface area of each of the following figures.

A.

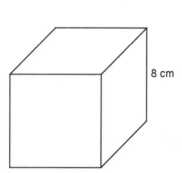

8 cm

B.

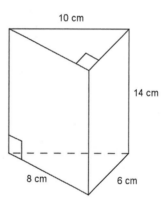

10 cm

14 cm

8 cm   6 cm

C.

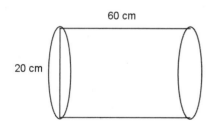

60 cm

20 cm

12. Simplify the following expressions.

A. 4!

B. 3! g3!

C. $\dfrac{5!}{2!}$

13. Rosalina bought a picture frame that can hold 3 photos. She has 10 photos to choose from to put into the frame.

A. How many combinations of photos can she choose?

B. How many permutations of photos can she choose?

14. A jar contains 12 red, 15 blue, and 23 yellow gumballs. A gumball is chosen at random from the jar. What is the probability that the gumball is—

A. red?

B. yellow?

15. Daytime temperatures were recorded every Monday for 10 consecutive weeks. The results are shown here.

Week	1	2	3	4	5	6	7	8	9	10
Temperature (°F)	82	78	85	89	92	90	88	92	101	84

A. Find the mean.

B. Find the median.

C. Find the mode.

D. Find the range.

E. Find the first quartile.

F. Find the third quartile.

G. Create a stem-and-leaf plot of the data.

16. A car is traveling at a constant speed. The graph shows the distance the car traveled over several hours.

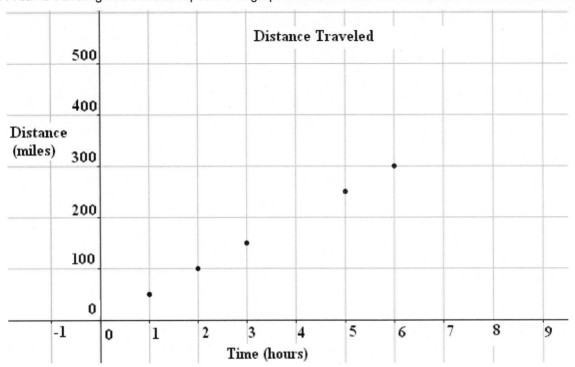

A. Find a reasonable estimate for the distance the car traveled after 4 hours.

B. Suppose the pattern continues. Find a reasonable estimate for the distance the car traveled after 9 hours.

C. If the pattern continued, how much time would it take for the car to travel 500 miles?

17. The histogram displays the weights of children who visited a pediatrician's office in one day.

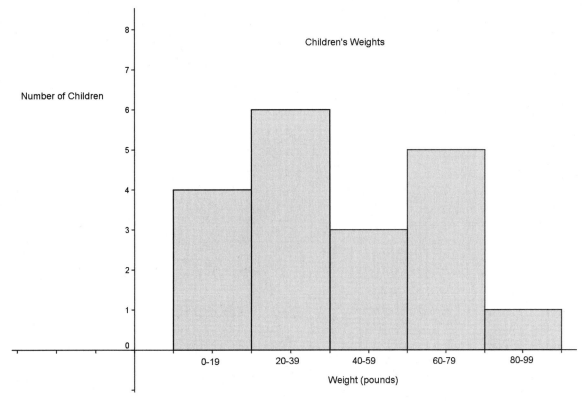

A. How many children weighed less than 20 pounds?

B. How many children weighed more than 59 pounds?

C. How many children weighed 20 to 79 pounds?

Answers

1. $\dfrac{6}{12}$ or $\dfrac{1}{2}$

2. A. $\dfrac{10}{15} = \dfrac{x}{90}$; $x = 60$ problems

   B. $\dfrac{10}{15} = \dfrac{45}{n}$; $n = 67.5$ minutes

3. A. 25%
   B. 12.5%

4. A. slope $= \dfrac{1}{2}$
   B. slope $= -2$

   A. 3
   B. −6

5. $\sin A = \dfrac{5}{13}$; $\cos A = \dfrac{12}{13}$; $\tan A = \dfrac{5}{12}$

6. Parallelogram

7. A. 44.0 cm
   B. 56.5 cm

8. A. 4
   B. $2\sqrt{5}$
   C. $3\sqrt{5}$

9. 11 ft

10. 16.8 units

11. A. SA = 384 cm^2 ; V = 512 cm^3

    B. SA = 384 cm^2 ; V = 336 cm^3

    C. SA = 4396 cm^2 ; V = 18,840 cm^3

12. A. 24

    B. 36

    C. 60

13. A. 120

B. 720

14. A. $\dfrac{6}{25}$

B. $\dfrac{23}{50}$

15. A. 88.1°F

B. 88.5°F

C. 92°F

D. 23°F

E. 84°F

F. 92°F

G.

Stem	Leaf
7	8
8	2, 4, 5, 8, 9
9	0, 2, 2
10	1

Key: 7|8 = 78

16. A. 200 mi
B. 450 mi
C. 10 hr

17. A. 4
B. 6
C. 14

Semester Assessment Answer Key

Semester 2 Test, Offline

(8 points)

1. A printer can print 40 pages in 1.6 minutes.

    A. Write and solve a proportion to find the number of pages that the printer can print in 5 minutes. Show your work.

    B. Lana wants to use the printer to print 150 pages. Find the amount of time, in minutes, it will take to print 150 pages. Show your work.

(6 points)

2. The population of fish in Lake Elson has been steadily decreasing. The graph shows some data about the number of fish in the lake over time.

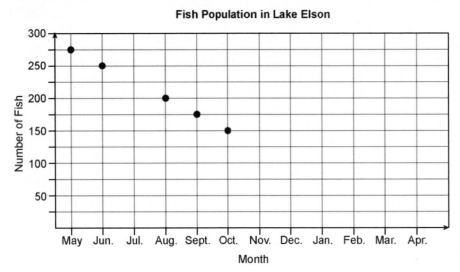

Fish Population in Lake Elson

Score

A. Find a reasonable estimate of the number of fish in July. Explain your answer.

B. Suppose the pattern continues. Find a reasonable estimate of the number of fish in December. Explain your answer.

C. If the pattern continues, in what month will there be no fish in Lake Elson? Explain your answer.

(10 points)

3. A garden is going to be built in the city park. The garden region is shown below.

Score

A. A short fence will be built around the perimeter of the garden region. Find the number of meters of fencing required. Round your answer to the nearest tenth. Show all your work.

B. Find the total area of the garden region. Round your answer to the nearest tenth. Show all your work.

(6 points)

4. A shipping company is considering using this box to ship products.

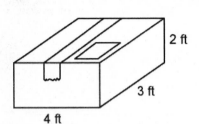

Score

Using the box will be cost effective only if the surface area to volume ratio of the box is less than 2. Determine whether it is cost effective for the company to use this box. Show and explain your work.

Score	___ of 30